C000060732

KINGS
OF THE KING'S
ROAD

KINGS
OF THE KING'S
ROAD

Clive Batty

VSP

Vision Sports Publishing
2 Coombe Gardens,
London, SW20 0QU

www.visionsp.co.uk

First published in 2004 by Vision Sports Publishing
First published in paperback in 2007 by Vision Sports Publishing

© Clive Batty 2004, 2007

ISBN 10: 1-905326-22-X
ISBN 13: 978-1-905326-22-8

The right of Clive Batty to be identified as author of this work has been asserted by
him in accordance with the Copyright, Designs and Patents Act, 1988.

All rights reserved. No part of this publication may be reproduced, stored in a
retrieval system, or transmitted in any form or by any means, electronic,
mechanical, photocopying, recording or otherwise, without the prior
permission of the publishers.

This book is sold subject to the condition that it shall not, by way of trade
or otherwise, be lent, re-sold, hired out, or otherwise circulated without the
publisher's prior consent in any form of binding or cover other than that in
which it is published and without a similar condition including this
condition being imposed on the subsequent purchaser.

Editor: Jim Drewett
Design: David Hicks
Cover photography: PA Sports

Set in Bembo 11pt/13pt
Typeset by Palimpsest Book Production Limited, Grangemouth, Stirlingshire

Printed and bound in the UK by Creative Print and Design, Wales

A CIP catalogue record for this book is available from the British Library

CONTENTS

WHAT HAPPENED NEXT?

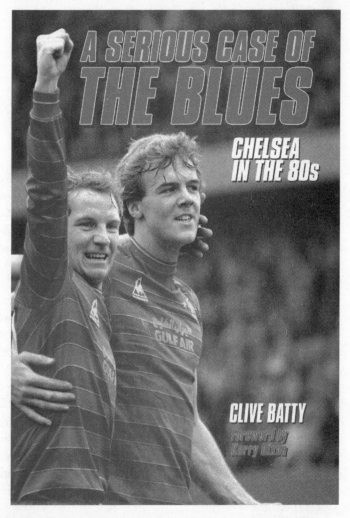

Available online at www.visionsp.co.uk for £11.49 (RRP £16.99)
(Copies signed by Kerry Dixon also available)

ACKNOWLEDGEMENTS

This book would not have been possible without the generous contributions of the Chelsea players who were more than willing to discuss every aspect of their careers at the club. Special thanks, then, are due to Tommy Baldwin, Alan Birchenall, John Boyle, John Dempsey, Tommy Docherty, Mickey Droy, Steve Finnieston, Ron Harris, Tony Hateley, Marvin Hinton, Alan Hudson and Peter Osgood.

Doug Hayward, Alvaro Maccioni, Terry O'Neill and Eric Swayne provided some great stories for the chapter on the King's Road, while Mark Colby, Tony Easter, Ron Hockings, Andy Jackson, Jim Luck, Fred Roll and Ray Taylor made equally valuable contributions to the fans' chapter.

Thanks also to Matthew Hirtes, who lent me a number of reference books and pointed me in the direction of some useful websites. Despite being an ardent Manchester United fan, Dave Hicks did a superb job designing the cover and the lay-out. Jim Drewett, my editor/publisher at Vision Sports, was a constant source of (mostly excellent) ideas and encouragement. I would also like to thank his business partner Toby Trotman for giving his backing to this project.

Finally, thanks to my father, Robert, who took me to my first Chelsea match in 1971 shortly before my ninth birthday.

FOREWORD
BY ALAN HUDSON

I am delighted to add my memories to this terrific book. Playing in this magnificent Chelsea team was unbelievably exciting, and it's fantastic that Clive Batty has re-united us all on these pages so we can all re-live those great days.

I was just 17 when I broke into the Chelsea team in 1969. The youngest member of a wonderful side, full of talented individuals and colourful personalities. It took me a little while to settle in, and I didn't feel I'd really arrived until just before Christmas that year when we went up to Old Trafford and beat Manchester United – George Best, Bobby Charlton, Denis Law and all – by a couple of goals. After that anything seemed possible. And with the team we had, anything *was* possible.

Every player in the side contributed something special. When Charlie Cooke, that great entertainer, was on the ball I could just stand and watch, marvelling at his skill. Then, when Peter Osgood got the bit between his teeth and was really in the mood, nothing or nobody could stop him. His sidekick Hutch, the bravest of the brave, was like a walking time bomb, ready to explode into action at any time. McCreadie was another class act, simply breathtaking in his early years when no one had ever seen a full back whizzing up and down the pitch like that before. Eddie could also pick opponents off like a sniper in waiting. So could the rest of our defence. Ronnie 'Buller' Harris was one of those players who love seeing an opponent in pain while Webby just revelled in being a part of this band of rogues. Dempsey and Hinton were two unsung heroes who were both vastly under-rated, and the same was true of 'Nobby' Houseman – an educated player who took a lot of stick without batting an eyelid, and kept raking in those crosses for our deadly duo, Ossie and Hutch. John Hollins, running all over the pitch, was the 'here, there and everywhere' man of the team. Then there was Tommy 'the Sponge' Baldwin, a player who just loved shooting at the opponent's goal at every opportunity. He'd run until he dropped for our band of brothers and, if there was any consolation in my missing that epic Cup Final against Leeds, it was that the Sponge took my shirt. But it still never really eased the blow! Last, but far from least, was 'the Cat'. How this slim, not especially tall man could leap above those giant centre forwards of the time almost defied logic. He was a class act and every Chelsea supporter will agree we would not have swapped him for any other keeper in the world!

So many gifted individuals, so many strong personalities. For managers Tommy Docherty and Dave Sexton putting the whole thing together must have been a bit like working on a jigsaw puzzle, an analogy I explore further in my new book, *The Tinker and Talisman*, an in-depth account of more recent developments at the Bridge and much more besides. Tommy and Dave had a tough job, and the players didn't always see eye-to-eye with them.

Perhaps that was because off the pitch we were like a bunch of desperadoes riding into Dodge City looking for excitement. Pubs, afternoon drinking clubs and nightclubs were all part of our regular itinerary. We'd tie up our horses and the whole saloon would turn their heads. When Charlie and the Sponge were out it was a case of 'watch out' – that pair of pranksters were far more dangerous than anything Jeremy Beadle could come up with. As for me, the King's Road was my hunting ground and the boys used me as their scout, tipping them off about all the latest pubs, clubs, restaurants and clothes shops. The sixties were in full swing and the upbeat tempo of that very special period was reflected in our style of play – both on and off the pitch.

I can't write about those times without mentioning our wonderful supporters. Coming home on the train from away games we used to drink with the fans, and we did the same after home games in the pubs near the Bridge. In those days players would mix with their supporters almost as if they were part of the team – well, of course, they were!

Kings of the King's Road is a complete one-off: a brilliant recreation of some incredible times, told through the words of the players and the fans. Clive has done a superb job in bringing all the stories together and, over a pint or two on the King's Road, it's been a real pleasure chatting to him about a truly fabulous era.

INTRODUCTION
LONG LIVE THE KINGS

Chelsea v Bruges, 24th March 1971. Stamford Bridge. European Cup Winners' Cup Quarter Final. Alan Hudson, his long hair almost reaching down to the white number 10 on the back of his royal blue shirt, dribbles the ball to the by-line at the Shed end. A Belgian defender, having spotted the danger, lunges in but it's too late. Hudson has already pulled the ball back to Peter Osgood, lurking unmarked near the penalty spot. Osgood, dark frizzy sideburns covering most of his cheeks, steadies himself before smashing a left-footer into the back of the net. It takes a fraction of a second for the crowd to react, and then Stamford Bridge is engulfed by a tidal wave of noise. The place goes mad. Chelsea have come from two goals down to book a place in the semi-final. Later that evening Osgood, Hudson and the rest of the Chelsea team will relive the goal as, surrounded by jubilant fans, they sink a few celebratory pints in the Lord Palmerston pub, a short distance from the ground at the top of the King's Road. Who says the glory days have only just arrived at Stamford Bridge?

In July 2004, shortly before Chelsea set out on a pre-season tour of America, club director Paul Smith was asked by a reporter from *The Times* to outline the "brand image" the Blues would be attempting to build in the States and elsewhere around the globe. Smith's response was curt. "It's not as if Chelsea came out of nowhere," he replied. "There's still something [at the club] reminiscent of the 'Swinging Sixties'"

It is perhaps ironic that Chelsea – a club powered by Roman Abramovich's millions, and generally considered to be drivingly ambitious and forward-looking – should seek to define itself by harking back to the past. Yet, for many older fans especially, Smith's comments made perfect sense. If anything, they rather understated the influence that the late sixties and early seventies continue to exert at the club.

The casual visitor to the Bridge will find few visible signs of this decades-old heritage – in stark contrast to Anfield or Elland Road, for instance, where statues of club legends Bill Shankly and Billy Bremner are monuments to past glories. At Chelsea, lounge bars named after former heroes Peter Osgood, Bobby Tambling and Roy Bentley are virtually the only reminders of the great triumphs of yesteryear.

Dig a little below the surface, however, and modern-day Chelsea's connections with the 'Swinging Sixties' – an era of change which, incidentally, most social commentators agree continued well into the 1970s, possibly even until the birth of punk in 1976 – become more apparent. Take two of the songs played in the pre-match build-up at every game at the Bridge, for instance. The club's 1972 League Cup Final theme tune *Blue is the Colour* is still the Chelsea anthem, more than 30 years after it made the top 10. Likewise, *The Liquidator* – a hit for Harry J and the Allstars way back in 1969 – remains a vital, not-to-be-missed, foot-stomping, hand-clapping three minute demonstration of support for the Blues nearly 40 years after it reached the charts and was adopted as a battle-cry by the Shed. A straw poll of fans attending the Bridge, meanwhile, would almost certainly reveal the following: a) a disproportionate number of supporters are aged 40 or over; b) a similarly disproportionate number of fans who date their support for the club back to the 1970 FA Cup Final (or a little bit before – after all, no supporter cares to be lumbered with the 'glory hunter' tag); and c) the 1970s royal blue Chelsea kit, unsullied by sponsors' logos and featuring the original club badge, is most fans' all-time favourite Blues kit.

Cynics may dismiss all this as misty-eyed nostalgia, but there's no denying that the 1970s still resonate at Stamford Bridge. Most importantly, the flamboyant Chelsea team of the period gave the club a legacy of entertaining, attractive, attacking play – 'sexy football' if you like, a quarter of a century before Ruud Gullit coined the term – which lives on to this day. Playing with style, panache and a swaggering self-confidence which bordered on the arrogant, the Chelsea sides created by managers Tommy Docherty and Dave Sexton helped define the club's image for years to come. Even now, if you ask any football fan which words come to mind when they think of Chelsea the answer is likely to include the following: 'flashy', 'stylish', 'cocky'. All of which, with plenty of justification, was said about the seventies team.

Individually, the players possessed personality and character in abundance. In goal, Peter Bonetti was a breathtakingly acrobatic keeper who lived up to his famous nickname, 'the Cat'. In defence, skipper Ron 'Chopper' Harris' scything tackles made him a cult figure on the terraces, while fellow defender David Webb was the team's 'Mr Versatility', filling virtually every position on the pitch, including goalkeeper, at one time or another. At the other end of the pitch Charlie Cooke and Alan Hudson, two midfielders blessed with exquisite technique and oodles of imagination, provided much of the side's hallmark flair and creativity. The focal point of the attack, charismatic centre forward Peter Osgood, 'The King of Stamford Bridge' to his adoring fans in the Shed, was a genuine superstar for whom the spectacular was the norm. With their fashionably long hair and bushy sideburns, their shirts hanging out and their socks rolled down, the Blues team of the seventies had a rock star image and, increasingly as the decade wore on, the rebellious attitude to match.

Although deadly serious about winning, the Chelsea lads also had a highly developed sense of fun which was wholly lacking in some of their stern-faced rivals. This was sometimes expressed in a well-rehearsed routine which invariably hoodwinked even the top referees of the day.

"Alan Hudson used to come out at half time and put the ball down to kick off, even if we'd already done so in the first half," Ian Hutchinson once revealed. "Huddy did that about ten times a season and usually got away with it. The odd time we would get caught. That summed up playing for Chelsea – taking the piss and having a laugh. Nevertheless, when the nitty-gritty came, we were up for it too."

Off the pitch, meanwhile, most of the team fully embraced the goodies – sexual freedom, fashionable clothes and groovy hairstyles – thrown up by the Swinging Sixties. From their base just off the King's Road, the cultural capital of London at the time, the Chelsea boys – especially those like Hudson, Baldwin and Cooke who lived up in town, rather than in the stockbrokers' belt in leafy Surrey – enjoyed a champagne lifestyle. They mixed with pop stars, actors and some of the most glamorous women of the age, including Raquel Welch, the dancers from Pan's People and, when George Best didn't get in there first, a Miss World or two. At the same time, they never lost contact with their fans, and were just as likely to be spotted downing a few post-match pints in a pub round the corner from the Bridge as dining at an exclusive King's Road eaterie.

"It was an absolutely fabulous era," says Alan Birchenall. "I don't care who you are or what the players earn today, anyone who was around in the sixties and seventies will say the same. I've got great football memories, but I've got even better memories from the life we lived. When I turn my toes up I probably won't remember a single match, but I'll remember everything around the game. The present day players think they've got it made, they think they invented having a good time, but it's simply not true."

Sometimes the quest for a good time landed the players in trouble – usually with the Bridge management, frequently with the football authorities and, occasionally, with the Metropolitan Police. The English game has always produced its fair share of rebels, mavericks and non-conformists but, perhaps, no team has ever boasted as many such characters as the Chelsea side of the late sixties and early seventies.

"If anybody had filmed what went on all this stuff about what the celebrities get up to in the jungle would be second-rate," says Alan Hudson, summing up his days as a member of the King's Road rat pack.

Well, the cameras may not have been there but that matters little when the main players have such vivid memories of one of the most colourful periods in Chelsea history.

CHAPTER ONE
BUILDING THE TEAM

I n the autumn of 1961 Chelsea, not for the first time in the club's history, were in some disarray. Six years earlier, in 1955, thousands of fans had celebrated on the pitch at Stamford Bridge as the Blues had marked their 50th anniversary by winning the league championship for the first time. The intervening years, however, had been mediocre ones, redeemed only by the remarkable goalscoring feats of the young Jimmy Greaves.

Now, though, Greaves had gone – sold to AC Milan for £80,000 after a final prolific season at the Bridge in which he had scored 43 goals, including four in his last match for the club at home against Nottingham Forest. Gone, too, were nearly all the old championship-winning heroes: captain Roy Bentley, Eric 'The Rabbit' Parsons and future England manager Ron Greenwood. Indeed, just two regular members of the 1955 side remained: full-back Peter Sillett, whose Easter Saturday penalty against Wolves in front of 75,000 fans at the Bridge had virtually clinched the title; and fleet-footed winger Frank Blunstone, the youngest member of the class of '55 at just 21.

After a poor start to the 1961/62 season saw the Blues win just one of their first six matches, Chelsea chairman Joe Mears decided that manager Ted Drake, who had been in charge of the team since 1952, would benefit from the services of an assistant. Having made enquiries among his contacts in the game, Mears offered Arsenal's Tommy Docherty, a former Scottish international wing-half, the role of Chelsea player/coach.

"Mr Mears contacted the FA, and they suggested Jimmy Adamson, who was at Burnley, and myself," recalls Docherty. "Jimmy wanted to continue playing, but I was 33, and quite happy to get involved in coaching. At the interview Mr Mears said he knew nothing about football, and his directors even less – so I thought, 'Well, that'll do me'."

Docherty immediately made his playing debut for Chelsea, helping the Blues to a morale-boosting 6–1 win over Sheffield United, a match in which 19-year-old striker Bobby Tambling confirmed his potential as a possible successor to Greaves by scoring his first hat-trick for the club. The result, though, did not kick-start a recovery and Drake's mix of old stagers and inexperienced youngsters continued to flounder.

The life of a football manager has always been perilous but in those days poor results did not inevitably lead to the sack. Moreover, having steered the Blues to their greatest triumph, Drake could rely on the residual loyalty of most board members. All the same, the directors' patience was not infinite and, apart from understandable worries over the team's unimpressive form, there was a growing feeling among the board that Drake had become something of yesterday's man.

In the early 1960s football was moving into a new, more glamorous era. The abolition of the maximum wage was fundamental to this sea change in social perceptions of the game. Overnight top players, notably Fulham and England captain Johnny Haynes, were able to negotiate wage increases from £20 to £100 a week. At last, fortune as well as fame beckoned the successful. Drake, though, gave little impression of being the man to lead Chelsea into this exciting, if unknown, territory. His greatest achievements – winning the championship, his bold introduction of the teenage Jimmy Greaves and his successful campaign to replace the old

'Pensioners' tag with a new nickname, 'The Blues' – were all firmly in the past. Regarded as an aloof figure by many of the younger players, and presiding over a divided team with low morale, his stock was no longer high. Finally, in late September 1961, after a crushing 4–0 defeat at Blackpool, the Chelsea board decided to act.

"I was about to fly up with Ted Drake to Scotland, because we were interested in signing Celtic's Pat Crerand," remembers Tommy Docherty. "But before we left we were asked to wait until after the board had met. I was waiting outside the boardroom when Mr Battersby, the club secretary, came out and said, 'Ted Drake has gone.'

'What, to Scotland?' I said.

'No,' he said. 'He's gone.'

He'd resigned, or been sacked – whatever you want to call it. So the board asked me to take over as caretaker and I agreed."

Docherty's appointment was made permanent in January 1962 and the new manager's wages were doubled from £30 to £60 a week. An ebullient, energetic and dynamic figure with a gift for a sharp one-liner, 'the Doc' quickly set to work, tightening discipline, organising more rigorous and physically demanding training sessions, and swiftly assessing which players fitted into his new Chelsea vision. The ones who didn't, or didn't care for the new regime, were soon sent packing.

"The big problem at the club was that there were too many old players swinging the lead," says Docherty. "There was a real split between them and the youngsters coming through, who had won the FA Youth Cup two years running. Some of the established players – Ron Tindall, Reg Matthews, the Sillett brothers – even wanted the young ones to call them 'mister'. It was ridiculous. Anyway, I soon got rid of the dead wood and the players who weren't up to it."

Although the club was struggling, Docherty knew that Chelsea's future was potentially a bright one. For some years, the Blues' youth system had been renowned as one of the best in the country, rivalled only by Manchester United's. Drake's predecessor, Billy Birrell, deserved much of the credit as he had established the club's first junior scheme, called 'Tudor Rose', in 1947. Renamed Chelsea Youth two years later, under the direction of Dick Foss, a former Blues player, a stream of talented footballers emerged from the youth team's base at the Old Welsh Harp ground in Hendon. In the second half of the 1950s players such as Peter Brabrook, Les Allen, Ron Tindall and, of course, Jimmy Greaves were among those to come through the junior ranks to make a mark in the professional game. Ultimately, though, the so-called 'Drake's Ducklings', with the obvious exception of Greaves, had failed to fulfil their promise. Now another generation of highly-rated young players – some of whom had already been thrust into the first team by Drake – had been developed on the Hendon production line.

Among the players falling into this bracket was Peter Bonetti, an extraordinarily agile goalkeeper whose quick reflexes had earned him the nickname 'the Cat'. Unlike most other keepers at the time, Bonetti was not afraid to come off his line to collect crosses and would even advance beyond the penalty spot to claim corners and free-kicks. His biggest weakness was his kicking which lacked power, a deficiency he compensated for by throwing the ball out swiftly and accurately whenever possible.

Then aged just 18, Bonetti had taken the place of former England international Reg Matthews in the Chelsea team in April 1960, the same month in which he also helped the Blues win the FA Youth Cup. His first full season in the Chelsea side, 1960/61, had not been an easy one: playing behind a defence which was little more than a shambles, the Cat had only managed to keep one clean sheet in 36 league appearances. Nonetheless, this depressing statistic could not disguise his outstanding natural ability.

Chelsea's defence, which had conceded a club record 100 league goals in Drake's last full season at the club, was by far the weakest area of the team when Docherty arrived on the scene. True, the same could be said for many other clubs, yet even in an era of attacking formations which tended to encourage high scoring games Chelsea's back line was well known for its generosity. For some time under Drake a lack of defensive organisation had been apparent, regardless of which players he picked. If the Blues were to have any chance of avoiding the drop, Docherty needed to remedy this flaw – and fast.

One of his first decisions, then, was to fill the two full back positions with youth products Allan Harris and Ken Shellito. On the left, Harris was a steady if unspectacular performer, while on the opposite flank Ken Shellito was a pacy, technically accomplished player who liked to get forward. However, there was no short-term solution to the lack of an effective partnership in the centre of defence, a bugbear for a number of seasons. Docherty tried several players in this key area but, whatever the combination, the goals still flooded in – another 94 in the 'goals against' column by the end of the 1961/62 season.

There was better quality in midfield, where Terry Venables was already building a reputation as a sharp, quick passer with an eye for the killer ball. On the wings Blunstone and Bert Murray, yet another youth product, were pencilled in by Docherty as mainstays of his revamped side, particularly after long-serving right-winger Peter Brabrook moved on to West Ham in the summer of 1962. Up front, meanwhile, Tambling and fellow Chelsea homegrown Barry Bridges both possessed blistering pace and could be guaranteed to score their share of goals – 42 in total by the end of Docherty's first half season in charge.

The duo's goals, though, were not enough to prevent Chelsea finishing bottom of the table. Relegation, which had always appeared likely, was duly confirmed a couple of games from the end of the campaign and the Blues went down with Cardiff City. Despite this setback, Docherty was far from down-hearted and remained convinced that, once his rebuilding work was finished and the 'dead wood' had been completely rooted out, he would have the basis of a decent team.

While the Doc continued his sweeping purge, new players came in. Welsh international striker Graham Moore was signed from Cardiff and East Stirling left-back Eddie McCreadie, who had impressed when Docherty visited Stirling's Firs Park ground on a scouting mission for another player, was snapped up for a paltry £5,000. Strong, quick, skilful on the ball and a forceful tackler, McCreadie possessed all the attributes Docherty was looking for in a full back and would prove to be an inspired signing. In the dressing room, meanwhile, the new arrival's poor eyesight quickly gained him the nickname 'Clarence', after the cross-eyed lion in the hit TV series *Daktari*.

Back in the Second Division for the first time since 1930, Chelsea faced stiff competition for the two automatic promotion places. Middlesbrough, Newcastle and Sunderland, who had just missed out on promotion by one point, were all expected to mount a strong challenge from the north-east. Leeds, under new manager Don Revie, had only just escaped relegation to the Third Division the previous season but, like Chelsea, had an exceptional crop of youngsters coming through the ranks. Stoke, who still had wing maestro Stanley Matthews on their books at the age of 47, were also fancied to do well.

Realising that it would be a huge gamble to take on such powerful rivals with youthful promise alone, Docherty fortified his young side with three experienced pros: Blunstone, long-serving centre-half John Mortimore and, alongside him, Frank 'the Tank' Upton, a tough defender Ted Drake had signed from Derby shortly before his departure from the Bridge. Their role would partly be a paternal one, encouraging the younger players when form and confidence dipped.

Tactically, Docherty had been influenced by the Brazilian side which had won the 1962 World Cup using overlapping full-backs in an innovative 4–3–3 formation which the Chelsea manager was keen to copy. The Blues had the players to duplicate this newfangled attacking ploy, as Ken Shellito on the right and Eddie McCreadie on the opposite flank both possessed the pace, skill and stamina needed to make regular forward raids from deep. The rest of the team was also set up offensively, with Venables directing play from his position as the midfield lynchpin, Murray and Blunstone providing width and Tambling, Bridges and Moore forming a three-pronged spearhead.

Second Division defenders in 1962 weren't really designed to counter South American-style attacking manoeuvres; given the choice they preferred to battle, scrap and trade broken noses with a couple of heftily-built centre forwards. So, in this unsophisticated environment, Chelsea's fluid movement, quick-fire passing and supercharged counter-attacks had a surprise factor that proved irresistible. By Christmas the Blues were seven points clear of the chasing pack and still unbeaten at home. Among the teams to have left the Bridge empty-handed were Charlton (5–0), Cardiff (6–0) and Newcastle (4–2). The fans were impressed and so, too, were the critics.

"They possess the poise, speed, method and spirit of a side that could flower into a commanding force over the coming seasons," one reporter predicted after a 2–0 win over Norwich at the Bridge in November 1962. "No doubt there are two or three positions that need developing if they are to live on more than mere nodding terms with the Tottenhams, Evertons and Burnleys of this age . . . but it is the future that beckons. It could be rich and full indeed if Chelsea's young men fulfil their promise."

Throughout the first half of the season Barry Bridges and, especially, Bobby Tambling had been scoring goals at a Greaves-like rate, while Docherty's new look back four had rediscovered the art of defending, conceding an average of less than a goal per game. Nothing, it seemed, could stop Chelsea's promotion bandwagon. Except, perhaps, the weather. The winter of 1962/63 was one of the worst on record: temperatures plummeted to Siberian levels, thick snow covered the country from Cornwall to the Clyde and toboggan sales soared. Inevitably, football fell victim to the Arctic conditions with hundreds of matches being postponed.

By the time the Blues eventually resumed their league campaign in February 1963 the fizz had completely evaporated from the side. A run of five straight defeats saw Chelsea's lead eaten up and prompted Docherty to move into the transfer market for West Brom striker Derek Kevan and veteran schemer Tommy Harmer, a former Tottenham player. Neither, though, figured prominently in the initial stages of the run-in which saw the Blues' erratic form continue. Far from being favourites for promotion, Chelsea were now just one of a number of clubs, including Stoke, Sunderland, Leeds and Middlesborough, with aspirations of filling one of the top two places. Everything would depend on the Blues' last three games, at home to Stoke, away to Sunderland and at home to Portsmouth.

On May 11th, Chelsea's biggest crowd for three years, 66,199, squeezed into the Bridge for the visit of Stoke and their ancient winger Matthews. Stan, soon to become Sir Stanley, might have been a pre-war relic but he was still capable of giving the Chelsea defence a torrid time. So, in a bid to nullify the winger's influence, Docherty instructed 18-year-old Ron Harris, playing in one of his first games for the Blues, to follow Matthews all over the pitch.

The brother of Allan and a talented all-round sportsman who had played schoolboy cricket for England, Ron had made his Chelsea debut the previous season and Docherty had been sufficiently impressed by the young defender to recall him for the promotion run-in. A specialist man-marker who stuck to his prey like a limpet, Ron was quickly making a name for himself as one of the toughest tacklers in the game.

The match against Stoke was pivotal in establishing this reputation. On a number of occasions Harris hacked down Matthews as he dinked his way down the wing. Even the home fans, upset by what they saw as the unnecessarily brutal treatment of a national institution, booed the youngster. Harris, though, remained unperturbed and would joke later that the reason why Matthews struggled to get up after being repeatedly felled was because he suffered from arthritis. Still, on this occasion, Matthews had the last laugh as his side's 1–0 win virtually guaranteed Stoke promotion

The defeat left Chelsea needing to win at Sunderland to retain their hopes of going up. A home win or draw, meanwhile, would see the Rokerites promoted at the Blues' expense. Essentially, the match was a cup final and the whole of Wearside wanted to see it. "We stayed in a hotel near the ground," remembers Docherty, "and the day before the match you could see people queuing up outside to get in the next day."

In what he would later describe as "the biggest gamble of my life", Docherty dropped Bridges and Moore and replaced them with a heavyweight strike force of Kevan and Upton, who was more used to stopping goals than scoring them. If the plan was to batter the Sunderland defence into submission, it wasn't one which appeared to worry the home team.

"On the way into Roker that day, I met Brian Clough, who was out of the Sunderland side through injury," recalled Frank Upton. "He said, 'What are they playing you up front for – a joke?'" The joke, though, was on Sunderland as Chelsea hung on for a 1–0 win after a first half corner flicked off little Tommy Harmer's groin and bobbled over the line.

"We went up there with a side packed with defenders and people who could look after themselves," said Bobby Tambling later. "We knew it wasn't going to be pretty, but the result bore out the tactics. It was tremendously windy and Peter Bonetti couldn't reach the 18-yard line with his kicks. I think we played the whole of the second half pinned in our box, after Tommy Harmer scored probably the most important goal of his career."

In the dressing room afterwards there was much discussion about which part of Harmer's anatomy had got the vital touch. Was it his thigh, stomach . . . or somewhere else? Harmer ended the debate in unconventional manner, as Bert Murray related later: "He whipped his little dick out and was swinging it around, pointing to it and saying, 'It hit this, it hit this.'"

Buoyed by the crucial victory at Roker Park, Chelsea approached their final match against Portsmouth three days later in good spirits. A win would put the Blues level on points with Sunderland, who had finished their campaign, leaving the second promotion spot behind champions Stoke to be decided by goal average. Chelsea just had the edge in this department so a victory by any margin over Pompey would guarantee promotion.

Fielding the same team that had beaten Sunderland, the Blues tore into a Portsmouth side containing future Chelsea manager Bobby Campbell. To the joy of the home fans, Derek Kevan gave them a second minute lead and after that it became a rout. Three-nil up at half-time Chelsea went on to win 7–0 with Bobby Tambling hitting four of the goals to take his season's tally to 37. At the final whistle, hundreds of youths poured onto the pitch, thrilled that the promotion which had seemed a certainty before Christmas had finally been achieved.

In truth, Chelsea had limped over the line. A haul of 15 points from the last 18 matches was near-relegation form – even in those days of two points for a win – and didn't augur well for the coming season back in the big time. Not that Docherty was worried. "I was very confident we'd do well because the players could only get better," he says. "We had a young team – some of the boys were just 18 or 19 – but that year in the Second Division gave them all a bit more experience."

Nonetheless, the First Division would be a different matter altogether. A little over a year earlier the Blues' young team had struggled in the top flight and some fans, especially those of a more pessimistic disposition than the Chelsea manager, couldn't help wondering if history was about to repeat itself.

CHAPTER TWO
DOCHERTY'S DIAMONDS

I n the early 1960s clubs that had won promotion to the First Division, unlike their Premiership counterparts today, could look forward to rather more than a fight for survival. In season 1961/62, for instance, Alf Ramsey's Ipswich Town amazed everybody, including their own fans, by becoming league champions a year after winning the Second Division title. The following season Liverpool, after nearly a decade out of the top flight, had made a less spectacular but nonetheless worry-free return to the First Division finishing eighth. Doing 'an Ipswich' might be beyond them, but Tommy Docherty had every expectation that his youthful Chelsea side could perform at least as well as the Merseysiders.

In preparation for the forthcoming season, Docherty made few changes to the squad that had won promotion. In the summer of 1963 Derek Kevan, having played just seven games for the Blues, moved on to Manchester City for £40,000. Graham Moore followed soon afterwards, joining Manchester United. In the newspapers, meanwhile, there were rumours that the name Chelsea might be changed to 'Kensington FC' as the Royal Borough of Chelsea became the Royal Borough of Kensington – predictably, the stories turned out to be nothing more than 'silly season' gossip. Suitably relieved, the fans looked forward to the new season with keen anticipation. Season tickets, priced at £6–£12, were much in demand, while the less affluent supporter only needed to stump up two shillings (10p) to get on the terraces. For fans who liked something to read on the tube or bus home, the Chelsea programme was available for a further sixpence (2p).

After beginning the season with two disappointing 0–0 draws against West Ham and Burnley, the Blues adapted quickly to life back in the First Division. The team certainly didn't look out of place in the top flight and, following a good run of form in November and December, remained tucked in behind title contenders Liverpool, Manchester United, Everton and Spurs.

Peter Bonetti, his confidence boosted by a dependable back line in front of him, was rapidly emerging as one of the best and most spectacular goalkeepers in the country, although the imperious Gordon Banks blocked his path to international honours with England. The back four of Ron Harris – now christened 'Chopper' by the fans, in tribute to his ferocious tackling – Mortimore, McCreadie and Shellito was solid and uncompromising, but also possessed attacking flair on the flanks. In midfield, Terry Venables revelled in his role as the team's conductor, threading astute passes forwards for the pacy Tambling and Bridges to race onto, while wingers Murray and Blunstone provided a stream of crosses and their fair share of goals.

Among the season's highlights were a 5–1 Boxing Day win at Blackpool and a 4–0 thumping of former champs Ipswich at the Bridge in February. Before the final match of the season at home to Everton, Chelsea fans were treated to a display by the Butlins' Young Ladies dancing troupe before settling back to watch a Bert Murray penalty give the Blues the points to secure fifth place, seven points behind champions Liverpool. "We were all quite happy with that after having just come up," says the Doc. "We had a great side, full of skill and speed."

The major disappointment of the campaign came in the FA Cup, the Blues surprisingly losing 2–1 at home to Second Division

Huddersfield in the fourth round after having knocked out Tottenham in the third.

The summer of 1964 produced more changes in the side. Frank Blunstone was forced to retire after suffering an achilles tendon injury in training, although he stayed on at the club to coach the Chelsea juniors where future star Alan Hudson was one of his protégés. To fill the gap left by Blunstone's retirement, Docherty toyed with the idea of promoting Peter Houseman, an 18-year-old left-winger from Battersea who had made a handful of appearances the previous season. Deciding that Houseman was too raw, the Doc bought Aston Villa's tall, elegant striker George Graham for a mere £5,000, partnered him with Barry Bridges up front and moved the left-footed Tambling to the wing. Problem solved.

A second new face in the team was youth product John Hollins, a tireless box-to-box midfielder with a strong shot whose equally tireless chatting earned him the nickname 'Ena', after the *Coronation Street* gossip Ena Sharples.

With Ken Shellito's appearances restricted by a chronic knee injury, in September 1963 Docherty had splashed out £30,000 on Charlton's Marvin Hinton, a cultured, smooth-passing defender who was just as happy playing in the centre of defence as at right-back. And by the start of the 1964/65 season Hinton would be a regular in the team, while Shellito's ongoing injury problems made him an increasingly peripheral figure. "Marvin was a fantastic player; he was great at coming out with the ball and, because he hated having to run, he never made a bad pass," says Docherty.

A further change was to the team strip. The shirts, of course, remained blue but the colours of the old shorts (white) and socks (blue) were reversed, giving Chelsea a snazzy, modern look which suited the team's fast, upbeat, vibrant playing style. By now, too, the Blues had a second nickname, 'Docherty's Diamonds', which was born after the manager had been captured by the TV cameras high up in the East Stand shouting, "Come on, my little diamonds!"

Following a series of pre-season friendlies against strong continental opposition, the Diamonds were ready to sparkle.

Chelsea got off to a scorching start – in fact, the best ever in the club's history in the top flight – winning seven and drawing three of their opening ten games. For the first time in a long while, the football world was having to take the Blues seriously. "Chelsea, now bubbling over with youth and vitality, no longer look the sort of team music hall comedians can joke about," commented Geoffrey Green in *The Times*.

A significant factor in the team's improvement was the promotion of Dave Sexton from assistant coach, a position he had held since February to 1962, to first-team coach in September 1964. Thoughtful, quietly spoken and with a football brain the size of a small planet, Sexton was the ideal man to complement the bubbly, irrepressible Docherty and the players responded well to their chalk-and-cheese partnership.

"Dave and the Doc were the perfect pair," said Bobby Tambling some years later. "Docherty was the greatest motivator of players I have ever known. He used to build us all up so that we felt ten feet tall. He would pick his moment to boost the confidence of an individual and we all got the treatment at some time or another. He would tell the boys from the press that so-and-so was a great player and when you read the things that were written about you, you started to believe you could play a bit. Dave, on the other hand, was more reserved. But his knowledge of the game was tremendous and he really knew how to bring the best out of each player by concentrating on their qualities. If you had skill, Dave would bring it out."

John Boyle, yet another teenager who made his debut in the 1964/65 season, was also hugely impressed by the Docherty-Sexton combination. "Tommy and Dave were very open to new ideas," he says. "Tommy was almost like a revolutionary figure in football – along came this wisecracking Glaswegian, who was only about 35 at the time, and he thought the best thing he could do was to get rid of the old players. Luckily enough, all the young players were ready to come through to the first team. And he added a few astute signings. As a manager he was great. If he said, 'There's a wall, I want you to go through it', you'd only say 'How?' not 'Why?'

"He dramatically improved the work-rate. Suddenly there were people all over the field running hard. The athleticism was greatly improved. If you look back to videos of games in the fifties they are very pedestrian, but Tommy really worked on that. He wanted to play a high tempo game. He got midfield players who would put people under pressure rather than giving them time to play, full-backs who would get forward and strikers with loads of pace."

Ron Harris agrees. "Tommy transformed Chelsea Football Club," he says. "I think his attitude, wherever he's been, is that young-sters never cheat you. In the side at that time we only had a couple of older heads, people like John Mortimore, Frank Blunstone and occasionally Tommy Harmer. So he got rid of all the older fellows, and I think one of the reason loads of young-sters went to Chelsea was that even at 17 if Tommy thought you were good enough he'd give you a chance."

In a revealing interview with *The Times* during the 1964/65 season, Docherty outlined the key elements of the football philosophy he was seeking to instil in his young players. "Tactically, we aim at the man over in attack," he said, referring to his overlapping full-back ploy. "It is a kind of concertina movement. We demand mobility, and though only Venables, at the hub of things, is given free reign to improvise, we encourage the others to play by ear, not sticking to rigid positions. As they develop they are thinking more."

The high levels of fitness, skill and mental agility required by the players in this free-flowing playing system in turn demanded an intensive training regime. "The accent is on accuracy, high speed and endurance, a mixture of strength and finesse, with no player in practice games allowed more than two consecutive touches of the ball," the Doc continued. "Running off the ball, and playing the ball off quickly, are the basic things for us."

In the same interview, Docherty admitted that many of his best ideas had been copied or adapted from other teams. The ploy of using full backs as auxiliary wingers, for example, had stemmed from a fortnight Docherty had spent in Spain, watching Real Madrid's training methods.

"I picked up their tactic of players overlapping in attack. Only their forwards did it. I have extended it at Chelsea to the backs and half backs. We have picked up useful things, too, from West Ham United. Our free-kick play around the edge of the opposing penalty area – glancing the ball through the defensive 'wall' – we copied and adjusted from Burnley. Even the numbers on the players' shorts in our new all-blue strip was developed from a suggestion by one of our supporters."

Confident, brash and fearless, Docherty gave every impression that his young Chelsea team were on the verge of greatness. Only one thing, it seemed, could hold the Blues back. "Stamford Bridge is our biggest enemy," he said. "It lacks warmth and intimacy. The players themselves feel remote out there in the middle, detached and watched from a distance as if they were puppets – as if the audience was set too far back from the footlights."

Docherty had a point. At the time, Stamford Bridge was a very different stadium to the one that fans know today. Originally an arena for athletics events, the oval-shaped ground was unusual in having a greyhound track running round the pitch. Although this facility provided the club with extra income, it also pushed the fans back from the action on the pitch which, in turn, made the Bridge a much less intimidating venue for away teams than compact grounds like Anfield or Upton Park.

At the Fulham Road end, a roof had been erected in the 1930s to provide cover for bookmakers at evening greyhound meetings and 'the Shed', as it became known in the mid-sixties, quickly gained a reputation as the focal point for Chelsea's most enthusiastic fans.

But they were still a long way from the pitch. The terracing at the North End was uncovered, although some fans could seek refuge from bad weather under the pre-war North Stand, a peculiar stilted structure in the north-east corner with seating for just 1,000. Next to the North Stand, the 5,000-capacity East Stand, which dated from the club's foundation in 1905, ran along the full length of the pitch. On the opposite side, meanwhile, the club was planning to build a stand on the massive West terracing. Eventually unveiled in January 1966, three-quarters of this new West Stand were traditional seats, while the front quarter was made up of unreserved concrete slabs known as 'the benches'. Taken as a whole, the ground was a strange mish-mash, reflecting the evolution of stadium design over the past 60 years.

Consequently the Bridge was no fortress, and the Blues crashed to their first defeat of the season at home to Manchester United at the end of September 1964, Denis Law and George Best grabbing the goals for the Reds. The 2–0 reverse was only a temporary setback, however, and Chelsea continued to challenge for the championship throughout the winter and spring.

In fact the Blues were fighting on three fronts as they made good progress in the two domestic cup competitions. In the FA Cup, Northampton were crushed 4–1 in the third round before a Bobby Tambling goal decided a London derby at West Ham in the fourth. Another derby in the fifth round, this time at home against Tottenham, was settled by Barry Bridges' first half goal. In the quarter-finals, Third Division Peterborough were hammered 5–1 at the Bridge, setting up an enticing semi-final with Liverpool.

As the Blues entered March, the League and FA Cup Double – previously only won by Preston, Aston Villa and Tottenham – was very much a possibility. But, optimistic fans wondered, could Chelsea make it an unprecedented Treble by winning the League Cup as well?

The brainchild of Football League secretary Alan Hardaker, the League Cup had been launched in 1960 with the intention of providing another source of revenue for cash-strapped lower division teams. Many big clubs, though, saw it as an unwanted addition to the fixture list and boycotted the competition. Having entered the League Cup in its first season, Chelsea had then joined the long list of non-competing clubs in the next two years.

In 1963/64 Chelsea had re-entered the competition with a weakened team and promptly gone out to Second Division Swindon at the first hurdle. The following year, Docherty maintained his policy of using the competition to blood promising youngsters. Peter Osgood, Joe Fascione and future Scottish international Jim McCalliog all made their debuts in the League Cup in 1964, while rarely called upon squad members such as Frank Upton, Allan Young and Ian Watson were also given run outs.

After disposing of Birmingham, Notts County, Swansea and Workington in front of crowds ranging from the small to the pitiful (fewer than 6,000 attended the home tie against the Swans), the semi-final draw pitted the Blues against Aston Villa. Villa were the first winners of the League Cup and one of the few First Division clubs to treat the competition completely seriously.

Anticipating a tough match in the first leg at Villa Park, Docherty recalled his first-choice players, although there was also a debut for young Scottish midfielder John Boyle. "It was a terrible pitch, covered in snow, mud and sand but it was wonderful to be playing," recalls 'Boylers'. "It was 2–2, then with five minutes to go, I got the ball about 30 yards out and whacked it into the corner of the net for the winning goal. Incredible." Boyle's goal in the 3–2 win proved decisive as a 1–1 draw in the second leg at Stamford Bridge put the Blues into the final against the holders of the competition, Leicester City.

A week after the return with Villa, Chelsea flew to Duisberg to play the West German national team in a friendly. The match had been arranged at the request of the West German manager Helmut Schoen as part of his team's preparations for the 1966 World Cup in England. Schoen had particular reasons for choosing Chelsea as warm up opponents, telling Docherty, "You play like a South American team. You don't play like an English team at all. Your full-backs come like wingers. We haven't seen this before in Europe."

Lining up against the Blues for the Germans were four players who would go on to play in the World Cup Final against England the following year: goalkeeper Hans Tilkowski, defender Horst-Dieter Hottges, striker Uwe Seeler and new midfield *wunderkind* Franz Beckenbauer.

"I think it was Franz Beckenbauer's first game for West Germany," says John Boyle, who was playing just his sixth match for Chelsea. "Uwe Seeler was coming back from an achilles injury and Helmet Schoen wanted him to have a game to test it out. So we got Ronnie Harris to mark him." How thoughtful.

Watched by 3,000 British troops in a crowd of 32,000, the Blues pointed the way forward for Bobby Moore, Geoff Hurst, Bobby Charlton and co, with Barry Bridges scoring the only goal of the game late on. No overlapping full-back was involved but the goal was still a typical example of Chelsea's attacking play at the time, Hollins lofting the ball forward for Bridges to burst clear of the German defence and shoot past Tilkowski. Schoen was gracious in defeat.

"Considering their average age is under 22, Chelsea are a marvellous team," he said. "They are the best English club side I have seen for a long time."

One German sports writer was equally enthusiastic about the Blues' performance. "Chelsea gave the national team a lesson with their cultured football and played like a top-class continental side as they fell back in defence with eight or nine men, or moved smartly forward with seven or eight."

There was no question either of the game being a kickaround friendly in which neither side was especially concerned about the result. "It was a real match," insists Boyle. "Obviously, when a club team plays a national team there's a huge incentive for the club side. I'm not saying we'd have beaten them every time, but we managed a win and for us it was incredible to play against all those famous names. It was a great boost for us."

It may have been after this game, or another similarly impressive Chelsea display, that Tommy Docherty congratulated one of his players in a rather unorthodox way. "I'll never forget the time when, after we'd put in a particularly good performance, he took all his clothes off and jumped in the bath with us," says Terry Venables. "He started messing around and then gave Marvin Hinton a love bite on his neck. On his neck! I mean can you imagine the amount of explaining Marvin had to do when he got home to his wife."

A month after their German adventure the Blues lined up against Leicester in the first leg of the League Cup Final. The match came at a bad time for Chelsea who had suffered their heaviest defeat of the season two days earlier, going down 4–0 at championship rivals Manchester United. Again, United's brilliant young winger George Best had got on the scoresheet and generally run the Blues' defence ragged.

There was more worrying news, too: leading scorer Barry Bridges had picked up a knock at Old Trafford and would miss the final. To the irritation of reserve team centre forward Peter Osgood, Docherty handed Bridges' number nine shirt to a surprising choice, left-back Eddie McCreadie.

The 20,690 fans who tore themselves away from *Coronation Street* to attend the match at the Bridge were bemused by McCreadie's change of position. Yes, Eddie was quick and skilful, but he was a defender and his goals record – two in more than 100 games for the club – hardly inspired confidence. On the other hand, one of those goals had been against Leicester earlier in the season in a 4–1 home victory. Could he do it again?

The answer was yes. With the scores tied at 2–2 after Bobby Tambling and a Terry Venables penalty had twice given the Blues the lead, McCreadie collected a throw from Peter Bonetti. Charging up the muddy field he outpaced the Leicester defence and, as Gordon Banks rushed off his line, poked the ball past the England goalkeeper and into the net for the winner. It was, said McCreadie later, "one of the best goals you've ever seen", although unfortunately the lack of interest in the League Cup meant there were no TV cameras present to record it for posterity.

For the return leg three weeks later the unlikely match winner was back in defence. So, pretty much, was the whole Chelsea team after Docherty instructed his players to get behind the ball and make it difficult for Leicester to score. The plan worked perfectly as the match ended 0–0, giving the Blues their first piece of silverware for a decade. The home fans, though, were incensed by Chelsea's negative tactics and demonstrated their feelings with loud boos when skipper Terry Venables went up to collect the cup from Football League President Joe Richards.

"In the second leg we showed what we had learned against the various European teams we'd played in friendlies," says an unrepentant John Boyle. "Basically, we played for the 0–0 draw from the kick-off. It was great to win the cup, especially as it was so early in my career and because we'd only recently come up from the Second Division, but it wasn't the competition it became a few years later. Quite a few of the top teams were missing because they were involved in Europe." Chelsea, too, were bound for the continent the following season and would choose not to defend their trophy.

The League Cup was in the bag, but there would be no Treble. Between the first and second legs of the final Chelsea had lost 2–0 to Liverpool in the FA Cup semi-final at Villa Park. The Blues could feel slightly aggrieved as John Mortimore, playing one of his last games for the club before a summer move to QPR, headed what appeared to be a legitimate goal at 0–0 only for the referee to disallow it. That decision apart, Chelsea could have no complaints. Liverpool were there to be beaten, having played a tough European game in Rotterdam which went into extra-time just two days earlier. Unfortunately, Chelsea captain

Terry Venables had unwittingly fired up the tired Reds, as former Liverpool hardman Tommy Smith later told the Chelsea programme.

"We were knackered and we were sitting in the dressing room before the game when [Bill] Shankly came in fuming and pinned this brochure to the wall. 'You won't believe it,' he told us, 'but those cocky lot think they're in the final already. Look! They've made up a mock-brochure for the final.' And they had. Terry Venables had done it to show off to his mates."

The bizarre 'Cup Final programme' proved to be the ultimate motivational tool for the Liverpool manager. "Shanks was fuming and so were we," said Smith. "We went out there and your lot never stood a chance!"

At least the Blues exacted some revenge on Good Friday with a 4–0 thrashing of the Reds at the Bridge, keeping them in a three-way title race with Manchester United and Leeds. However, a dropped point the following day at home to West Brom and then a 2–0 defeat at Anfield on Easter Monday meant that Chelsea would have to win their last two fixtures – at Burnley the following Saturday and away to Blackpool two days later – to have any chance at all of lifting the championship.

Rather than returning to London after the Liverpool defeat, the Blues elected to stay in the north-west, choosing Blackpool as their base. It turned out to be an unfortunate choice as the resort went down in Chelsea history as the scene of the infamous 'Blackpool Incident'.

Accounts of the incident vary, but what is not in dispute is that eight Chelsea players – captain Terry Venables, Barry Bridges, George Graham, Eddie McCreadie, John Hollins, Bert Murray, Marvin Hinton and Joe Fascione – broke Tommy Docherty's curfew, slipping back into the hotel via the fire escape in the early hours of the morning. Tipped off by an eagle-eyed porter, the Doc had known for some time that half his squad were not in the hotel.

"We'd only just come back from the pictures when the night porter came to see me and said, 'They've all gone out again.' I said, 'No, it can't be, they've all just come in from the cinema.' But they weren't in their rooms and the porter was getting upset because it broke the fire regulations if guests went out without informing the hotel. So we waited until nearly 3am, and after they'd sneaked back in, I went into one of the rooms, and there was John Hollins pretending to be asleep. But when I pulled the cover back, he was still wearing his jacket and tie!"

The rest of the night owls were soon rounded up to be faced by an incandescent Docherty. "This sort of thing had happened before," he says, "and I'd turned a blind eye. But this time I had to make a decision, and I sent the eight of them home."

The players were shocked. It was a Wednesday night and the Blues weren't playing again until Saturday – it wasn't as if they had gone out on the razzle the evening before a match. And while they were a little bit tipsy, they certainly weren't reeling drunk.

"We'd just been out to a late-night drinking bar for a couple of drinks," says Marvin Hinton. "We weren't looking to get hammered, we were just a group of lads who fancied staying out a bit longer."

Docherty, though, could not be swayed. The gang of eight players, he insisted, would get the first train home to London and wouldn't play against Burnley. What's more, according to Hinton, the manager also told the group that none of them would ever play for Chelsea again. At the time Docherty made no mention of this ultimate sanction in his comments to the press. He was, though, more than willing to explain the reasons for his drastic decision.

"I feel this was the only way to do it," he told reporters. "I lay down the rules and if players break them they must take the consequences. The club is more important than individual players or league championships. How can you win the championship with disloyal players?"

By sending home the players Docherty had all but conceded defeat against Burnley and, consequently, thrown in the towel in the championship race. Effectively he had sacrificed the club's title ambitions for a point of principle: namely, his right as manager to set boundaries for the off-field conduct of his players. Some club bosses may have felt that, under the circumstances, the 'blind eye' Docherty referred to might have been given another run out. But Chelsea chairman Joe Mears, who enjoyed an excellent relationship with his manager, publicly backed the Doc's action, telling pressmen, "I am sure Tommy has done the right thing and will have the fullest support of the board."

Returning to London, the players had an unpleasant surprise waiting for them. News of the scandal had leaked out and the media was out in force to greet the disgraced 'Chelsea Eight'. "We couldn't believe it when we got to Euston and saw all the photographers, cameramen and reporters," recalls winger Bert Murray. "We had to cross a police cordon to get to our Chelsea van parked down the platform."

And Marvin Hinton remembers: "The story made the front pages the next day. I think we were treated unfairly; a large fine would have been more appropriate. It wasn't as if we had done anything terrible while we were out."

However, it didn't help the players' cause that one elderly guest was quoted as saying, "I was woken up by a great rumpus. Doors were banging and people stamping along the corridor. I thought we were being invaded."

Fired by a sense of injustice, the players released a joint statement to the press, intensifying the war of words with their manager. "We have done nothing to be ashamed of," it read. "We have not been the subject of any complaint from a member of the public or any member of the staff of an hotel in Blackpool. We have done nothing which we could not talk freely about. We admit to a breach of club discipline in that we were late back at the hotel and if necessary we can obtain proof of the way we spent every minute of the evening. We are shocked by the punishment, which we believe is out of all proportion."

The players were soon on their way back to the north-west, attending the Burnley match at the invitation of a TV station. "We met up with Docherty who brought us back to Blackpool," remembers Murray. "He was the one who apologised. He told us he wouldn't do anything like that again and that would be the end of the matter."

Although he didn't regret his actions, Docherty recognised that some sort of gesture of reconciliation was necessary to bring the episode – which, by now, had become so notorious it even had its own name, the 'Blackpool Incident' – to an end. He decided that a 'happy family' picture of himself with the eight miscreants back at the hotel would fit the bill nicely.

The photo that appeared in the following day's newspapers was designed to reassure fans that all was now well in the camp. A close study of the picture, however, reveals the underlying tensions that existed between manager and players. Docherty, staring into the camera, has his arms around the shoulders of George Graham and Marvin Hinton. Friendly enough, you might think, except the slightly manic grin on his face – think Jack Nicholson in *The Shining* – suggests he's about to bash the two players' heads together.

The players' expressions and body language, too, give away something of their true feelings. George Graham has turned his scowling face away from Docherty towards his mate Terry Venables on his right. Venners, his eyebrows arched quizzically and his hands stuffed in his pockets, looks thoroughly fed up. Barry Bridges, meanwhile, is chuckling away to himself as though the whole thing is a huge joke. To his left, Eddie McCreadie is yawning, his night on the tiles having apparently caught up with him. Only the two youngest players, John Hollins and Joe Fascione, wearing the glum expressions of naughty schoolboys summoned to see the headmaster, and Bert Murray, his eyes cast down, look remotely sheepish or remorseful.

The Blackpool Incident of April 1965 proved to be a pivotal moment for the Chelsea team of the mid-sixties. A little over a year later, four of the late-night revellers, all of them first-team regulars, would have been shipped out of the club. Docherty's smile, as the photo hinted, really was that of an assassin.

After a severely weakened Blues team, filled with reserves who had been hastily summoned from London to replace the 'Chelsea Eight', had been thrashed 6–2 at Burnley, Docherty restored six of the miscreants to the team for the game at Blackpool. The Blues lost that one as well, ending a season which had promised so much on another sour note.

While Chelsea fans should have been reflecting on an excellent season – silverware in the League Cup, an FA Cup semi-final and a creditable third place in the league behind Leeds and champions Manchester United – instead they were mulling over the consequences of the players' late-night shenanigans on the Golden Mile, which continued to excite much press comment. The fear for the fans was that the episode might create an irretrievable rift between manager and players, a concern shared by former Tottenham captain and future Chelsea manager Danny Blanchflower.

"It was a brave-looking action at the climax of their championship challenge and it will please the partisans and hypocrites up and down the country," he wrote in a newspaper column, referring to Docherty's decision to send the eight players home. "But will it prove very wise in the end? I don't think so. It was not a public crime and Tommy was impulsive to make it public. I think there's no-one more sincere about the game and the club. But I feel he's been a bit rash as most young managers would be. I think his young team have been a bit rash, too, as young men often will. But young men have a way of remembering hard punches; they continue to think they were not fair."

Certainly, the relationship between Tommy Docherty and Terry Venables, who the Doc believed to be the ringleader of the

Blackpool Incident, never recovered and continues to be spiky to this day. Yet, initially, the pair had got on well, with the Chelsea manager recognising Venables' leadership qualities by making him captain. "Not only could he play, but I liked the boy's inquisitive nature," says the Doc. "He had an old head on young shoulders, and I reckoned he would handle the extra responsibility."

Soon, though, Docherty felt Venables was, if anything, trying to take too much responsibility. "He was a very disruptive influence," he says. On the training pitch, we'd be working on something, and he'd say out loud: 'That won't work!' He was always criticising, though he'd come and see me later and apologise. It didn't undermine my authority, though, because I was too strong to let that happen. On the field, too, more and more of what went on was revolving around Terry and eventually he wanted to run the show."

"That's Docherty's assessment," Venables once retorted. "That's his truth. My recollection of it was that I would always ask questions and he encouraged that. I was deadly keen to learn and that was misconstrued by Docherty. He was a young manager and I was a young player. We had our differences of opinion. But it wasn't only me he fell out with. He was unpredictable, one of those guys who'd do something different to what he said he was going to do. He fell out with everybody. It'd get to the stage where you felt you didn't want to talk to him and then he'd have you laughing within a couple of minutes. He really was a hysterical bloke. Looking back, it was a clash of two strong personalities."

Providing an outside view of the relationship, Bobby Tambling says: "Terry was very tactically minded and I think they clashed in that area. And they clashed as comics because they were both comedians trying to be the funnyman in the dressing room, which Tommy shouldn't have been competing for anyway because he was the manager and above that. But, being so young, Tommy still felt like a player."

A psychologist might suggest that the two men – both of whom were confident to the point of cockiness and had a supreme belief in their own abilities – were competing for the role of 'Alpha male' in the Chelsea dressing room. If this was the case, who would come out on top? And what would be the implications for the club as a whole? The coming season would provide all the answers.

CHAPTER THREE
QUEST FOR THE CUP

f it ain't broke, don't fix it' is an adage that has served generations of craftsmen well down the years, but it's clearly not
one that Tommy Docherty subscribed to. Having created a
Chelsea team bursting with talent, enthusiasm and youthful
promise the Doc might have been expected simply to sit back
and enjoy the results of his handiwork. Instead, within a year of
seeing his young Blues side come close to pulling off a remarkable Treble, Docherty had more or less dismantled the team and
started afresh.

Although the Blackpool Incident had aroused his destructive
urges, Docherty kept them in check for a while. There were no
departures from the Bridge before the start of the 1965/66 season.
The most significant arrival was Jimmy Andrews, a Scot who had
played for three London clubs, as team coach, filling the gap left
when Dave Sexton had taken the manager's job at Leyton Orient
a few months previously.

One of Andrews' first tasks was to attempt to improve morale
in the camp. The fallout from Blackpool hung over the club like
a toxic cloud, which even a summer tour of Australia had failed
to disperse. Bobby Tambling later remarked that the atmosphere
on the trip Down Under was "like a morgue", a clear illustration
of how far management/player relations had deteriorated. Still,

there was plenty to look forward to. By virtue of finishing third in the League, the Blues had qualified for Europe for the first time since a brief foray in the Fairs Cup – the forerunner of the Uefa Cup – in 1958/59. To help prepare his team for this continental adventure, Docherty arranged a series of testing pre-season friendlies against strong German and Swedish opposition, including a re-match with the West German national side in Essen.

At half-time against Beckenbauer and co, the Blues appeared on course for another famous victory. Goals from Jim McCalliog, a teenage forward from Scotland who would soon be on his way to Sheffield Wednesday, and Barry Bridges gave them a 2–0 lead. In the second half, though, the Germans scored three times to win 3–2. For Peter Bonetti in the Chelsea goal the dramatic turnaround in fortunes provided a slightly eerie foretaste of things to come. Five years later the Cat would again be on the receiving end of a German recovery from two goals down – only this time the game was a somewhat more important affair: a World Cup quarter-final in Mexico which saw England blow their chances of retaining the Jules Rimet trophy.

Once it got under way, the 1965/66 season had the fans in a state of almost perpetual excitement. The Fairs Cup (see Chapter Nine, *Kings of Europe*) served up a heady mix of glamour, euphoria, violence and, with the final in Chelsea's sights, ultimate disappointment. Another long run in the FA Cup, meanwhile, prompted dreams of Wembley only for these to be shattered by a surprise 2–0 semi-final defeat at the hands of relegation-threatened Sheffield Wednesday. "We were big favourites," says Ron Harris of this setback, "everybody thought it would be a one-sided game but it was a quagmire of a pitch at Villa Park and we didn't perform."

Gallingly, one of the Wednesday goals was scored by McCalliog, just a few months after Docherty had decided he was surplus to requirements at the Bridge. The Doc had offloaded the Scot primarily because another young striker had come through the ranks to make the number nine shirt his own. Peter Osgood, the son of a Windsor builder and an occasional hod-carrier himself, h. made an electrifying Chelsea debut aged just 17 the previous season, scoring two goals against Workington in the League Cup. Banner headlines the following morning hailed a new hero, but they were soon forgotten as Docherty consigned the young starlet to the reserves for the next nine months.

In October 1965, however, Docherty finally decided the time was right to unleash his exciting protégé, giving Osgood an extended run in the team at the expense of Barry Bridges. "Barry was an England centre-forward and a big idol at the time," recalled Ossie, "but Tommy said, 'I'm going to give you ten games no matter how you play.' To hear that gives you a lot of confidence to try things which may not always come off."

After a quiet settling-in period, during which some fans campaigned for the return of Bridges, Osgood won over the crowd with a series of dazzling displays. Tall, quick, beautifully balanced and an elegant, almost balletic, figure on the ball, Ossie possessed magnificent control, a deft touch and superb vision. While not a traditional English centre forward, he also had some of the attributes of that breed: strength in the air, physical presence and a powerful shot in both feet. Above all, though, it was his precocious ability to strike spectacular goals – perfectly-timed volleys, full-length diving headers, solo efforts that left a couple of defenders on their backsides – which had the fans excitedly chanting his name. For the press, too, Osgood's dramatic arrival on the London football scene was little short of a sensation.

After a 2–1 victory over Spurs at the Bridge on January 8th 1966, a match which saw the opening of the new West Stand, *The Times* described Osgood as 'a west London Hidegkuti' (a reference to the famous deep-lying Hungarian centre-forward who, along with Ferenc Puskas, had starred in the Magyars' legendary 6–3 win against England at Wembley in 1953).

"His artistic footwork and shooting power mark him as one who could yet lead England's attack for the World Cup," gushed

rovided he is not weighed down by the praise
the event, England manager Sir Alf Ramsey
along with Bridges, Bonetti, Hinton, Hollins and
venables in his original squad of 40 players, but only the Cat
made the cut for the final 22. Two weeks after the Tottenham
match, a mazy Osgood dribble from inside his own half to the
edge of the Liverpool area in the Blues' third round FA Cup
victory at Anfield had BBC commentator Kenneth Wolstenholme
drooling on *Match of the Day.* "This boy Osgood . . . he really is
good!" he cooed.

Later that month, Osgood scored a stunning solo goal at Burnley
which he later nominated as the best of the 150 he notched for
the club. Unfortunately, Wolstenholme and the BBC cameras
weren't at Turf Moor to record the event but, happily, Ossie
himself had a vivid recollection of his Lancastrian masterpiece.

"They had a corner, Peter Bonetti caught it, threw it out to
me and I ran almost the length of the pitch, beat about five
players, took the ball round their keeper and put it in the back
of the net. I remember the whole ground applauding me as I
went back to the centre circle, which was a fantastic feeling. I've
been back to Burnley a few times since and people still come
up to me to talk about that goal."

While great news for Chelsea fans, the rise of the teenage prodigy
was not so welcome for England international Barry Bridges,
who found himself occasionally consigned to the substitutes'
bench. After a few weeks on the sidelines Bridges demanded a
transfer, which Tommy Docherty turned down. Another player
keen to move was Eddie McCreadie. After his successful cameo
display as a striker in the 1965 League Cup Final the Scotsman
had become convinced that he was the new Jimmy Greaves. "I'm
a great centre forward," he told Docherty, "but you've been playing
me out of position for three years."

The Doc said he'd alert other clubs to the availability of this
new striking talent and, the following morning, informed McCreadie

that a number of clubs were interested . . . headed by Mansfield Town. Surprisingly, Eddie seemed less keen to quit the Bridge after that.

With Osgood contributing seven league goals the Blues finished the season in fifth place, ten points behind champions Liverpool. Add in the pair of cup semi-final appearances and the season could be viewed from two distinct perspectives: reasonably satisfactory and full of promise for the future on the one hand or, on the other, somewhat disappointing.

Docherty took the latter view, being particularly annoyed by the Sheffield Wednesday FA Cup debacle. His reaction was typically impulsive, impetuous and extreme. Where another manager might have opted for a bit of tweaking with a screwdriver, Docherty took a sledgehammer to the team he had so painstakingly put together. Within a space of a few months the side was split apart, as Terry Venables moved to Spurs, George Graham joined Arsenal and Barry Bridges and Bert Murray left for Birmingham City. Peter Bonetti also looked set to depart, having put in a transfer request ahead of his involvement in England's World Cup campaign. If Chelsea fans were distraught by this sudden turn of events, so too were the players.

"It was so frustrating that Tommy Docherty lost his patience and that side was not allowed to fulfil its potential," Barry Bridges reflected years later. "We were a young team and team spirit was excellent. A lot of the players had played together all the way through from the youth team. We were inexperienced and we were getting better all the time. We played some great football as well. All off the cuff, the sort of thing only youngsters can get away with. Docherty overreacted to the Blackpool Incident when he sent us all home. We lost the last three games to cost us the championship and it all went wrong from there. Terry Venables has told me that it is his biggest disappointment in football what happened to that Chelsea team."

Peter Osgood may not have been that concerned about the

departure of Bridges, his rival for the number nine shirt, but he was sorry to see Terry Venables leave the club. "Terry was brilliant. I loved him to death and I thought he was a fantastic footballer. I thought he was superb, one of the best passers of the ball I've seen since Johnny Haynes. Johnny was the best passer of a ball I've seen in my life and Terry was his equal – that's how good a player Terry was. On top of that, he had a great engine on him, he could score goals and he was the leader of the pack. He was just a fantastic character to have around."

For Tommy Docherty, though, Venables and the others had been an irritant for some time. The rift created by the Blackpool Incident had not healed and, according to the Doc, his only option was to show the malcontents the door.

"Eddie McCreadie said to me, 'You've broken the team up.' But I told him, 'No, you lot broke it up, not me. If everyone had played the game, things could've been different.' Some of the lads started getting a bit stroppy after the Blackpool Incident and I decided to move them on. I don't regret doing that. Barry Bridges, for instance, wasn't a great player. He was quick and he scored goals, but he missed more than he scored. As for Venables, I should have sold him earlier than I did."

Having lost four components of his side, Docherty set about finding replacements. He had already strengthened the defence by buying West Ham full-back Joe Kirkup in March 1966. The following month he re-signed Ron Harris' brother, Allan, from Coventry for a second spell at the Bridge which would end in July 1967 when Harris joined QPR. Next, he moved to fill the gap in midfield left by the imminent departure of Terry Venables. The Doc's target was Charlie Cooke, a supremely gifted playmaker with Dundee. Cooke needed little persuading to move south and proved to be an instant hit with the Bridge crowd, who had always had a weak spot for an old-fashioned, ball-juggling entertainer.

"He was my best signing," enthuses Tommy. "What I loved about him was that when he came down to London he didn't say anything about money. He just said, 'Boss, isn't it great that I'm going to be playing for Chelsea?' And, of course, he was a marvellous player, far better than Terry Venables."

In truth, they were very different players who could not easily be compared. Venables was a team player, an organiser and a tremendous passer of the ball; Cooke, on the other hand, was a far more individualistic talent, a hypnotic dribbler who could send an opponent the wrong way with a snake-like swivel of his hips before accelerating away into the distance.

Meanwhile, Peter Bonetti's future at Chelsea remained uncertain. Relations between manager and player were hardly improved when Docherty refused to allow the Cat to report a week late for pre-season training after the goalkeeper had performed his understudy duties to Gordon Banks at the World Cup. Bonetti took a week off anyway, and Docherty responded to this latest flouting of his authority by promptly buying a new keeper, Millwall's Alex Stepney.

"The reason he got Alex was purely out of spite for me," Bonetti remarked later. "That's no disrespect to Alex because he was a brilliant keeper. Tommy and I were in dispute because I wanted to leave. He fined me and said Alex was going to play, so I put in another transfer request. There was speculation I was going to leave. But when the season started I was in the team and Tommy said he was going to play us in alternate games. Neither of us were going to put up with that; we both said the best keeper should be chosen on merit. But he sold Alex to Man United straight away so it didn't apply. Manchester United was my favourite club when I was a kid and I was just choked that it wasn't me going up there instead of him."

At the other end of the pitch, Docherty bolstered his striking options by signing Tommy Baldwin from Arsenal in exchange for George Graham in September 1966. "That was a great deal," the Doc says. "Tommy was the less established player so we also got around £50,000 from Arsenal as well." A wholehearted, unselfish performer who could be relied upon to harass defences for the full 90 minutes, Baldwin was also an intelligent, opportunistic striker who specialised in supplying the finishing touch at the near post. Having replaced the popular Graham, Baldwin might have worried about the reception he'd get from the crowd. The fans, though, couldn't resist such a transparent trier and the Gateshead-born forward proved to be an instant hit.

By this time the dust had settled after all the comings and goings and, somewhat surprisingly considering all the rumblings of discontent, the Blues had got off to a magnificent start to the 1966/67 season. An impressive opening day win at West Ham, where the Hammers' World Cup-winning trio of Bobby Moore, Geoff Hurst and Martin Peters had been paraded before an adoring East End crowd prior to kick-off, set the tone and helped to propel the Blues on a scintillating 10-match unbeaten run.

What's more, Chelsea were playing with a verve and panache which suggested a trophy of some sort was very much on the agenda. A 6–2 away thrashing of Aston Villa in September, a match in which Bobby Tambling scored five goals, only seemed to confirm the widespread view that Chelsea would be among the league title contenders. For new man Tommy Baldwin, who made a scoring debut in another emphatic away win three weeks later at Manchester City, the free-flowing style he discovered at Chelsea was a revelation after the tactical rigidity he had experienced at Highbury.

"It was a complete change," he says. "As an Arsenal player I was taught that you had to defend all the time – even as centre-forward I had to be running back and chasing. The accent was on defending. From being in the youth team they told us that if you got a 0–0 draw that was okay, you'd got a point. You had to keep a clean sheet – that was the emphasis all the time. It was very different at Chelsea. When Tommy Docherty signed me we had a team meeting before the game. All he said was, 'You've all met Tommy, haven't you? He's playing up front, so knock the ball up to him, he'll hang onto it and we'll play from there.'

"That was it. It was a real breath of fresh air. He didn't say anything like, 'Oh, this full back likes to bomb on so make sure you close him down.' He didn't worry about the other teams at all. Of course, he'd tell the defence about the opposition strikers and if they had a guy who was a bit quick or whatever, but with me he just said to concentrate on attacking. My game was always about running back and chasing so I still carried on doing that, but it was nice to be able to concentrate on scoring goals. Anyway, we went out and won that first game 4–1, which was a great start for me."

Baldwin had another reason to be happy as his bank balance showed an instant improvement after his move across London. "My wages jumped from £25 to £80 a week and I got a signing on fee," he says. "But the idea of just playing for Chelsea really appealed to me, because they had a young team full of good players."

Arguably the best of those young players was Osgood, who with six goals in those first ten games had maintained the form which had catapulted him into the nation's consciousness the previous season. But, just four days after helping the Blues to the top of the table after the win at Maine Road, the young striker's season came to an abrupt end when he broke his leg in a tackle with Blackpool's Emlyn Hughes – a devastating blow for both player and club. Chelsea's season – in the league, if not the FA Cup – never really recovered and a final placing of ninth was well below the heightened expectations of the early autumn.

Deprived of his talismanic centre forward, Docherty wasted little time in recruiting a replacement, signing Aston Villa striker Tony Hateley (the father of 1980s England centre forward Mark Hateley) for £100,000. A former schoolboy high jump champion, Hateley was rated as one of the best headers of the ball in the game. His ground skills, though, were altogether more prosaic and Chelsea fans soon became used to intricate passing moves coming to a sudden halt at the feet of the floundering forward.

"Tony was a lovely lad and a good pro, but we were a quick,

skilful and very fit side and he didn't fit into our style of foot-ball," admits Docherty. "He was great in the air and we had very quick players down the wings who could put over good crosses, so I thought he'd give us another outlet. But he turned out to be a bad signing. Probably my worst."

Despite that blunt assessment, it's only fair to point out that Hateley played a central role that season in Chelsea's run to their first ever Wembley FA Cup Final (the only other final the Blues had reached, when they lost 3–0 to Sheffield United in 1915, had been played at Old Trafford). The route to the Twin Towers began with a 2–1 win at Huddersfield, where Bobby Tambling and left-winger Peter Houseman, enjoying his longest spell in the side since making his debut three years earlier, were on target. In the fourth round, the Blues were drawn away to lowly Brighton and took the opportunity to spend a relaxing week on the south coast in preparation for the game.

"We went down there on the Tuesday and met up with a local bookmaker, George Gunn, who was a friend of Dave Sexton's," recalls John Boyle. "He took us to a club that night and then we went to the dog track on Wednesday evening where we had a meal and a drink. Then, on Thursday, we went to a casino. Tommy was with us the whole time, so there was no problem."

Maybe, though, the accent was just a little too much on fun rather than training, as the Blues survived an almighty scare at a packed Goldstone Ground, holding on for a 1–1 draw after Boyle was dismissed.

"It was really quite rare in those days to get sent off, it had to be a pretty bad foul even to get a booking," says Boylers. "They had a guy called Wally Gould and I got sent off for fouling him. I got changed immediately. I felt so upset about it I left the stadium and went for a walk along Brighton beach. I remember sitting by the sea, thinking, 'What have I done? If we lose it'll be my fault.' I thought I'd put us out of the FA Cup. Fortunately, we got the draw and Tommy Docherty was very good about it.

He picked me for the replay four days later which we won 4–0. I felt a whole lot better after that."

The Blues repeated their Brighton sojourn before the fifth and sixth rounds, both won at home against the two Sheffield teams, United and Wednesday. The benefits of the bracing sea air and a change of scenery weren't the only factors in Docherty's *Groundhog Day* policy, according to Ron Harris.

"Tom was superstitious," he says, "so we had to do the same thing every round. We used to go down to Brighton and stay in the same hotel, the Dudley Hotel. We trained nearby at Worthing. He used to give us some money to go to a Chinese restaurant or go to a club to have a couple of drinks. It became our Cup routine."

In the semi-final draw Chelsea were paired with Leeds at Villa Park while Tottenham and Nottingham Forest were due to meet at Hillsborough in the other tie. The longstanding, and frequently tempestuous, rivalry between the Blues and the Yorkshiremen is often traced back to this match but, as John Boyle recalls, there had been a good number of ugly incidents in the clubs' previous meetings.

"One of the first matches I played for Chelsea was against Leeds at Elland Road in January 1965. The pitch was very icy, and the Leeds players had these leather studs which were screw-ins but also had nails in them. They'd actually clipped off half their studs and left the nails sticking out. Chelsea complained afterwards, and I think it was soon after that refs started inspecting studs.

"Then, about a year later back at Elland Road, I dived to head the ball and Billy Bremner booted me in the face, knocking me out. Harry Medhurst, our trainer, came on and gave me some smelling salts; the game restarted, and I was looking around, thinking 'Um, nice lights.' I could just about make out Ossie screaming, 'Get 'im off!' Even when I got to hospital I didn't have a clue where I was!"

Boyle describes Leeds as "cynical bullies", a description which seems generous given the treatment meted out to him in the semi-final by the Yorkshire side's goalkeeper, Welsh international Gary Sprake. "I was chasing a long ball," he says, "Sprake came out to catch it and kicked me in the face. I had a thick lip and bloody nose, but we won the game, so it didn't matter. Anyway, a couple of years later we were up in a club in Leeds after playing at Elland Road, and Sprake was there, so Ossie went over and said, 'You took a right liberty when you kicked John in the face!' Gary looked at me and said, 'John, I promise you, I only meant to kick you in the chest!'"

Boyle downplays the incident, but according to Tommy Baldwin and other witnesses, the injury he sustained in the semi-final was one of the goriest they have ever seen on a football field. "It was a terrible sight," says Baldwin, "there was blood dripping all down his face and onto his shirt. But great credit to John Boyle, who played on regardless. At half-time we were absolutely furious about the incident."

Ironically, Sprake needed treatment himself in the second half after an accidental collision with Tony Hateley knocked out a couple of his teeth. And Hateley made an even more telling contribution later in the game, scoring the all-important goal which took Chelsea to Wembley. "Charlie Cooke picked the ball up on the halfway line, beat about five players and slung a great ball in," he remembers. "I just powered it in past Gary Sprake from around the penalty spot. I remember Ossie, who still had his leg in plaster, jumping out of the dug out and hopping on the pitch."

If a header from 12 yards sounds impressive, then think again. Ron Harris, who admittedly would have been some way back from the crucial action, reckons Hateley scored from double that distance. "Honestly, I've never seen anybody head a goal so far or so hard," he says. "It was well outside the penalty area."

The champagne was out on the train home, with even teeto-taller Hateley joining in the wild celebrations. No doubt some of the toasts were to referee Ken Burns who had controversially disallowed a trademark Peter Lorimer piledriver free-kick because he hadn't blown his whistle. The Blues, though, could convincingly argue that they deserved that spot of luck, after the misfortune of losing in the semi-final in both 1965 and 1966.

It didn't take long, however, for the champers to go flat. At a time when the players should have been solely focused on the final against Tottenham, the victors in the other semi-final, much of their energy in the build up to Wembley was taken up by a heated dispute with the club over bonuses and the allocation of Cup Final tickets.

"In our contracts we were on £250 for reaching the final and £500 for winning the Cup," explains Tommy Baldwin. "But, obviously, players talk to each other and we found out that the Tottenham team were on £1,000 for getting to Wembley and £2,000 for winning the game. Initially, the Spurs players had been on similar bonuses to us but the club had increased the money as a reward. Chelsea, though, just wouldn't budge.

"Another problem we had was with the distribution of Cup Final tickets. Under FA rules we only got 13 tickets each. Why 13, I don't know. But you can imagine that if you get to the Cup Final with all your family, relations and friends to consider, 13 tickets doesn't go anywhere. Again Tottenham were doing better than us. I know the club gave them about 100 tickets each. So that didn't help."

Indeed, gripes about players' tickets had been a feature of the Cup run with the squad holding protest meetings over what they claimed was an insufficient allocation before both the fourth round tie at Brighton and the semi-final with Leeds.

"The whole thing was a bit of a shambles, to be honest," adds John Boyle. "Whatever the FA said, the unwritten rule was that each player would get 100 tickets from his club for the Cup Final. They used to keep 20 or 30 and the rest went to touts. Stan Flashman was the big name but there were a few other well-known touts as well. For the married guys, especially, the extra money was a bonus because it wasn't listed on their pay slip and so the wives didn't know about it. It was money in your pocket. Usually Marvin Hinton, who was one of the married players, would collect all our tickets and do the business for us.

"Anyway, before the Cup Final Tommy Docherty read the riot act to us. 'If anybody is thinking of selling their tickets, I can tell them they're going to be in serious trouble,' he warned us. Then, a few minutes later, the groundsman came in with a brown paper bag for Tommy. 'Here's your bag, Tommy,' he muttered. As he passed it to him, somebody caught a peep inside and there was a load of cash there. We thought 'he's only gone and sold his tickets!'"

Tommy Docherty, though, strongly denies that he sold any of his tickets above their face value. "As manager I received 100 tickets from the club for the Cup Final and I had to pay for them myself," he says. "It's ridiculous to say I sold them to touts. The tickets went to family and friends. When you have an allo-cation like that you have to write down the names and address of every person you give a ticket to, which you wouldn't be able to do if a tout bought them off you. The only 'deal' I made was to swap four tickets for four seats at Wimbledon.

"In those days players signed a contract every year and the bonuses would be included. Whatever the players say, the contract could not be altered during the season without permission from the Football League – Alan Hardaker, the Football League secretary, was a stickler for that. So I doubt very much that Tottenham adjusted their bonuses. As for the dispute about the tickets, they wanted a bigger allocation so they could sell them and make a few quid. In fairness, they were only on about £50 a week then, but all the same how could they justify doing that to the supporters who ended up having to pay well over the odds for a ticket?"

The players' ticket allocation was eventually increased to 20, still way below the unofficial norm. The dispute over bonuses, though, took longer to be settled and, incredibly, was still a matter of bitter debate on the morning of the Cup Final.

"We had a meeting at the hotel in Hendon, and seven players including myself said to Tommy Docherty that if we didn't get a better offer we weren't going to play," says Tommy Baldwin. "In the end they doubled the original offer to £500 for making the final and £1,000 if we won it. But that was still half what Tottenham were on."

The strike threat may have been little more than a bargaining chip but, all the same, the whole episode was hardly the best preparation for the final, the first ever between two London clubs. Dubbed, inevitably, 'the Cockney Cup Final' by the popular press the match was a hard one to call. Tottenham had finished the season in third place behind champions Manchester United and Nottingham Forest and were the form team, having put together a long unbeaten run. Chelsea, by contrast, arrived at Wembley with no momentum at all, after having lost five of their last seven league games.

On the other hand, the Blues could point to a good record against Spurs in their head-to-head meetings that season: a 3–0 win at the Bridge in October and a 1–1 draw at White Hart Lane in March – a match in which 16-year-old Ian 'Chico' Hamilton set a double record as both Chelsea's youngest ever player and youngest goalscorer.

In his Cup Final preview in *The Times*, Geoffrey Green alerted readers to "a strong feeling in my boots that Chelsea will win the Cup at last." His hunch seemed to be based more on an appreciation of the Blues' fluid style of play than anything else. "Chelsea are fashioned in the modern idiom," Green wrote. "They do not boast accepted wing players: numbers on players' backs are for mere identification in the programme and bear no relationship to old-fashioned positions on the field; full backs and wing halves overlap as the pattern unfolds playing, as it were, positional leapfrog."

If the Chelsea game plan was to confuse the opposition with unlikely players popping up in unexpected places, it didn't work. Tottenham, with Terry Venables prominent in midfield, took control of the game through goals by Jimmy Robertson and Frank Saul, and although Bobby Tambling replied late on it was the scantest of consolations for the Blues. As with so many Cup Finals, the game was a flop as a spectacle, primarily because Chelsea had under-performed so badly.

"No doubts about it, we were completely outplayed," admitted John Hollins some years later. "I was nervous. I think we all were. Nerves can destroy a team. They drain you, and when the time comes to raise your game, you can't because you're exhausted."

Other players also blame nerves for the disappointing showing but Marvin Hinton has a different slant on the main reason for the defeat. "Tommy Docherty changed the system," he says. "I'd been playing sweeper all season, and he put me in as marker. I had to mark Alan Gilzean, who was a good touch player and quite slippery. I was awful, I admit it. The argument about tickets and bonuses didn't help either."

"Players are always great tacticians after the game," responds the Doc. "I don't remember him complaining before the match. In any case, Marvin hadn't been playing as a sweeper. He played just like Bobby Moore, off the centre half. But it's true we didn't play well in the final. Neither did Tottenham – it was a dreadful game. I always think the best cup finals are between a northern team and a southern team."

A few days after the Cup Final Chelsea set off on a three-week tour of America, Canada and Bermuda. The trip was meant to be little more than an end-of-season jolly, and seemed to provide the perfect opportunity for the players to put the heartbreak of Wembley behind them. Life at Chelsea, though, was rarely so uncomplicated and for Tommy Docherty and his players events on the tour were to have far-reaching and dramatic consequences.

CHAPTER FOUR
KINGS OF THE KING'S ROAD

Despite stiff competition from Wembley and Arsenal's Emirates Stadium, Stamford Bridge can claim to be the capital's premier football venue. As former chairman Ken Bates was fond of pointing out, its location – "ten minutes by taxi to Harrod's" – is unrivalled, particularly for the well-heeled supporter who enjoys a spot of up-market post-match shopping. Almost entirely redeveloped in the last decade (only the East Stand dates back to before the mid-90s), with seating for 42,000 fans, the ground itself features a host of first-rate facilities, including two hotels, a health club, a night club and numerous bars and restaurants.

The Fulham Road, running past the front entrances to the ground, also provides hungry fans with a wide variety of dining opportunities ranging from hot dogs to sushi, as well as an ultra-convenient underground station and, in Fulham Town Hall, a focal point for exuberant cup-winning celebrations. Backing onto the East Stand, meanwhile, beyond the railway line, Brompton cemetery, with its ornate gravestones and elaborate tombs, makes for a tranquil and relaxing approach to the ground for fans arriving from Earl's Court tube station. A little further away, but still within walking distance, the route over Battersea Bridge, offering splendid views of the Thames up to Vauxhall and the hugely expensive Victorian townhouses along Cheyne Walk, is popular with fans living south of the river.

Above all, though, it's the nearby King's Road, one of the most famous streets in the whole of London, which has always given an extra buzz to any trip to the Bridge. Designed by Charles II as a royalty-only thoroughfare providing a short cut to Hampton Court, the King's Road finally opened to the public in 1830. More than a century later the street's fame spread worldwide as it became an informal stage set for the 'Swinging Sixties'.

Although still featuring on many tourists' 'must see' list, today the King's Road is not what it was: high rents have forced the smaller, quirkier shops out and the familiar big chains – Boots, Starbucks, various mobile-phone retailers and Rymans to name but a few – have moved in. Most depressingly of all, a branch of the Abbey National building society now stands on the site of the Markham Arms, a favourite haunt of the Chelsea players during the 1960s and 1970s, while the Chelsea Drugstore bar, once celebrated by the Rolling Stones on their classic track *You Can't Always Get What You Want*, became a part of the ever-expanding McDonald's empire many years ago. All the same, a few landmark sites have survived the culling process including the flower-festooned Chelsea Potter pub, cowboy-boot retailers R Soles and Pucci Pizza, a long-established Italian restaurant where model Sophie Dahl used to work as a waitress, serving cheap but tasty pizzas to the likes of Jack Nicholson and George Best.

Happily, for the players at the time, the heyday of the King's Road coincided with the emergence of Chelsea as London's most glamorous team in the mid-sixties. "There was so much going on then," says Alan Hudson, who was born just around the corner from the Bridge. "When I got in the first team it was the real Swinging Sixties. The King's Road was incredible. There were a lot of nice girls walking around, and the pubs were great as well. The Palmerston was the main pub where the players would go, and boxers went there too. Further down the King's Road you had the Trafalgar which was Tommy Baldwin's favourite pub. The Markham was the main pub that I used to go to because my favourite restaurant, Alexander's, was next door down in the basement."

Alexander's was owned by Alexander Plunkett-Green, who was married to the fashion designer Mary Quant. The couple were well-connected and the restaurant attracted an A-list clientele, ranging from pop and film stars to royalty. "Adam Faith was a regular in Alexander's," recalls Huddy. "Marc Bolan had a place over the road from the restaurant, so he would use it. Everybody went there. Apart from Annabel's in Berkeley Square it was the place where you could walk by and see all sorts of famous faces, even kings and princes. As you walked in the door there was a round table called the Royal Table, and when there was no royalty in that was where the Chelsea boys sat.

"I didn't discover the place to begin with – that was down to my brother, John, who was on Chelsea's books at one time. He used to clean the windows there – not that they had many. So, I was the one who introduced Alexander's to all the lads and it became very popular with everybody. We'd go in there after training for lunch – especially on a Friday, after we'd been training at Stamford Bridge. Then we'd go on to a drinking club, because pubs weren't open in the afternoons in those days."

Despite claiming that "it's a bit of a myth that I was part of the King's Road gang", Windsor-based Peter Osgood was also a regular diner at Alexander's. "It was definitely the 'in' place," he said. "You'd get Conners – Sean Connery – in there and Princess Anne and so on. Sir Richard Attenborough would go down there with his actor mates. We knew who they were and they knew we were the Chelsea boys. They were brilliant to us; we'd leave them alone and they'd leave us alone but if they wanted to come over and say 'Hello' that was fine, too. It was smashing. We got introduced to quite a few people down there. I didn't speak to Princess Anne, she was royalty, after all. We'd have loved it if she had come across to said 'Hello' but you can't approach, can you?" Surely, though, the onus was on Princess Anne to pay her respects to Ossie – after all, he was 'King of the Bridge'.

Another popular spot with the players was Alvaro's restaurant, which opened in April 1966 virtually next door to Alexander's at 124 King's Road and opposite Royal Avenue – the street where James Bond had his London address in the Ian Fleming books. "There were just a couple of other Italian restaurants in the area at the time," remembers owner Alvaro Maccioni. "When I bought the site off the man who owned it the place was the Magic Carpet Inn, a traditional old English-type bistro. He shook my hand when we completed the deal and said, 'I wish you all the luck in the world, because as far as I'm concerned the King's Road is finished.' Maybe his type of King's Road was finished, but it was the beginning of the new fashionable one.

"It took off immediately. It was as though people were just waiting for us to open. To begin with I didn't know any of the Chelsea players, but within one week of the restaurant being open we had Sammy Davis Junior and Princess Margaret come in on the same night. Princess Margaret said she would love to meet Sammy Davis Jnr so I went over to him and had a word, and then they had a chat. The following day it was all over the papers, not just the *Evening Standard* but the nationals."

Alvaro's was so successful that a year later, in 1967, Signor Maccioni opened a nightclub in the King's Road called the Aretusa which soon became a favourite with the players. "When we opened the Aretusa club I sent invitations to Peter Osgood and Peter Bonetti," says Alvaro, "because they were the only two I knew well from Alvaro's. From then onwards we met them all. The restaurant in the club was booked a month ahead in advance, and we didn't let anyone in off the street even if we were empty as it was a strictly members only club. In those days you had to be strict about the membership because otherwise you could have lost your licence as we were allowed to serve alcohol outside normal pub hours. But, as a member, you could drink from 11am to three o'clock the following morning."

In this era of strict licensing laws, the Aretusa's liberal policy made it an especially appealing venue to the heavy drinkers among the squad. "There were days when they were in there a long time," Alvaro says. "But, having said that, I don't remember them overdoing it. Of course they had a drink. They used to come in the evening, they used to come in the afternoon. It was open all day long and it was the place to come in the sixties and seventies for Chelsea players. We had lots of pretty girls coming too, which was another attraction – many models, film and TV people, the Rolling Stones, David Bailey, all the James Bond crowd, Michael Caine and so on. The club attracted a very creative crowd." Another frequent visitor was the hard-drinking actor Richard Harris, who would occasionally challenge Tommy Baldwin to a drunken bout of arm wrestling.

"During the day the Rolling Stones and Beatles often used to come to try out their new records before they released them," continues Alvaro. "We had one of the best sound systems in any discotheque and they wanted to hear how their records sounded in that environment. Often they would leave the record behind afterwards so I've got a big collection of records with a label on only one side. At the time I didn't realise how valuable they would become. It was only a few years ago when I saw something on the internet about rare records that I realised they would be worth something. So I went back in the loft to search them out."

It wasn't only players from Chelsea who came to the club. Despite playing for Manchester United, George Best, the most famous and most talented footballer of the era, was a regular. "He had his own chair at the bar," remembers Alvaro. "He used to come in most nights, often with a different woman. It was a shame he didn't play for Chelsea, but he still spent lots of time in London. I couldn't understand how he did it. I remember once he was still at the club at 2am and the next evening United were playing AC Milan in the European Cup in Manchester. He'd had a few drinks but he wasn't in a bad way; in fact, I never saw him in a bad way, he could hold a drink so well you could never tell if he was drunk or sober. Anyway, George gave me a pass to go and watch the game, I left him in the club and went home.

"The following day I arrived at Old Trafford and I only had this pass, not a proper ticket. I needed to meet George at a particular door where he'd let me in. I was thinking, 'I'm sure he won't be playing, not after last night . . .' But I got to the door and there he was. And when the game started he was brilliant and scored two goals. I couldn't believe it, it really was unbelievable."

Alvaro sold his club and restaurant in 1972. Three years later he opened another eaterie, La Familigia, just off the top of the King's Road in Langton Street. "Carlo Cudicini uses us as his canteen," jokes Alvaro, a loyal Chelsea fan who has graduated over the years from the Shed to a box in Di Matteo's hospitality suite. Roman Abramovich, Claudio Ranieri and Ken Bates have also been spotted in the restaurant, which is so popular on match-days customers need to book months in advance to be sure of getting a table.

In the 1960s the King's Road, along with Carnaby Street, was prime clothes-shopping territory for the fab, groovy and 'with-it' young. Signalling their own fabness, grooviness and 'with-it-ness', simple clothes shops became boutiques – part of a wider trend which saw restaurants turn into bistros, dancehalls reinvent themselves as discotheques, and even plain old barbers' re-emerge as salons. For High Street shoppers everywhere 'O' level French had never seemed so useful.

Mary Quant had opened Britain's first ever boutique, Bazaar, on the King's Road in 1955. Selling skinny rib sweaters, plastic raincoats, colourful tights and, later, Quant's own ground-breaking creations such as the mini, micro-mini and hot pants, the store was a huge success and was soon joined by similar outlets along the length of the King's Road. Among the more famous names were Take Six, Topgear, the hippy store I Was Lord Kitchener's Valet and Let It Rock, which was opened by Vivienne Westwood and Malcolm McLaren in 1971, and later became the legendary punk shop, Sex.

Being a local lad, Alan Hudson was especially in tune with the fast changing fashion scene and, although younger than the other players, he was considered something of a style guru. "Ossie asked me to take him down the King's Road a couple of times," he says. "He didn't know how to dress because he came from Windsor. I took him along to some top-notch places like Just Man and Take Six there and we bought a load of gear. Personally, I was having suits made up for about £200 a pop. I also used to like the shirts and the ties in the same colour, especially the floral ones."

A valued adviser on fashion matters, Huddy's clothes sense, shoulder-length hair and popularity with young female fans also made him a target for the modelling agencies. "I did a bit of modelling, but only for fun," he says. "I did a thing for a shampoo company and there was ads all over the underground with my picture on them. I also did some modelling for Limited Edition shirts. They didn't pay me, but I got to keep the shirts."

As the sixties progressed, fashions became more bizarre or 'far out' in hippy-speak. The Chelsea boys had broadly adopted the sharp-suited 'mod' look in the mid-sixties, but although their hair grew longer as the seventies approached, kaftans, bandannas and tie-dye T-shirts did not become a part of the typical player's wardrobe.

"We didn't get into wacky clothes," says John Boyle, "partly because we always had to wear a suit when we travelled away. We used to get our suits from Soho. Terry Venables and George Graham had a few friends in the business and we used to go with them to get fitted up. You'd pick your own material, take it down and they would do you a suit. We never did much shopping on the King's Road because we were mostly pretty conservative. It was more about being smart and smooth than being flamboyant.

"To begin with we all had short hair – it got a lot hairier later. The Beatles were a big influence on us because they grew their hair long in the late sixties. Before that we didn't like long hair at all. I can remember coming back from a game in Barcelona in 1966 we bumped into the singer Crispin St Peter at the airport. There were a few comments about 'long-haired pop stars' because he had a ponytail and very few men had them in those days."

In fact, far from embracing the sandals-and-cheesecloth 'counter-culture' style, some of the players looked more like the city toffs or 'bread heads' the hippies actively despised. "Eddie McCreadie was the best-dressed man of the squad," claims Alan Birchenall, who joined Chelsea shortly after the hedonistic, psychedelia-soaked 'Summer of Love' in 1967. "He's the only guy I ever met who would come to training wearing a three-piece suit: jacket, waistcoat, trousers. He looked like a banker, more of a city investor than a footballer. He even had the rolled up umbrella."

It's unlikely that Eddie, by then Chelsea manager, would have chosen to buy his clothes from the shop on Elleston Green that his old team-mates Tommy Baldwin and Charlie Cooke opened in 1977 along with Baldwin's wife, Gabrielle, and former *Ready, Steady, Go* presenter Cathy McGowan. "We sold second hand stage gear we'd got from pop stars, people like Elton John," says Tommy. "It was quite successful. I used to serve in the shop sometimes with Charlie who was still at Chelsea at the time."

The Elton John connection went back a few years when Tommy was offered the chance to provide financial backing for the singer, who was then just beginning his showbiz career and was still in the process of casting off his old identity as plain Reg Dwight from Pinner. "I knew his PR guy, Ray, who was looking for a couple of investors to put in £1,500 to start Elton off," recalls

Tommy. "Everyone was saying he was going to be the next big thing, but I didn't think much of the demo tape Ray sent me. In fact, I threw it out of the car window. Then I was invited to his first gig at a club called the Speakeasy. Everyone was raving about him but I was more interested in having a few drinks. Anyway, I was always more into country and western. I didn't take Ray up on his offer."

Unlike some of his players, manager Dave Sexton was an infrequent visitor to the King's Road, preferring to buy his clothes in Mayfair. A conservative man who had served with the army in Greece, Sexton preferred the clean cut style of an earlier period and was unimpressed by the increasingly scruffy appearance of his players. On one famous occasion, he even dropped David Webb for growing a beard.

"Dave was a very nice man and would come in every so often to buy a suit," says his tailor Doug Hayward. "One day he came in and gave me the tracksuit they wore at Wembley – blue trousers and a red top with the 1970 FA Cup Final motif on it. I had it upstairs for years until my daughter found it and she started wearing it to Chelsea games. Lots of people would come up to her and ask her where she got it. It caused quite a stir."

Doug, who still runs Hayward's outfitters in Mount Street W1, was a regular at the Bridge throughout the sixties, and organised tickets for a group of fans who included actors and film directors. "I used to buy 12 season tickets every year and everyone would pay for one," he says. "I would hold the tickets during the week and if a couple of people were away filming or whatever we had a list of substitutes to fill in. We used to meet before the game at a small restaurant on the King's Road. Then, when Alvaro's opened, he invited us along for the opening night. The paint was still wet and everyone was getting white marks on their jackets. Custom was a bit slow at first so he asked us all to come along and have lunch every Saturday before going to the football. He only charged £1 a head, which was a really good gesture as the meal was probably worth £5. But he just wanted a regular group of people to come every Saturday.

"That £1 a head continued for about eight or nine years and he never put the price up. It was lovely food too. Tommy Steele used to pop into my shop and say, 'Have you got a spare ticket this week?' He'd come along to lunch at Alvaro's and when it was time to put the £1 in he used to hold the note in his hand above the pot and then take it back without dropping the pound in. I bought an old taxi – I think it cost me £15 – and we used it to deliver stuff to the shop. But on Saturday afternoons we had this boy who came by and we used to give him two bob each to pick us up at Alvaro's and run us to Chelsea. Then he'd go away and come back at ten past five and we'd all pile in again. We got about ten or 12 people in that taxi, it was a real crush. Even then Tommy Steele wouldn't cough up the two bob. I couldn't believe it!"

One of those subsidising the long-pocketed entertainer was the photographer Terry O'Neill. In 1972 he created one of the iconic images of football in that decade when he snapped a group of London players, including Alan Hudson, David Webb and Terry Venables, smoking cigars and drinking brandies in a Fleet Street restaurant. "The idea was to make them look like the football mafia," he says. "I did that one in London and another in Manchester with Malcolm Allison, Rodney Marsh and Francis Lee. I did film stars normally but I loved sports. *The Sun* had just launched and was the first paper to go for pictures of footballers off the pitch. So I thought up this 'clan' idea and sold them the pictures. It was difficult to get all the players together; if you think they're unreliable now they were mega-unreliable then. But I got them all together somehow, although it was all a last minute rush."

Chelsea have always had a showbiz following, but in the 1960s the Bridge could probably have supported a branch of Equity. Among the many actors following the Blues during the

Docherty and Sexton eras were Dennis Waterman, Michael Crawford, *Man About the House* star Richard O'Sullivan, Bill Gaunt and Rodney Bewes, better known at the time as Bob Ferris from *The Likely Lads*.

"Because of *The Likely Lads* and all the other filming I've done in the north east, people think I'm a Geordie," Bewes said a few years ago. "Actually, I was born in the middle of Yorkshire and then came down to London at 14. I used to stand in the Shed at every home match and travel away a lot, too. I was one of a group of North Country actors who followed Chelsea all over the place. The players were heroes of mine and I always made a conscious effort not to meet them. When you appear on TV you can normally get to meet most people, but I went out of my way to avoid the Chelsea players – I didn't want my illusions shattered.

"I was offered tickets for the Chelsea Ball and that type of thing, but always flatly refused. But then I bumped into Peter Bonetti in a King's Road restaurant. We'd never met, but it was as if we'd known each other for years. First name terms and an instant friendship. Then Peter turned to me and said: 'Who's that tasty looking blonde in the corner?' I told him that it was my wife Daphne and thought to myself that even the great Chelsea players have human instincts like the rest of us. I actually took Daphne to Stamford Bridge on my first date with her. I met her at a midweek party and asked her to Chelsea the following Saturday. She told me that she'd been frantically trying to get hold of me to say she didn't fancy going to watch a football match. But as I was ex-directory, she couldn't make contact. In the end, though, she enjoyed herself."

Bewes would often attend the Bridge with the actor Tom Courtenay, a Hull City fan who also adopted Chelsea as his London team. "I remember one occasion when Tom was having enormous success in the title role in the film Billy Liar. Tom was a little reluctant to go, because he thought people might start pulling his leg. But I managed to persuade him. Sure enough, after a few minutes of the match, some wag started shouting: 'Billy Liar, Billy Liar.' Tom told me that he should have stayed at home. 'No, I replied, it's okay. Just smile at the chap.' Tom did just that and promptly had an orange thrown in his face!"

Based in a studio next door to Stamford Bridge, fashion photographer Eric Swayne knew just about everyone who was anyone on the King's Road scene in the sixties. Mary Quant and Vidal Sassoon were among his clients, he was on friendly terms with members of The Who and Rolling Stones and, even more impressively, Jane Birkin and Patti Boyd figured among his many girlfriends. Over the years he got to know a number of Chelsea players, although he might never have met any of them if the Blues had been able to keep the ball on the ground . . .

"In 1962 I went freelance and rented my first studio. It was in a block called West London Studios right next to the main entrance of Stamford Bridge. Our block was packed with really well known photographers, which I wasn't at the beginning. It was a bit of a celebrity photographer and model block, a lovely place. At that time the Chelsea team used to have a kickaround every morning in the car park. Their practice balls would occasionally come over the wall, so I often used to rush down to nick one. The players used to come round looking for the balls, but if I'd been around they very rarely found one. I had quite a collection, and I used to take them along to Parsons Green for a kickaround. Anyway, that's how I got to know the players – when they called round to ask for their ball back.

"Three of us in the block of studios had season tickets at Chelsea in the old East Stand and we had two spares as well. There was me, two art directors and in our little cluster of seats we were near Alan Price, Tom Courtenay, and the actor from *The Likely Lads*, Rodney Bewes. Pricey used to come along on one of my tickets sometimes. We had fantastic seats right next to the Directors' Box. I started supporting them the year they came up from the Second Division, 1963. I was immediately hooked on the Blues, like my son now who has a couple of season tickets. It was a very exciting team at the time. They had a devil-may-care attitude which made them great to watch. Alright, they didn't have the discipline of some of the players today and they probably didn't do the same amount of training but they had lovely talent. They were real stars, kind of like pop stars. They were marvellous. A super set of guys.

"Throughout this time I was very busy with my work as a photographer. Ian Quick, who was an art director with a design group called Yellowhammer wanted to do a poster of me for my own publicity. His father, Norman, was the sports photographer with *The Daily Express* and he arranged that some of the Chelsea team would appear in a photo shoot for me at Stamford Bridge.

"I paid a small fee, £50 or so, which was enough in those days. The idea was to have Peter Bonetti in goal with a defensive wall in front of him consisting of me, Johnny Boyle, Keith Weller and Tommy Baldwin. In the end we never did the poster because the guys weren't allowed to wear their Chelsea kit. We took the photos but it would have meant a lot of retouching and strip-ping the crowd in at the Shed end so we scrapped the idea. Anyway, I remember being very proud that I was wearing Ossie's shorts, which I'd found in the dressing room. Before the photo shoot started we were mucking around and having a kickabout with Keith Weller and the others. Keith put in a cross from the right and I hit it on the volley – pretty well, I felt. I thought 'Yes, goal!' but Peter Bonetti just nonchalantly flicked out a leg and kicked the ball clear. That was annoying enough, but what really got me was that at the time he had his back to me and was deep in conversation with the groundsman!"

In September 1973 Eric was asked by John Boyle to take the photos at his wedding in Walworth, south-east London. Peter Osgood was best man and most of the other Chelsea players were guests. "I knew the footballers who were there but I hadn't met his wife, Madelaine, before or any of his and her family," says

Eric. "I just photographed anything that moved, sent off the contacts to John Boyle at Chelsea FC with a little note saying, 'Phone me, when you want to order prints' and he never phoned me. So, I thought, 'Funny bloke, doesn't like the pictures', which I found a bit strange because I did about ten or twelve cassettes of film. I really went for it."

What Eric didn't realise is that Boylers had gone out on loan to Brighton and the photos hadn't been forwarded to him. The pair lost contact and the wedding photos remained lost somewhere in the bowels of Stamford Bridge. Eventually, 28 years later, after Boyle had put out an appeal to readers of the official *Chelsea Magazine* to help him find the photographer, John, Eric and a copy of the snaps were reunited in a heart-warming encounter at the Shed Bar which would surely have brought a tear to the nation's eye had it been captured by daytime TV.

Interestingly, although he was on friendly terms with some of the team, Eric used to steer clear of the players' favourite King's Road pub, the Markham Arms. "I avoided it because the Kray twins used to drink there," he says. "I used to go to the Chelsea Potter instead."

Yet, it was the Potter which was the scene of a massive police raid in 1968 when the Met were on the tail of Great Train Robber Bruce Reynolds. The police had intercepted a telephone message from Reynolds in which he said he would meet his associate at the pub. What they failed to realise, though, was that 'Chelsea Potter' was code for 'Sloane Square tube' so the police ended up missing their prey by a mere couple of hundred yards.

Such excitement was unusual. Most of the time, the King's Road was simply a place to chill out and watch the beautiful people stroll by. "The King's Road was a just marvellous place to be back then," says Eric. "On Saturday mornings I'd drive down the road in my Mini Cooper S with the window down and the stereo on and the number of attractive women you'd see was amazing. In the King's Road I found, so to speak, Roy Boulting's daughter,

Enid and Jane Birkin, who I went out with for a while – both stunning girls. The King's Road was a magnet for them."

Fellow photographer Terry O'Neill agrees. "It was always a happy place, everyone was eyeing up the girls. It's not the same now, although the excitement's come back a bit. The girls were all in mini skirts – it was a bit like the south of France, St Tropez or somewhere. It was definitely the best place to go to see beautiful girls in London. Some of them were models, others were ordinary girls but they were all good-looking. You didn't see any rubbish down there!"

London's top totty, some of the capital's best shops, restaurants and bars and all on the doorstep of Stamford Bridge. No wonder the players couldn't keep away from the King's Road.

CHAPTER FIVE
THE END OF THE DOG

After playing a series of matches against local opposition and fellow tourists Dundee in North America on their 1967 summer tour, the Blues moved on to Bermuda where they were lined up to play three more games. Often described as 'an island paradise', Bermuda proved to be anything but as one of the matches threatened to spiral out of control.

"We were playing a Caribbean Select XI," remembers Docherty, "and we were six or seven goals up when the local referee sent off Tony Hateley and Peter Houseman for arguing – which was quite unlike either of them. Anyway, they wouldn't go off; so I went on the pitch to sort it out. The ref said, 'Get off my pitch, or I'll report you.' I told him to 'fuck off', and he reported me for swearing."

Tommy Baldwin, meanwhile, has a totally different recollection of the incident which, in time, would come back to haunt Docherty. "We played this game in Bermuda against a local island team and we were about five goals up just before half-time. We were attacking and someone crossed the ball when the lights went out. The lights came on again, went off again and it carried on like that all through the second half. Tommy got fed up with this and took us off the pitch at one stage, which made the referee go mad. We finished the game eventually – I think we won 8–0 or something. After the game we had to walk from the ground along a sandy lane back to the hotel. As I walked along with the other players I could hear Tommy still ranting and raving at the referee, and he was having a go back. Tommy must have said something – I don't know what exactly – and the referee reported it to the English FA."

Whether it centred on a debatable double sending off or faulty Caribbean floodlights, the incident didn't go down well with the Football Association, particularly as the Doc had appeared before their disciplinary panel only the previous year. On that occasion he had been fined £100 for 'ungentlemanly remarks' to a referee after a Youth Cup match at QPR.

As usual, the FA's convoluted disciplinary procedures took a while to whir into motion so Docherty's case was not heard until the start of October 1967. The new season was already well under way by then, with Chelsea having got off to a desper- ately poor start. Not only were the Blues hovering in lower mid-table, but they had also suffered a couple of consecutive four-goal defeats by Newcastle and Southampton and been pitched out of the League Cup by Second Division Middlesborough. One reporter described the Blues at this time as "a machine for the moment run down, a team out of confidence and lacking their former character."

Charlie Cooke, a complicated individual who was prone to self-doubt, was suffering a low period and was one of those out of form. Meanwhile Peter Osgood, back from injury and leading the attack again following the departure of Hateley to Liverpool, was understandably rusty. The fact that he had put on weight during his long lay-off hadn't helped, and increased the percep- tion among some fans that, although gloriously gifted, Osgood was also a 'lazy' player.

As well as the bad results, Docherty's strained relationship with Chelsea chairman Charles Pratt, who had taken on the role in July 1966 after the death of Joe Mears, provided him with another headache. "Joe Mears died, which was real tragedy for Chelsea," says the Doc. "The new chairman, Charles Pratt, really lived up to his name. I fell out with him at our first meeting when I told him if I wanted his advice I'd ask for it. He didn't like that. Things came to a head when I took a team to the London five-a-side tournament. He asked me what my team was for the first game, and I said, 'I haven't got a team, I've got 12 players.' But he insisted on knowing my team. 'Well,' I thought, 'if that's how he is over a five-a-side, what'll it be like when we play a big match?' I knew I wouldn't be able to work with him, so the next day I told him it would be better if I left."

Docherty, who had signed a five-year contract with Chelsea in December 1966, resigned on the same day as the FA announced their verdict on the incident in Bermuda – a 28-day suspension from all aspects of the game. Under the terms of the suspension Docherty would not even be able to pay to see a game at the turnstiles, let alone coach or manage.

"There was no pressure brought to bear on Mr Docherty to resign, but I can say we were not very pleased at the FA suspension," Chairman Pratt told reporters. "This was something derogatory to a club of which we are very proud." Docherty himself issued a short statement, saying, "This was the time to part company".

The team's dismal form and the FA suspension didn't help but, ultimately, it was the mutual lack of trust and respect between manager and chairman which led to Docherty's departure. Like many Chelsea bosses after him, the Doc had discovered that when manager and chairman fall out there is usually only one winner.

The players were shocked by the news of their manager's departure and were clearly adversely affected the following day when they slumped to a 7–0 defeat at Leeds. Today, affection for the man is still apparent, even amongst those players who suffered the full whirlwind force of the Doc's frequently unpredictable nature. "Tommy was a good motivator," says Docherty lovebite victim Marvin Hinton. "He made you feel you were a much better player than the one you were up against. He was great at building you up."

Tommy Baldwin, who Docherty helped transform from a bit-part player at Arsenal to a Shed legend, is another big fan. "He was very different to my Arsenal manager, Bertie Mee. He was still quite young, about 38 to 40, and he wasn't the tough regimental man that people make out. He didn't mind us having a beer – not before a game, of course – and he would come and join us and have a beer himself. I got on well with him, I think we all did in the team I played in."

John Boyle, one of many young players to be given his Chelsea debut by the Doc, says simply, "He was a wonderful manager, he just encouraged all us youngsters to play."

In assessing Docherty's managerial reign at Stamford Bridge, it is clear that the positives hugely outweigh the negatives on the balance sheet. When he arrived at the club Chelsea were widely regarded as something of a joke and were wholly lacking in direction. A few months earlier the club had failed to hang onto their prize asset, Jimmy Greaves, and 'The Pensioners' tag, despite Ted Drake's best efforts, still attached itself to the team – appropriately, in many ways, considering the large numbers of veteran players in the squad. By clearing out the old stagers and promoting a generation of home-grown youth players to take their places Docherty not only produced a new, energetic young team, he also helped to create a fresh image for the club: dynamic, progressive and forward-thinking. The introduction of the new all-blue kit was symptomatic of this root-and-branch transformation. On the whole, his transfer policy was a success, too, with the likes of Eddie McCreadie, Marvin Hinton and George Graham proving to be genuine bargains. The fact, too, that attendances at the Bridge increased by 30% over the course of his period in charge, rising from an average 27,000 in 1961/62 to 35,000 in 1966/67, demonstrated that Docherty's efforts had the support of the fans.

On the debit side, critics will point to the lack of tangible success of the Docherty era. Yes, his side won the League Cup in 1965 but then, as now, this was not a competition regarded particularly highly by the leading clubs. This criticism, though, is harsh. Chelsea, after all, had only ever won one trophy in the 55 years of their existence prior to Docherty's arrival. To win silverware – of any sort – was a major achievement in that historical context. Nor should the numerous near misses of his reign be dismissed lightly: they showed the football world that Chelsea were a force to be reckoned with, raised the collective pulse of the fans and, crucially, provided the players with all-important big match experience.

A more pertinent criticism is that Docherty's volatile personality sometimes clouded his judgement and, ultimately, led to his downfall. His heavy-handed handling of the Blackpool Incident is a case in point. Was it really necessary to send the players home? And was it wise to sell four of the miscreants soon afterwards? On this second point, though, Docherty can point to his swift purchases of Charlie Cooke and Tommy Baldwin and his careful nurturing of the young Peter Osgood. Few would argue that these were inferior players to the trio they replaced – Terry Venables, George Graham and Barry Bridges.

On the other hand, there is no doubt that Docherty's sharp tongue and fluctuating temper sometimes created problems for himself. It is perhaps significant that of his many run ins with referees Docherty's most violent outbursts came in two essentially meaningless matches – he simply couldn't restrain himself. Nor could he resist some blunt straight talking with the new chairman when another manager might have opted for a more tactful approach. As it turned out, if Docherty had tried harder to muddle along with Pratt he would only have had to put up with his interfering ways for a few months longer. The Chelsea chairman died in March 1968 to be succeeded by Leonard Whithey, and then the following year by Joe Mears' son, Brian.

The past, though, cannot be altered; the ifs, buts and maybes count for nothing. So how will Chelsea history judge Tommy Docherty? Flawed though he was, there can surely only be one answer: despite the limited trophy return, the dressing room bust ups and his cavalier attitude towards the bigwigs in the boardroom, the Doc will be remembered as one of the club's finest and most influential managers.

In the immediate aftermath of Docherty's departure the players publicly lobbied the board to appoint ex-Blues coach Dave Sexton, formerly a player with West Ham, Brighton and Leyton Orient, as his successor.

"We are not trying to tell the directors their job," an unnamed spokesman was quoted as saying, "but we feel it is a good idea if they give us the chance to help choose the new manager. If Ron Stuart [acting manager] takes over, that will be fine by us. But if the board are going to look outside for a new man, we would like them to consider Dave Sexton for the job. He proved he was a great coach when he was here a couple of years ago. He would do a great job for club morale, and his coaching technique could take us right to the top."

For once, the board appeared to listen to the players and offered the job to Sexton, who by now was working as Bertie Mee's assistant at Arsenal. Sexton accepted the offer, and was warmly welcomed back to west London by Charles Pratt. "We regard him as the best man in the world to do the job for which he has come back to Stamford Bridge," said the delighted Chelsea chairman.

Certainly, considering Sexton's track record, it seemed a good choice. After resigning as manager of Leyton Orient in December 1965, Sexton had moved to Fulham as coach and played a big part in saving the Cottagers from relegation to the Second Division. In August 1966 he joined Arsenal, initially as coach, and helped guide the Gunners to their highest place for eight years. True, 7th place didn't exactly turn Islington into a sea of red-and-white bunting, but it represented an improvement in what had been a dire decade for the north Londoners. Above all, Sexton's abilities as a coach and his potential as a manager were well known to the board after his previous spell at the Bridge. Reserved and mild-mannered, Sexton was a very different personality to the maverick Docherty. Not that this counted against him – quite the opposite, in fact. After the turbulence of the Doc's reign, the directors were anxious to appoint a manager who would steer the club into calmer seas.

One of the few people at the Bridge to have reservations about Sexton's appointment was Tommy Baldwin, who confronted the new manager after his first game in charge, a 1–1 home draw with Everton.

"When he got the Chelsea job I thought, 'Oh no, he got rid of me when I was at Arsenal.' The night after the Everton game he had a party for the supporters. We were all at that and I bumped into him and said, 'Are you going to boot me out again, like you did at Arsenal?' He told me to go and see him in his office on Monday but I never went."

Sexton had inherited a talented squad from his predecessor, but one which was under-performing in a manner which would become all too familiar to Chelsea fans over the years. The team was struggling at the wrong end of the table and shipping goals at an alarming rate, so the new manager might have been tempted to concentrate his attention on defensive matters. Sexton, though, had different priorities.

"I got some good advice from Malcolm Allison when I started the Chelsea job," he said some years later. "He said attack should be your number one priority. It's okay boxing clever and all that – but if you want something, you've got to go and get it, haven't you? We never used to take the brakes off. In the long run, it paid off. That's the beauty of taking a positive approach."

Sexton signalled his commitment to attack by his first signing, Sheffield United striker Alan Birchenall. The blond forward, who possessed a sweet left foot he dubbed 'the Claw', arrived with a handy reputation, having struck an average of one goal every three games in a low scoring side. With Osgood, Baldwin and Tambling all still on the payroll, the Chelsea manager now had the luxury of selecting from four quality forwards, or rather he would once the £100,000 new boy had managed to find Stamford Bridge in the A-Z . . .

"I'll never forget my first day at Chelsea," says Birchenall. "I drove down in this red Triumph Spitfire soft top that I'd just bought, thinking I looked the dog's whatsits. So what happens? I only go and get myself lost in the backstreets of west London and end up having to stop and ask this cockney where the ground is. 'Jesus Christ,' this bloke splutters. 'We've lashed out a hundred grand on you and you can't even find your way to the poxy ground. Tell you what, piss off back to Sheffield, you big ponce.' So I'm thinking, 'Well, that's a great start.'"

Once he'd got his bearings, however, Birchenall quickly adjusted to his new surroundings, scoring on his Chelsea debut in a 3–2 win at Sunderland and hitting both goals later that month in a 2–1 Boxing Day defeat of Arsenal at the Bridge. "I should have had a hat-trick, too," he recalls. "We got a penalty near the end, Johnny Hollins let me take it and I almost hit the corner flag!"

Thanks to improved form after Sexton's arrival the Blues eventually finished in sixth place and qualified again for the Fairs Cup, a creditable achievement given their early season troubles. Peter Osgood's 16 goals made him the club's leading scorer, and allayed fears that he wouldn't be so effective a player after his bad injury. The clean sheet count had picked up, too, especially towards the end of the season when Sexton bought uncompromising defender David Webb from Southampton, with Joe Kirkup moving in the opposite direction in part exchange.

Webb, who had played under Sexton at Orient, was so keen to join Chelsea he even agreed to take a pay cut to join the Blues – an unselfish attitude that epitomised his unflagging commitment to the club in the years that followed. Although he sometimes dived in unnecessarily, Webb tackled like a tank at full speed, passed the ball simply and effectively and, to the initial surprise of his team-mates and the Bridge crowd, proved to be a handy emergency striker when required to play that role.

Webb, though, was cup-tied for the crucial sixth round FA Cup tie at Second Division Birmingham, who included former Docherty Diamonds Barry Bridges and Bert Murray in their line up. The old boys had the last laugh, too, as City beat the Blues 1–0. The Cup would have to wait for at least another year.

At the end of the season Chelsea played QPR in a testimonial for Ken Shellito, who after numerous attempted comebacks had retired from the game through injury. There was a surprise for the 21,000 fans when Alan Birchenall trooped off to be replaced by Jimmy Tarbuck. "Dave Sexton decided to take off one comedian and put on another," quips the Birch. "Tarby was a Liverpool fan but like a lot of London-based showbiz people at the time he adopted Chelsea as his second team. But the main thing was we got a decent crowd along because Ken had been a good servant to Chelsea."

Sad though it was, Shellito's retirement represented another broken link with the Docherty era. Gradually, over the course of the 1968/69 season and beyond, Sexton began to forge a team which was increasingly in his own image. But it was most definitely a process of evolution rather revolution. Trimming his squad, Sexton moved on a number of fringe players, including occasional winger Joe Fascione, and back-up defenders Geoff Butler, Colin Waldron and Jim Thomson.

Among those to benefit from the Sexton regime, meanwhile, were Peter Houseman and Ian Hutchinson. After five years in the squad, during which he had made fewer than 100 first-team appearances, Houseman finally made the left-wing slot his own in the 1968/69 season. Many fans had doubts about a player who lacked two ingredients often thought essential to the winger's craft: pace and trickery. However, Sexton gradually became convinced that Houseman's crossing ability, allied to his stamina and the natural balance his left-footedness gave the side, merited his inclusion in the team.

Ian Hutchinson, a rough-round-the-edges striker with then non-league Cambridge United, was spotted by Sexton's assistant Ron Suart and snapped up by the Blues for a bargain £5,000 in July 1968. Initially raw, awkward and lacking in self-confidence, Hutch took a while to adapt to life at the Bridge and seemed destined to be used mainly as cover for the likes of Osgood, Baldwin, Tambling and Birchenhall. In only his second game for the Blues, though, he unleashed his party piece, a massive long-throw which flicked off Ipswich's Bill Baxter and into the net. Sexton was impressed: this was a new tactic which clearly unsettled defences and, along with Hutchinson's strength in the air and fearlessness in the box, made the newcomer a more interesting proposition than he first appeared. The only problem facing Sexton was how to best utilise the vast attacking talent at his disposal. This dilemma led him to employing Peter Osgood in midfield for much of the season, an experiment which was only partially successful.

The battle for places in defence was equally fierce, particularly after Sexton bought Fulham centre half John Dempsey in January 1969. An uncomplicated stopper who was commanding in the air, a strong tackler and tidy in his distribution from the back, Dempsey would go on to form solid central defensive partnerships with both Ron Harris and, when Chopper later moved across to full back, David Webb.

Inevitably, some players found themselves being less involved than they had been under Docherty. Marvin Hinton was one player who found himself watching from the bench or the stand more often than he would have liked, while John Boyle was another who could no longer be sure of a starting position.

"I don't think that Dave liked me as a player," he says candidly. "The funny thing is, though, that he used to get the players to mark each other out of 10 in different categories to find out if you'd had a good game or not – and I always did well. We'd all put the marks down on a form, hand it to Dave and he'd work out the average. I usually figured near the top of the list because it was all about what Dave thought was important in the game – tracking back, chasing, tackling, lasting till the 90th minute and so on. I had all those qualities, you see. I remember it was always a problem what to put down for Ossie. I mean, chasing back . . . 0 out of 10?"

Sexton had good cause to study his prototype Opta-style stats during the 1968/69 season, which followed a now familiar Chelsea pattern. The Blues finished fifth in the league, without ever seriously challenging runaway champions Leeds. Again, the various cups promised much but delivered nothing but disappointment. In the League Cup Chelsea were once more the victims of a giant-killing, going out to Second Division Derby County in the third round. In the Fairs Cup, the Blues had an even more unpleasant shock, succumbing to little-known Dutch outfit DWS Amsterdam on the toss of a coin following two 0–0 draws.

Yet again, the FA Cup appeared to offer the best chance of glory. After goals from Peter Osgood and Bobby Tambling saw off Carlisle in the third round, the Blues drew 0–0 at Preston and were leading 2–0 in the replay when the Bridge floodlights failed in the second half and play had to be abandoned. To prevent a possible repeat of this fiasco, the rematch was held on the following Monday afternoon yet still attracted a crowd of more than 36,000. Many local schools, perhaps appreciating that double maths couldn't compete with the prospect of seeing the Blues in action, simply threw in the towel and took their pupils along to the game. As it turned out, Chelsea provided a useful lesson for the youngsters in the merits of perseverance as Webb and Cooke scored in the closing minutes to wipe out Preston's first half lead.

After Stoke had been accounted for in the fifth round, the Blues were rewarded with a home draw in the quarter-finals against the Cup holders, West Bromwich Albion – a tricky but eminently winnable tie. The result, a 2–1 defeat, had pessimistic fans in the 52,285 crowd wondering whether the Londoners' name would ever appear on the Cup. Frustratingly, the Blues travelled to the Hawthorns the following week for a run-of-the-mill league match and cruised to a 3–0 win. "That summed up how inconsistent we were at that time," admits John Dempsey.

You could, it seemed, change the manager, change the team and change the chairman. Changing the Blues' erratic nature was another story.

CHAPTER SIX

THE BOOZE

A few years ago, an hour or so after Chelsea had famously thrashed Manchester United 5–0, Blues fans celebrating in a Fulham Road pub were a little surprised but nonetheless thrilled when Dennis Wise walked through the doors for a post-match pint. For the lager-swilling, blue-clad throng, life couldn't get much better than this: a hugely enjoyable massacre of the despised 'Manure' followed by the sight of their beloved skipper joining them in a few rousing choruses of 'Carefree', 'Blue Flag' and 'Who put the ball in the United net?'

Although it was only a fleeting, incident-free visit, Wise's swift half in an unfashionable Fulham boozer still made the tabloids. It wasn't exactly 'Scoop of the Year' material but, in an age when Premiership players have become increasingly remote from their public, enjoying mind-boggling salaries and glittering lifestyles almost beyond the comprehension of the average supporter, the Chelsea's captain's unexpected pub appearance was seen as worthy of a few column inches.

Rewind the clock 30 years, however, and any hack who suggested to his editor that 'Chelsea player spotted in King's Road pub' might make a good splash would be given short shrift and, quite possibly, his P45. News, after all, by its very definition, is something that is out-of-the-ordinary rather than an everyday occurrence and, much to manager Dave Sexton's dismay, the sight of one or more of his star players knocking back a pint or six in one of the local hostelries around the Bridge was far from uncommon.

Back in the sixties and seventies most teams had players who spent more time in the pub than on the training ground, but the Chelsea lads could make a good claim for being top of the unofficial drinking league. By all accounts, their appetite for alcohol was truly gargantuan. Yes, there were some notable exceptions, with the clean-living trio of Peter Bonetti, John Hollins and Peter Houseman, in particular, preferring to disappear off to their families in the suburbs rather than going out on the town. Little matter, the rest of the team, led by Peter Osgood, Charlie Cooke, Tommy Baldwin and Alan Hudson, did their boozing for them as they bar-hopped their way down the King's Road on a regular basis. Indeed, Baldwin's capacity for beers and spirits was so immense it earned him the nickname 'the Sponge'.

"It was John Hollins who coined it," says Tommy. "When I first came to Chelsea I was introduced to all the players and John said to me, 'Hello, you're the Sponge, aren't you?' I just laughed, but later on I asked him, 'What's with the Sponge?' He said he'd been away with England Under 23s and Jon Sammels, who played with me at Arsenal, had told him all about me. 'You drink so much you must have a sponge in your stomach,' John said, and the nickname stuck." From time to time the name would even appear in the club programme, although the implication was always that the unusual moniker stemmed from the striker's shirt-drenching efforts on the field rather than his insatiable thirst off it.

When it came to finding a place to sup, Baldwin and co had no shortage of choices. Among the numerous pubs within walking distance of the Bridge, the players' favourites included the Lord Palmerston, at the top of the King's Road near the old Shed entrance; the Ifield Tavern, around the corner from the ground in

Ifield Road; and the Markham Arms, a dark, cavernous pub halfway down the King's Road, next door to Alexander's restaurant. Sadly, none of these pubs are what they were in their seventies heyday: the Lord Palmerston, once a famous boxing-themed pub, is now the characterless Morrison's; the Ifield has been transformed into a yuppie gastro-pub; and, saddest of all, the Markham is now a branch of the Abbey National.

As Alan Birchenall recalls, the Markham was the most popular pub among the Chelsea boys for a lunchtime session. "We'd finished training at Mitcham and then, a bit later, we'd be on the King's Road sat in the Markham Arms with shepherd's pie and beans, looking out of the window at all the sights the street had to offer at the time. You didn't have all-day opening in those days but the pubs were never in a rush to throw us Chelsea players out at half two, and we managed to keep going through the afternoon. It was a similar story at the Ifield and the Lord Palmerston after evening games. We'd go round there, they'd pull the curtains and we'd stay in for a few after closing time."

In those days, 'lock-ins' were a part of London pub culture and, although illegal, the police tended to turn a blind eye as long as there were no complaints about rowdy, drunken behaviour. They might have adopted a more hardline approach, however, if they'd known what some of the late-night drinkers were planning.

"After the Fairs Cup tie against DWS Amsterdam in 1968 I went to the Lord Palmerston with Ossie," remembers the Birch. "The match was boring, a 0–0 draw. It was an early season game, a balmy evening, and everyone was in shirt sleeves. Ossie was by the fireplace, I went to get the drinks in at the bar where there was a guy with a thick black Crombie coat on. I looked at him and thought, 'God, he looks a bit dodgy.' He turned to me and said, 'You were fucking rubbish, you lot tonight.'

"He was a big bloke so I thought it best to agree with him. I wasn't going to argue. The bar was crowded and while we were waiting to get served, just as a matter of conversation, I said to him 'Blimey, aren't you hot in that?' pointing at his coat. He looked at me and said 'Yes I am, but there's a reason I'm wearing it.' Then he pulled open the coat and when I peered inside I saw the handle of a double-barrelled shotgun. I crapped myself, picked up the pints and went over to Ossie and whispered in his ear, 'Come on, let's get out of here!' He said 'Why? We've just got a pint in!' But I insisted we got out, because I thought the guy was about to do someone in the pub. You've got to remember those were the days of the Richardsons and the Krays, so there was no point taking chances.

"Anyway, the next day we forgot about it until we picked up an *Evening Standard* on our way back home from training. There was a huge great headline – 'Gangland Shooting on Fulham Palace Road.' Apparently a car pulled up outside a house, a guy got out, then another car came alongside and blew both the bloke's legs off. I said to Ossie, 'That's the geezer I was with last night in the pub.' A week later I was back in the Palmerston and asked the landlord about the bloke in the Crombie and he told me to zip it. I didn't need to be told twice, I can tell you."

If that was a case of a drinking bout coming to a premature end, the Birch more than made up for it on another occasion when he joined Charlie Cooke, Peter Osgood and John Boyle for possibly the longest and most inebriated lunch in Chelsea history. "We were all slightly injured," recalls Boylers, "and to stop us from swinging the lead, we had to report for treatment every few hours. Anyway, we went off to Barbarella's – the restaurant just outside Stamford Bridge – for lunch and the waiter said, 'Why not have a bottle of wine with your meal?' So we had a bottle which, inevitably, led to another one.

"Meanwhile, Dave Sexton had already been in, had his lunch and left. When a third bottle of wine arrived, the Birch actually went off for treatment leaving the three of us there; then a few minutes later he came running back and told us that Harry Medhurst, our physio, was doing his nut. But we had another bottle of wine opened, so we didn't want to leave. Fourteen bottles of wine later, there's Charlie waving a pen around, trying to sign a cheque. He needn't have bothered, the bank sent it back later as the signature was totally illegible. Unfortunately, one of the newspapers got hold of the story and Dave left us all out for the next match at Southampton."

One of the players to benefit from Sexton's crackdown was Alan Hudson, who replaced Cooke and made his Chelsea debut at The Dell in an eminently forgettable 5–0 defeat. It wasn't long, though, before Hudson himself had fallen foul of the manager in very similar circumstances, although the amount of alcohol involved on this occasion was a mere dribble in comparison. All the same, the incident is worth relating as it reveals the extent to which Sexton was angered and frustrated by what he perceived to be the dominant 'drinking culture' at the Bridge.

"The first team were having a bad time and me, Bill Garner and Stevie Kember were injured and having treatment," remembers 'Huddy'. "At lunchtime we went down the Markham to have lunch. They used to do a nice shepherd's pie so we had that and a couple of pints of lager. Then we went back for more treatment. We got back to the Bridge and Dave was waiting for us. He glared at us and said, 'Where have you three been?' We told him we'd been out for our lunch break but he still didn't look happy. 'You've been down the pub!' he said, and I replied 'Yeah, we've been down the Markham, but we're not fit to train this afternoon'. He went mad, absolutely crazy: 'Do you realise our team is struggling? And you're down the pub!' But I said, 'What can we do? We're not fit, we won't be playing on Saturday and we haven't gone down there to have 12 pints, we just had a couple.' But that just made him madder."

Incidents like that one, and the infamous 'Barberella's lunch' a few years earlier, led the Chelsea manager to take a number of unpopular measures in an effort to stop his players from drinking.

"Sexton used to get really upset when he saw the players in

the old East Stand before the game drinking with the showbiz stars – people like Dennis Waterman, Michael Crawford, John Cleese, Sean Connery, Richard O'Sullivan and Rodney Bewes," says Hudson. "He really didn't like us hanging out with them. Of course, you only did that when you were injured or hadn't been picked. But he'd do really stupid things like put a note up saying anybody who wasn't playing should not be seen with alcohol. It didn't make any difference, mind you. We'd still go up to the East Stand, where we used to watch the games, and have a nice large brandy in a coffee cup. When he walked by us, we'd smile at him and although he knew what was going on he wouldn't stop us. There were supporters around and there would have been trouble if he'd had a go at us. Anyway, if you're not playing what's the harm? It was almost as if he was on a crusade – you mustn't do this, you mustn't do that."

Top of the list of 'no-noes', of course, was getting plastered the evening before a game. To be fair to the players, it seems that they were sufficiently professional to realise that this was a reasonable demand and, when questioned, they'll usually say that they never drank on the eve of a match. The big boozy sessions, they stress, happened after games not before them.

That may be true, but it's equally the case that the players didn't always switch to orange juice or Coca-Cola on Friday nights. Even Alan Birchenall – who insists "You couldn't play at that level and abuse your body drinking all the time" – admits that there were occasions when the players' pre-match preparation included a few beers. In particular, he remembers a night out in Manchester before the Blues were due to play at Old Trafford.

"We went out of the hotel for a look around and popped into the local Mecca. It was the usual suspects – Ossie, the Sponge and so on. It was one of my first away trips and it amazed me that we were out at all. I thought, 'We're going to get an arseholing tomorrow' because we were up against George Best, Bobby Charlton and Denis Law – basically the United side that won the

European Cup. But we won it easily, 4–0, and I got one of the goals. I couldn't believe it. I was thinking, 'Is this the way Chelsea do things? Go out and have a couple of pints before a game and then go and put in a performance like that?' But it was just a couple of pints, not a session. Some of the boys were on a scouting mission for talent, but not the football type. One or two had a bit of success but I wasn't interested. I just stood in a dark corner because I couldn't believe what I was doing on a Friday night before such a big game. Friday night was sacrosanct at Sheffield United, you just never went out anywhere."

Stuffed like a plump Christmas turkey on their own patch, the United players would probably agree that the Blues showed no ill effects from their night on the town – quite the reverse, if anything. A year earlier, though, it had been a different story as a hungover Chelsea team crashed to one of their heaviest all-time defeats, 7–0 against arch rivals Leeds.

"It was the game after Tommy Docherty was sacked," says John Boyle. "We were leaving to go to Leeds on Friday lunchtime and we said goodbye to the Doc outside the gates at Stamford Bridge. It was a funny situation, the whole club seemed to be in turmoil. We got up there and after we went out to the cinema we brought a bottle of vodka back to the hotel. There were about five or six of us, including Eddie McCreadie who was the captain, sitting around getting drunk on the stuff. I wouldn't say we were especially affected by it the next day because we were so fit you could just work it out of your system. But it's not the sort of thing that you could do every week and, in fact, it was the only time in my ten years at the club that we went drinking the night before a game.

"The funny thing is we had a team meeting afterwards and McCreadie said something like 'Don't blame me, I played like three men out there', and somebody else said, 'Yeah, you played like Boyle, Baldwin and Cooke', because we'd all had shockers. 'You played like them three.'"

The Leeds debacle may have been the absolute low point of the period, but it was far from being unique. Some other surprising results from the Docherty and Sexton eras included a 5–1 defeat at Newcastle in August 1967, a 6–2 home thrashing by Southampton the following month and a 5–2 reverse at champions-to-be Everton in March 1970. Simple off days, the likes of which happen to all teams every now and then? Or could alcohol have played a part in the maulings, as surely it did at Elland Road? Certainly, Alan Hudson reckons that Chelsea's poor performance at Goodison Park could at least partially be explained by the fact that two players, David Webb and John Dempsey, stayed out well beyond the curfew imposed by Dave Sexton.

"The last person you want to be marking when you're hungover is Joe Royle," he laughs, referring to Everton's powerfully-built centre forward at the time. "Sexton used to have a fellow called Bill Edwards come along with the staff. He would look after the kit, but he was also a kind of spy. He'd stay up in the hotel on a Friday night and make sure all the players were back at the appointed time. It wasn't a surprise about Webby being out, but John Dempsey was another matter, because that wasn't him. But it came back through Bill that the two of them had been out."

Dempsey, though, strongly denies that he left the hotel at all and, in any case, Chelsea historians usually point to the absence of Peter Bonetti – Tommy Hughes, who had already conceded five against Leeds at Stamford Bridge earlier that season, replaced him in goal – as a crucial contributing factor to the massacre. Hudson himself, meanwhile, admits to being hungover during a couple of matches, including one at the Bridge against Crystal Palace when he needed a 'livener' in the Adelaide pub on the King's Road before he felt up to playing.

More generally, though, Alvaro Maccioni, the owner of the exclusive King's Road niterie The Aretusa, suggests that the players' protestations that they were always tucked up in bed with a warm cup of Horlicks at ten pm on Friday nights should be taken with the proverbial pinch of salt, if not a whole fistful.

"They used to stay in the club until late," he chuckles, "sometimes when they should not have been there at all. And they were out the night before matches – not regularly, but occasionally. I certainly remember one or two nights when they were in the club the night before games. Usually it was the ones who were local, Charlie Cooke, Tommy Baldwin and so on.

"One particular evening, at around 11pm, Dave Sexton called at the door when quite a few of the players were in the club. I didn't want them to get caught so I quickly sent someone down to tell the players 'The Boss is here!' while I chatted to Dave at the door. That gave them time to sneak out of the back entrance. I didn't want them to get into trouble because they were all great boys. Yes, they had a drink but they never got drunk or caused any problems. They just enjoyed themselves, whether they were having a quiet drink together or dancing in the disco downstairs."

With friends like Alvaro on the look-out for them, the players could often conceal their alcohol-fuelled antics from the manager. Sometimes, though, they so overstepped the mark that it wasn't Dave Sexton they needed to worry about, but those other boys in blue, the Metropolitan Police. One player to fall foul of the law was Tommy Baldwin who, early in his Chelsea career, unwittingly found himself caught up in a scene straight out of an episode of the popular seventies TV show *The Sweeney*.

"I was in the White Hart pub in Southgate with a few of the Arsenal players. It was a popular footballers' pub and Tottenham players used to go there as well. Anyway, this guy who I knew from my Arsenal days was there – he was always around the players – and he suddenly announced, 'I've got this party to go to.' So I said, 'Right, let's go.'

We got a bottle of vodka from the pub and headed off to the party – which was not far away in somewhere like Wood Green

– with a couple of girls we'd been out with. I was sitting at the back of the car with one of the girls, while the guy I knew was driving. Suddenly he said, 'Oh no, there's a police car following me.' I said, 'What's the problem?' and he told me he was either banned from driving or he didn't have a licence, I can't remember which.

"I tried to calm him down but he was getting very jittery. 'I can't stop, I've got to get away from here,' he said and he put his foot down and we shot off towards Hackney. The police were right behind us still and I could see that we would be stopped eventually. I wasn't worried about that but I couldn't help thinking about the bottle of vodka I had with me. I really didn't want Dave Sexton getting to hear that I'd been out drinking. So, as we went round a corner, I threw the bottle into a gap between the cars and it smashed into pieces on the road. We carried on, going down a one-way system the wrong way and banging into a few cars along the way. By now there were about 40 police cars chasing us and a roadblock had been set up at Old Street. To avoid the roadblock the driver turned off and we found ourselves in a back alley or dead end with a police car right behind us. I couldn't even get out of the car at first because it was jammed in – eventually I managed to get out of the back with the girl I was with.

"They took me to Old Street police station and the driver to another station. They kept saying, 'Who's the guy who threw the bottle at the police car?' In the police station there was a bit of a fracas when they tried to put me in a cell. I didn't want to go in there, and I just stopped dead. The sergeant blew his whistle, three or four policeman came running into the room and they literally picked me up, gave me a couple of belts around the face and threw me in a cell. They charged me with assaulting a policeman and throwing a bottle of vodka at a police car.

"It was all over the news that I'd been arrested. I went to Old Street magistrates' court for the case the next morning. I looked a right mess – my shirt was all ripped, I had dried blood all down my face and my nose was sticking out at a funny angle. I pleaded not guilty and the case went to Crown Court. I was charged with assault. 'You're joking aren't you,' I told my solicitor, 'drunk and disorderly maybe, but they can't do me for that!' But I was found guilty and I was given four months in prison.

"Back in the cells at Old Street police station I was sitting there thinking it through and, oddly enough, the one thing that kept going through my head was that at least I'd be able to get properly fit because I wouldn't be drinking inside. Then the solicitor came down and said, 'Sorry Tommy, I can't believe they've done that to you! What do you want me to do?' I said, 'I don't know, just get me out of here!' So he said he'd appeal against the sentence and ten minutes later he came back and told me they were letting me go, I was being let out on appeal.

"Chelsea were great about it, and Dave Sexton came along with me to court. At the appeal the police got into a bit of a muddle with their evidence and the magistrate decided their case wasn't proven, so he suspended the sentence."

The whole episode should have been a salutary lesson for the Sponge, but it wasn't long before he was in back in trouble – and, once again, drink was the root cause. "A bit later on I got done on the breathalyser," he admits, a touch sheepishly. "I got banned for a year. I think I must have been the first footballer to fall foul of the breathalyser because it was only introduced in 1967."

Baldwin was not the only Chelsea player to have a brush with the law. Peter Osgood was arrested after over-exuberantly celebrating the Blues' League Cup semi-final win in January 1972 (see Chapter 13, *Blue is the Colour*), although the fact that Chelsea's vanquished opponents were hated north London rivals Tottenham was surely a mitigating factor any judge or jury would have to take into account.

With incident piling on incident, Chelsea supporters must have been wondering whether Dave Sexton didn't have the right idea with his zealous anti-drink drive. At one point, in a bid to keep a closer eye on his wayward charges, Sexton persuaded the club to put the players up en masse at the Kensington Palace Hotel the night before home league games. The policy might have worked if the players hadn't started taking their dirty washing along for the hotel laundry to clean every week. Eventually, with the bills getting larger by the week, the expense could no longer be justified and the players were once again left to their own devices on Friday nights.

Drinking on aeroplanes was another issue Sexton tried to tackle, and during the Blues' European Cup Winners Cup campaign in 1970/71 he introduced a complete ban. "That didn't go down too well with everybody but it was sensible enough," says John Boyle, "because of the effects of drinking on a plane."

Other players, though, while accepting the policy for the outward journey, were unwilling to celebrate a good result on foreign soil with a glass of tonic water or lemonade. "We just had orange juice in our champagne and he didn't know then, did he?" recalled Peter Osgood. "We'd be at the back of the plane with the stewardesses having a great time, while Dave was up the front. The ban didn't work at all."

At times it sounds as though Dave Sexton would have had an easier life as headmaster of St Trinian's. However, he has always denied the suggestion that the players turned Stamford Bridge into an anarchic, drink-soaked playground. "My players weren't difficult – quite the opposite," he once said. "The problem is what success does. It's liable to change your outlook on life. When you haven't got anything, you get on with things – you're hungrier. Once you start getting money and fame, it becomes difficult.

"They were decent blokes, but they were subject to the same temptations as anybody else who comes into a degree of success. For example, you get invited to a lot of dinners and social events – and before you know it, they're professional athletes living the life of rich playboys. They're eating good food and drinking fine wines. With success come the trappings, and sometimes you get carried away. But basically they were good lads."

Nonetheless, he has admitted that there were occasions, such as the 'Barbarella's Incident', which tried his patience. "Mostly you're better off turning a blind eye, but sometimes you have to act. That day they were supposed to be back for treatment of their injuries."

Sexton's attitude to alcohol was very different to that of his predecessor, Tommy Docherty, who would often join his players for a beer. Indeed, as John Boyle recalls, the Doc was often the instigator of the drinking sessions. "When we were staying in a hotel Tommy Doc would order bottles of champagne in the bar and get them signed off as rounds of sandwiches and teas on the club bill. Another thing we used to do when we were on tour was to order drinks, get one in for the chairman Brian Mears as well, get him in a good mood and sign them off to the room number of the club secretary, John Battersby. And he used to pay it."

Compared to Docherty, Sexton must have come across at times as a right old party pooper yet, strangely, he didn't seem to mind the players having a quick pre-match snifter in the inner sanctum of the dressing room.

"There was tradition at both Arsenal and Chelsea where they used to have a bottle of whisky on the changing room table," explains the Sponge. "Everyone could have a nip to calm their nerves before they went out. A lot of them would go for it. Some players would have a cigarette or two, as well, especially Eddie McCreadie. He smoked 60 a day, but he was still one of the fittest players at the club. Before games you never saw him, he was always disappearing into the toilets for a fag."

Many famous footballers, including Bobby Charlton, Gianluca Vialli and Gerson, the midfield playmaker in Brazil's legendary 1970 World Cup-winning side, have been heavy smokers, so McCreadie was not alone in his addiction to the evil weed. More interesting, perhaps, is the question of whether the smokers in the Chelsea squad ever puffed on anything stronger than a John Player Special. This, after all, was a period when fashionable London was taking a lead from the growing hippy movement and starting to experiment with cannabis, thanks in part to its endorsement by leading celebrities such as Mick Jagger and Paul McCartney.

No doubt to Dave Sexton's huge relief, however, mind-altering drugs barely appear to have registered on the Chelsea players' collective radar. "To my knowledge, nobody in football dabbled in drugs in the sixties and seventies," insists Alan Birchenall. "We didn't need to get our kicks that way." Indeed, the Birch readily admits to being totally unaware of the burgeoning underground drugs scene in the country until he arrived in the capital following his transfer from Sheffield United.

"I went to a party at my agent's flat where Eric Burndon and the Animals, two Beatles and a Rolling Stone were among the guests," he recalls. "I'd just come down from Sheffield as one of the first £100,000 signings and I couldn't believe it. There I was, sat in the middle of a room surrounded by all these people who I'd only seen before on TV and in magazines. I sat on a settee next to a model, and we were chatting away although she didn't have a clue who I was. My agent was introducing me – 'This is Alan Birchenall, Chelsea's new £100,000 signing' and all this bollocks. The only thing I had in common with that lot was that I had long blond hair.

"The girl next to me was rolling her own. She lit it up, took a puff and then said, 'Can I interest you in this?' I looked at her a bit bemused and said, 'Sorry, I only smoke menthols.' So she took a couple of puffs and handed it to the woman on the other side of her. They both looked at me like I was from a different planet. Obviously it was the old wacky baccy. That's how ignorant I was about the drugs scene. Otherwise, you never saw it as a player.

"Over in California, where I played in the mid-seventies, it was a different ball game. Even the Mayor used to have a smoke of the stuff outside the town hall. It was almost obligatory. We had half a team of Americans smoking that stuff. My wife nearly got hooked by accident. One of the guys gave her a cookie one day and she didn't realise what sort of cookie it was – of course, it was one of those funny cookies and she was flying for about three days after eating it."

It seems pretty clear then that, although they may have looked like a bunch of toked-up hippies with their shoulder-length hair, pork chop sideburns and garish clothes the team weren't indulging in the illicit substances which, presumably, many Chelsea fans were enjoying in the late sixties and early seventies. On the other hand, some of the players with longstanding injury problems were already popping enough legal pills to fell an elephant.

"I was like a junkie," Ian Hutchinson told an interviewer a year before his death in 2002. "There was no way I would have passed a drugs test if they'd had them then. I used to be on eight anti-inflammatory tablets a day. And then there were the cortisone injections. You couldn't walk for two days afterwards, but the important thing was that you'd be all right for Saturday."

Hutch's dedication to the cause was well beyond the call to duty, but was by no means unique. Other Blues players, too, regularly played through the pain barrier in an effort to help the club gain valuable league points or go through to the next round of a cup. Little wonder, then, that once the final whistle went their thoughts turned pretty quickly to that first post-match pint.

As we've already seen, most of the players liked a drink or two, but just how much of the stuff were they putting away? As anyone who's ever had a skinful knows it all becomes a bit of a blur after the third or fourth pint so, unsurprisingly, the recollections of the players are not wholly reliable. Fortunately, the well-known London photographer Terry O'Neill, who was friendly with some members of the team, can shed some light on this crucial question.

"I used to go out with the players occasionally," he says. "At least I'd go out with them until a certain time, because they had a capacity for drink which was phenomenal. I don't know how they did it. I mean they'd start at lunchtime and they'd be drinking up to midnight and beyond. It was incredible. Most of the time it was Ossie, Alan Hudson, Charlie Cooke, Eddie McCreadie and a couple of others, John Boyle and John Dempsey. I'd stay with them as long as I could last, because I wasn't a big drinker. They always used to go round a set of the pubs and clubs in Chelsea.

"I only drank a couple of glasses of wine when I was out with them, and the wine wasn't much to shout about at the time. But they drank heavily. I kept a gap from them, really, because it was fun to talk to them about football but apart from that we didn't share the same mentality. I'm not being a snob, but they were lads looking to enjoy themselves and we had jobs to do, so you couldn't just disappear with them all day. They were a confident bunch but you couldn't help wondering what they'd do after football."

Dave Sexton may not have approved, but the fact that the players were using the same pubs as local Chelsea fans helped create a very special bond between the team and the supporters.

"We used to mix with the fans all the time, especially in the Lord Palmerston," says Tommy Baldwin. "The pub was run by the Mancinis, who were a big boxing family. The 'guvnor' was the uncle of Terry Mancini, who played for QPR and Arsenal. The pub was near the ground and it became our regular haunt. All the fans knew we'd be in there after games, so we used to get mobbed when we went in. We always had a whip but lots of time, especially if we'd won, fans would come up to us and offer to buy drinks. Most of the time we'd tell them we were okay, because we didn't mind getting our own drinks. The fans weren't slow to let you know what they thought – if you'd had a bad game you got slaughtered but if you'd had a good game you got the applause.

"After night matches we'd stay in the pub till closing time and then go on to a club. Quite often we'd go to the Aretusa – I used to be in there all the time as I lived locally – or we'd go the Sportsman on Tottenham Court Road because it had a casino. More often than not I was out with Charlie Cooke because he lived in the same area as me. A lot of the other guys were married and lived further out so we didn't see them socially so often."

All the players, though, are adamant that there were no splits in the camp between the hellraisers and the stay-at-homes, the big boozers and the apple juice drinkers.

"I think the one thing we had going for us was a fantastic, happy dressing room," says Ron Harris. "We had about 16 or 18 players and near enough everybody got on well. There was never a little clique in one corner and another in another corner. If we went up to Blackpool to stay before a match everybody used to go out together. Not just five or six of us. Peter Bonetti and Johnny Hollins were maybe the ones who didn't go out, but everyone else did. We didn't shun them, we always asked them, but they usually said they weren't bothered. Which was fine." Possibly, Hollins' reluctance to join the others stemmed from his involvement in the Blackpool Incident.

Alan Hudson makes a similar point to Harris, saying, "The lads never had a problem with Peter Bonetti, Johnny Hollins and Peter Houseman living their lives the way they did. It didn't matter that they didn't come out with us. We had a mix of characters which was good. What would have happened if those three had been as bad as the rest of us, I don't know!"

Dave Sexton, for once, would surely find it impossible to disagree with Huddy on that point.

CHAPTER SEVEN
THE CUP AT LAST

A few minutes before the start of the 1970 FA Cup Final at Wembley the players of Chelsea and Leeds were presented to the Royal Guest of Honour, Princess Margaret. "While we were chatting she said she hoped Chelsea would win," skipper Ron Harris told Blues programme editor Albert Sewell afterwards.

Now it's possible, of course, that the Princess' remarks were merely a part of Cup Final royal protocol and that she went on to make similarly encouraging comments to Leeds' captain, Billy Bremner. On the other hand, Mags might well have had a genuine affinity for Chelsea. The Blues were, after all, the local team to Buckingham Palace and her bohemian tastes often took her to some of the same King's Road haunts frequented by Ossie, Huddy and the Sponge. By contrast, the Princess was not known to have any close links with Leeds or, indeed, with Yorkshire.

Given Chelsea's appalling luck in the Cup in previous years they needed all the extra support they could get. And, for a change, they got a fair dose of good fortune throughout their 1970 campaign, never once being drawn to play outside London. The third round draw set the tone, with the Blues landing a home tie against Second Division Birmingham City.

In the build-up to the game with City Dave Sexton, along with five other managers, was asked by *The Times* to name his tips for the Cup. "May I give Chelsea as the winners?" he replied boldly. "We have gone close so often, I believe it is our turn. We are going well at the right time; confidence is sky-high, and Hollins and Hudson are now reliable midfield dynamos. There is skill on the ground, height near goal to knock in the crosses and we can play in any conditions."

The reference to Alan Hudson showed just how central the 18-year-old midfielder had become to Sexton's side. Having broken into the Chelsea team in the autumn, Hudson had swiftly become the Blues' playmaker, spreading passes around the pitch in the manner of his boyhood hero, former England captain Johnny Haynes.

Like many top-class players, he was an expert at shrugging off the attentions of opponents, either with his trademark drag back or by surging forward with the ball from deep positions. Perhaps, though, it was his ability to knit together team play with his unerringly accurate distribution which was his most valuable asset. Pre-Hudson, the Blues had often appeared somewhat disjointed, a collection of talented individuals lacking unity and cohesion; now, with the youngster directing play, his socks round his ankles and long hair flapping in the breeze, the Blues at last looked like a real team.

Apart from the introduction of Hudson, another important change came in defence where Sexton had switched from the man-to-man marking system most teams employed to zonal marking. "There were a few teething problems but it worked 90 per cent of the time," says John Dempsey. "Dave had bought me because he wanted somebody commanding in the air and, in my first season at Chelsea, I would always pick up the opposition's taller striker. Then, when we switched to zonal marking, I would mark the striker who was in my space. That was fine, but it would be a bit worrying if Ron Harris, who was quite short for a central defender, found himself on the far post marking a 6ft 3in striker like Tony Hateley or Ron Davies. Having said that, I can't remember any vital goals we conceded that way. I think Dave made the switch because he'd been influenced by the continental teams who used zonal marking."

As the 1969/70 season progressed, with Chelsea climbing the league after a slow start, Sexton's work with his players on the training ground could also be clearly seen in the team's shape and style of play.

"At the back our top priority was to defend," says Dempsey. "Eddie McCreadie, who had pace, would get forward down the left but we didn't really have an overlapping right-back. Both Ron Harris and David Webb played in that position, but they were not natural right-backs and didn't push forward much. In midfield, John Hollins was a very gritty player who would get up and down, he was the engine room of the team. Alongside him, Alan Hudson was very skilful and creative and would make a lot of openings. Peter Houseman on the left, who was a very underrated player, and Charlie Cooke on the right would both get forward and, when the opposition attacked, come back to help out the defence. Peter would tend to stay on the wing but Charlie, who had played in central midfield, would come inside more. They were both good crossers of the ball, which suited Peter Osgood and Ian Hutchinson, who were both very good in the air. So, we had a 4–2–4 when we were attacking which switched to 4–4–2 if the move broke down. The flexibility in the formation came from how the midfield was set up."

With the new midfield blending well, Chelsea's forwards had not gone short of scoring opportunities during the first half of the 1969/70 season. One of those to benefit was the rugged Ian Hutchinson, who established himself as Osgood's first choice strike partner ahead of Bobby Tambling, Tommy Baldwin and the injury-hit Alan Birchenall. And it was Hutchinson who wrapped up Chelsea's victory over Birmingham in the Cup, with two second half goals after Osgood had headed in a Hudson centre just before the break.

"Birmingham had knocked us out in the quarter-final two years earlier so we knew it wouldn't be easy," said Ossie. "In the end, though, it was a comfortable win for us. It was good to get revenge in front of our fans and get us off on our Cup run."

One spectator who was particularly impressed by Chelsea's performance was football commentator Brian Moore. "I would not bet against them reaching Wembley," he wrote in his match report for *The Times*.

In the fourth round the Blues were again drawn at home, but against stiffer opposition, Burnley. The Lancastrians were not as powerful a force as they had been a decade earlier when they had won the championship, but they were still a decent First Division outfit. "Burnley were a pretty good team in those days," confirms John Dempsey. "They had people like Ralph Coates, Martin Dobson and Steve Kindon who were all useful players."

Two goals in two minutes from Hollins and Osgood midway through the second half, though, appeared to have put an end to the northerners' challenge. But, with time ticking away, Dobson scored twice to earn Burnley a replay. The Chelsea supporters in the 48,000 crowd must have left the Bridge wondering whether this was to be another season of missed opportunities in the Cup.

Three days later at a foggy Turf Moor Ralph Coates, the proud owner of a wispy Bobby Charlton-style comb over, turned Chelsea fans' anxiety levels up a further notch or two by putting Burnley ahead in the first half. With 18 minutes left the Blues were still trailing when Peter Houseman scored a magnificent solo equaliser. It was Houseman, too, who crossed for Baldwin, deputising for the injured Osgood, to head Chelsea in front in extra-time and Houseman, again, who shot home the killer third goal.

"I think we really believed we could win the Cup after that game," says John Dempsey. "To fight back from 1–0 down to win 3–1 in extra time was the sort of result which gives you great confidence and we started thinking it could be our year."

The positive vibes only intensified when Chelsea were paired with struggling Crystal Palace in the fifth round. True, the Blues were the away team this time but a trip to Selhurst Park held few fears. "We'd already won 5–1 there in the league so it wasn't a bad draw," says Dempsey. "You'd look at it and think, 'yes, Chelsea should win'." Peter Osgood, who had scored four goals on that earlier visit to south London, headed the Blues in front on 37 minutes before Palace's Roger Hoy equalised shortly after half-time. Little matter, Dempsey restored Chelsea's lead with a powerful header from Hollins' free-kick and further goals from Houseman and Hutchinson secured another emphatic away victory.

The quarter-final draw produced four pleasantly symmetrical ties, with Second Division sides Watford, Swindon, Middlesbrough and QPR all playing hosts to First Division opposition: Liverpool, Leeds, Manchester United and Chelsea respectively. Of the four pairings, the west London derby naturally generated most interest, not least among the Chelsea players.

"QPR was a fantastic draw because of the rivalry between the clubs," says Alan Hudson. "For one thing, they had Terry Venables and Barry Bridges who had both played for Chelsea. Then there was Rodney Marsh, who some people were saying was better than Osgood. There were going to be duels all over the pitch. There was me and Venables, Ron Harris and Rodney Marsh, Osgood and Frank Sibley or someone like that. It was just set up to be a great game."

Marsh may have been the main Rangers threat, but he was no secret weapon. For John Dempsey, especially, the striker was far from an unknown quantity. "I knew his game pretty well because I'd played with him at Fulham," he says. "In training he'd put the ball through your legs, and then say 'nutmeg' over his shoulder as he sped off. As you can imagine, that was a bit annoying. Rodney was a difficult player to mark because he'd drift all over the field, so one minute he'd be up front with Mike Leach and the next he'd disappear off to the left wing or somewhere. But that was Rodney, he loved to entertain the crowd and the fans loved him back."

For once, the 90 minutes lived up to all the pre-match hype. On a mud-clogged Loftus Road pitch Chelsea got off to the perfect start with two goals in the first eight minutes from Webb and Osgood. Venables pulled one back for Rangers with a twice-taken penalty after McCreadie fouled Bridges and for a while the home side threatened an equaliser. Then, close on half-time, Osgood restored the Blues' two-goal advantage when QPR goalkeeper Mike Kelly failed to hold onto Hollins' long range shot. The Chelsea number nine took advantage of a defensive mix up to complete his hat-trick in the second half and, before celebrating with his team-mates, couldn't resist having a quiet word in the ear of the Rangers keeper.

"Kelly had failed Ossie on a coaching course not long before and after the third one went in Ossie said to him, 'Stick to fucking coaching!'" chuckles Alan Hudson. "Kelly didn't like that much."

Twenty-five years later relations between the QPR keeper and the Chelsea players hadn't improved much, the on-going feud resulting in a much-publicised tunnel bust up at the Bridge between Kelly, by then Middlesbrough's goalkeeping coach, and Hudson, who was working at Chelsea as a matchday corporate host. "I was about to do a presentation on the pitch at half-time," recalls Huddy. "It was 4–0 or something, we were playing great stuff, we'd murdered them. Kelly spotted me in the tunnel as I was waiting to go on. He looked at me and said, 'You, it's in the car park with you afterwards!'"

"So I went out and did the presentation on the pitch, went back to the box I was in and Ossie was there. I told him about Kelly, and Ossie said, 'Don't worry about that, I'll handle him'. Ossie went down after the game and they were chatting like best friends, but when he saw me Kelly went crazy. There was a bit of a scuffle but it was completely blown out of proportion by the press. I had to go off and do my question and answer thing in Drakes so I just walked away from it, but I made sure I had the last word. I told him that he should concentrate on coaching his goalie who'd just let in five rather than fighting. I got sacked after that."

Anyway, back to the QPR match and Peter Osgood grabbed all the headlines the day after the game, which finished 4–2 to the Blues, but an outstanding midfield display from Hudson had been equally crucial to Chelsea's success.

"Terry Venables said afterwards that with the heavy pitch he felt I wouldn't be strong enough and he could put me off my game," reveals Huddy. "He admitted he tried to give me a few knocks, but I just shoved him aside. He said he couldn't believe I was so strong at that age. But we won every battle all over the field, really. Ron kicked Rodney Marsh and he wasn't seen again, and Ossie proved that he was London's top striker."

Hudson's all-action performance didn't only impress Venables. After the game England manager Sir Alf Ramsey, who had been watching from the stands, said of the Chelsea midfielder, "There is no limit to what this young boy can achieve." This was praise indeed from the normally taciturn Sir Alf, a man who wasn't given to hyperbole and was so in control of his emotions that he had famously remained seated when the ref's final whistle signalled that England had won the 1966 World Cup. Although Ramsey hadn't said it directly there was a strong implication in his words that, aged just 18 and with less than a season's first team football behind him, Huddy was being considered for England's summer defence of the Jules Rimet trophy in Mexico.

That, though, was for the future. Of more immediate interest was who Chelsea might play in the semi-final. As expected, Leeds and Manchester United had overcome their lower division opponents but there had been a surprise at Vicarage Road where Watford had beaten Liverpool 1–0. Down at Chelsea's training ground in Mitcham the players gathered around a radio on the Monday lunchtime to listen to the draw. Unsurprisingly, there wasn't much debate about which team they wanted to be paired with.

"Of course, we wanted to play Watford," says John Dempsey, "and when we came out of the hat together there was a huge roar. We weren't frightened of playing Leeds or Manchester United but, obviously, you'd choose Watford out of those three. Mind you, we weren't going to underestimate them after they'd beaten Liverpool."

The Blues, though, had every right to be confident because they were playing some superb stuff at the time. A week after their trip to Loftus Road Chelsea strolled to a 3–0 win at high-flying Coventry, thanks to goals by Webb, Hudson and Baldwin. For Geoffrey Green in *The Times* the performance suggested that, finally, the team was becoming more than the sum of its parts.

"The secret of Chelsea nowadays is the harnessing and blending of their several skills," he wrote. "Where once the artistry of players like Osgood and Cooke tended to bring no end product and were showpieces on their own, set aside, as it were, from their colleagues, now there is real teamwork and co-ordination, built on craft, strength and spirit."

There was a growing feeling in the camp that not only could Chelsea win the Cup, they might also pull off the Double. "We just didn't think anyone could beat us, in the Cup or the league," says Alan Hudson. "In the league we were going pretty well, especially considering we were down the bottom at the start." The title, though, was a long shot, as Everton had a healthy lead at the top.

For the semi-final against Watford, played on another heavy pitch at White Hart Lane, Chelsea were the overwhelming favourites. Events appeared to be following the expected script when Webb put the Blues in front after just three minutes, but Terry Garbett quickly equalised and at the break the scores remained level. Watford had defended well but the Chelsea performance had lacked its usual zip. In the west Londoners' dressing room the players were in no doubt about the reason for their flat display.

"A day or two before the game Dave Sexton took us into town to have a sauna, somewhere around Kensington," recalls Ron Harris. "It's a bit like when you sit out in the sun for a long time: you feel a bit drained afterwards and a few of the lads were saying that at half-time. What didn't help, too, was that they were a Second Division team and you think to yourself it's just a matter of turning up and winning. But we had a helluva struggle for 60 odd minutes."

The goal which broke Watford's stubborn resistance arrived on the hour and, in many ways, epitomised Chelsea's bright, vibrant football that season. The move began with Hutchinson laying the ball back to Hudson who, surrounded by yellow shirts, cleverly turned away from his markers and slipped a pass out to Houseman in space on the left. With both Osgood and Hutchinson to aim for, Houseman picked out Ossie who powered his header past Watford keeper (and future Norwich manager) Mike Smith before hurling himself into the net in joyous celebration. Three more goals in six minutes from Houseman (2), his first following a superb run past three defenders, and Hutchinson confirmed Chelsea's place at Wembley. The 5–1 final score was the biggest FA Cup semi-final win since Wolves beat Grimsby 5–0 in 1949, although it was a little harsh on Watford. "The scoreline at the end looked like we pissed all over them but that wasn't the case," says Ron Harris.

On the other hand, the quick-fire salvo of goals which settled the tie was not untypical of Chelsea that season. When the team hit a purple patch – usually, this would involve the complementary talents of Osgood, Cooke and Hudson combining together in a dazzling array of flicks, feints and flourishes – the Blues were capable of putting a match beyond reach of the opposition in a matter of minutes. Dave Sexton knew this, but he also knew that outrageous skill and swaggering self-confidence alone were not enough for the team to be successful.

"Football isn't peaches and cream the whole time," he said a few years later. "Although you can win a game 3–0, you can always look back at moments in the match and say, 'By jingo, if we hadn't survived that particular spell, we wouldn't have been able to get in front.' So as well as playing attractive football, you have to be able to resist when these crises come along in a game and, believe me, they're cast-iron certainties." As if to underline this pragmatic philosophy, Sexton had a sign on his office wall reading, 'When the going gets tough, the tough get tougher'.

Chelsea would have to wait to learn who their Cup Final opponents would be. In the other semi-final at Hillsborough Leeds and Manchester United had drawn 0–0. The replay at Villa Park also finished scoreless so the teams would have to meet for a third time at Bolton's Burnden Park.

While this mini-epic was continuing, the Chelsea players had ample opportunity to reflect on which of the two teams they would prefer to meet at Wembley. Manchester United appeared to represent the distinctly easier option. Yes, they had three superstars in their team in George Best, Bobby Charlton and Denis Law, but the Reds were not the force they had been in 1968 when they won the European Cup. Moreover, Chelsea possessed a psychological advantage over United, having beaten them twice that season. Certainly, Ian Hutchinson must have been desperate for the Reds to triumph: remarkably, he had scored all four of Chelsea's goals against United that year.

Leeds, on the other hand, were arguably the best team in the country. The previous season the Yorkshiremen had won the league championship for the first time in their history with a then record number of points, losing just two matches in the process. In 1970, despite Chelsea's best efforts, they appeared to be the only team with a realistic hope of halting Everton's title charge, and they had also battled their way through to the semi-finals of the European Cup where they were due to meet Celtic. The demanding schedule of games didn't seem to worry Leeds' manager, Don Revie. His side were invariably referred to as the most 'professional' in the land – although, often, there was an implication that this was a euphemism for 'dirty' or 'cynical' – and would simply, as the football saying goes, 'take every match as it comes'.

Unlike Manchester United, who relied heavily on their glamorous forward line and were lacking in quality elsewhere, Leeds were very much a team. Virtually all of their players were internationals and there were no obvious weaknesses in their line-up, apart perhaps from their erratic goalkeeper, Gary Sprake. The rest of the side, which included famous names such as Jack Charlton, Norman 'Bites Yer Legs' Hunter, Billy Bremner, Johnny Giles and Allan 'Sniffer' Clarke combined skill, tenacity and hard-edged ruthlessness in equal measure. In short, Leeds were a fearsome proposition.

Leeds also held the upper hand in their head-to-head league meetings with Chelsea that season, having beaten the Blues 2–0 at Elland Road and 5–2 at the Bridge. Chelsea, though, had eased the Yorkshiremen's fixture congestion by knocking them out of the League Cup before falling themselves to Carlisle United – the third season on the trot that the Blues had gone out of the competition to lower league opposition.

On balance, taking into account all the different factors, the Chelsea players might have been expected to prefer a Manchester United victory at Burnden Park. Not so, according to Alan Hudson. "The glamour final would have been Chelsea and Manchester United, and it would have been George Best's only FA Cup Final," he says. "But I wanted to play Leeds because the rivalry with them was so intense. If there was one team we loved beating more than anybody else it was Leeds. Okay, they'd beaten us 5–2 in the league but we hammered them, we slaughtered them. Tommy Hughes threw a couple in and they didn't earn their goals at all. We played terrific that day and came off the field shaking our heads. It was probably the most unjust result of my time at Chelsea."

John Dempsey was equally unfazed at the prospect of meeting Leeds. "I didn't really mind who we played in the final," he says. "Just to be there was the important thing. Peter Bonetti didn't play in the game when they thrashed us 5–2 at the Bridge, and no disrespect to Tommy Hughes or John Phillips but I always felt we missed Peter when he wasn't in goal. As a defender he was great because you'd hear a shout and he'd come and catch the crosses, which took the pressure off you. Although he wasn't the tallest of keepers he had a great leap and he just used to command his area. You felt a lot more secure when he was playing."

In the event, it was Leeds who got through to Wembley to face Chelsea, thanks to a solitary Billy Bremner goal in the second replay. To have kept three consecutive clean sheets against Manchester United's prolific strikers was some feat, but one which only served to underline the meanness of the Leeds defence. Indeed, on their route to the Twin Towers – which also included wins over Swansea, non-league Sutton United, Mansfield and Swindon – Leeds had only conceded one goal.

At the end of March, two weeks before the final, Chelsea's Double hopes were ended in spectacular style as they were walloped 5–2 at Everton. This time there could be no complaints about the score which, but for late goals by Dempsey and Osgood, would have been even more embarrassing. Two days later there was even worse news for Chelsea fans as Alan Hudson suffered an ankle ligament injury during a 3–1 defeat at West Bromich Albion. With his left ankle in plaster and hobbling on crutches, Huddy's chances of making Wembley other than as a spectator looked bleak.

"There was nobody near me when it happened," he says. "I just landed badly, my foot went down a hole and that was it. I knew as soon as it happened that it was serious because I was in un-believable pain. It was a terrible idea to put the ankle in plaster because it glued the whole joint up. I tried everything to be fit for Wembley: I had acupuncture and even went to see a spiritualist, a lady in Victoria. It was like a palm reading, only she 'read' the bottom of my foot. I was just laughing while she did it and thinking, 'This ain't gonna work'. Anyway, she told me I wouldn't score in the final and she was right about that, but she didn't say I wouldn't play."

Two days before the final, Hudson failed a fitness test at Stamford Bridge. Although expected, this was a blow to Sexton as the 18-year-old was the creative hub of his team. "Alan Hudson is a tremendously gifted player, possessing all the skills," Sexton had written in the Chelsea programme. "He has superb close control when he's in possession, especially when he's forced to play his way out of a tight situation. When Alan is carrying the ball forward he is exceptionally smart at drawing defenders towards him and then slipping the ball past them to a team-mate. And that's not all – Alan has an explosive right-foot shot, a genuine net-stretcher."

These qualities would be sorely missed at Wembley, especially as Leeds' own central midfielders, Billy Bremner and Johnny Giles, were key figures in Revie's team. Meanwhile, skipper Ron Harris was also a doubt for Wembley, having sustained a hamstring injury against Sheffield Wednesday a couple of weeks before. If the worst came to the worst, Sexton could call on the experienced Marvin Hinton to fill the gap in defence, but the Chelsea manager was desperate not to lose his captain for such an important match.

"Ron was what I would politely describe as steadfast," he said later. "He was very mature for his age, and loyal to the club. Some players don't like getting moved around and being asked to play in different positions. That wasn't the case with Harris. You could ask him to play centre-forward, and he would. Ronnie Harris was a rock – and they're the sort of fellows you build your team on."

As it turned out, Sexton's 'rock' passed his fitness test, telling waiting reporters that he was "as fit as I'll ever be." The truth was somewhat different, as Harris now admits. "Until the Thursday before the final I couldn't even jog," he says. "I wouldn't have played if it had been a league game and I needed three cortisone injections just to get me out there."

With his skipper pencilled in, Sexton's main selection dilemma was who to pick to replace the absent Hudson. The natural alternative was hard-running midfielder John Boyle, but he had fallen out of favour that season and had barely appeared on the team sheet. The same applied to Bobby Tambling, whose long Chelsea career was nearing its end. Alan Birchenall, who had played the previous week against Tottenham when Ian Hutchinson was nursing a bruised hip, was another possibility but his own season had been marred by a knee injury. The obvious choice, then, was Tommy Baldwin, who had played in half of the Cup games anyway, and had pushed his case for inclusion by scoring the winner against Spurs. The only trouble was that the Sponge and Dave Sexton weren't seeing eye to eye.

"When I saw I wasn't on the team-sheet for the semi-final against Watford I slapped in a transfer request," says Tommy. It was by no means the first time Baldwin had demanded a move; in fact, it was an unusual week when he wasn't banging on Sexton's door, expressing a desire to quit the Bridge. "I know we had a lot of good players, but I couldn't understand why I was always the one who got dropped," he explains. "I put in loads of transfer requests but Dave never let me go. He just used to say, 'Get out of my office, you're worse than James Dean.' Well, I suppose I was a bit of a rebel."

While Sexton mulled over his team selection, the build-up to the Wembley clash in the outside world became increasingly intense. For football fans throughout England, the FA Cup Final was a hugely important occasion. Amazingly, considering the surfeit of football now served up on the small screen, it was the *only* domestic match of the entire season that fans were able to watch live on television. Seeing their club win the FA Cup, if only from the comfort of their sitting room, was the height of most supporters' ambitions – eclipsing even success in the league championship.

In those days both BBC1 and ITV had live coverage of the Cup Final, leaving only BBC2 as a possible televisual haven for non-football fans. In the *TV Times* and the *Radio Times*, which featured a picture of Manchester City celebrating their 1969 Cup win on the cover, the two main channels' schedules for the big day announced hours of preview material before the game itself, interrupted only by racing from Ascot on the beeb and all-in wrestling on ITV. If that wasn't enough, there was also the opportunity earlier in the week to see Peter Bonetti and John Hollins take on Billy Bremner and Johnny Giles in a special Cup Final edition of *A Question of Sport*, presented by David Vine.

For the newspapers, too, the Chelsea–Leeds clash was a massive story, not only on the day itself but in the week leading up to the match. Two days before the game, for instance, the *Mirror's* front page was devoted to a Cup Final hardy perennial, the trade in black market tickets. "Big probe into Cup tickets racket" screamed the headline, above a story about tickets marked 'Leeds AFC' being sold outside Stamford Bridge. Leeds chairman Percy Woodward was reported as promising a full investigation, saying, "If we find out that a player is involved, he will be in very serious trouble indeed."

Elsewhere, £4 stand tickets for the final were reportedly selling for £60. One tout gleefully told the *Mirror*, "You can't lose. Leeds are the team of the moment and every football fan in London is willing to pay to see Chelsea win the Cup for the first time."

Mind you, it was hard to see why anyone would pay over the odds when *Mirror* readers already knew the result of the match. "The *Mirror* has played the game by computer and it's . . . Leeds for the Cup," the paper's centre-page spread revealed. There followed a truly daft story about how a panel of experts, including three unnamed First Division managers, two Mirror sports writers, a scientific advisor and "the one girl in the side, a management scientist who helped with the mathematics", had fed in all the available information about the two sides into a computer and come up with the final score: Leeds 2 Chelsea 1.

Leeds were the slight favourites with the bookies, too, with William Hill quoting 8/11 for the Yorkshiremen and 11/10 for Chelsea. The odds suggested a tight match but Don Revie appeared confident that his team would win more handsomely than many were predicting. "It will be a hard game," he said, "but I don't think it will be as close as most people seem to think."

The mood in the Chelsea camp was equally optimistic. "We have none of the nervousness we felt before the final against Spurs in 1967," Eddie McCreadie told reporters, "and it's the right kind of confidence, the best kind, the quiet kind."

Another game from the 1967 Cup run was also a motivating tool for the Chelsea players. As we've already heard, the Leeds-Chelsea semi-final that year had been a physical and bloody affair. "Gary Sprake had put his studs in the face of John Boyle in the semi-final," recalls Alan Hudson, "so there was a lot of 'previous' going into the final. It wasn't like disliking a person, but when they put their kit on and we put ours on it was like 'Game on'. Leeds didn't have any rules and they would go to any lengths to win. They were like the Mafia in that respect. No one was dirtier than Leeds. Probably only Peter Lorimer and Eddie Gray out of all their team wouldn't go in over the top if they got the chance."

Tommy Baldwin agrees: "There were a lot of scores being settled from previous games whenever we played them. It always just seemed to go mad, with everyone kicking each other. But afterwards we'd have a drink with them in the bar and we got on okay."

And Ron Harris adds: "Chelsea-Leeds was never a game for faint-hearts. Everybody knows Jackie Charlton kept a black book containing the names of players he wanted to gain revenge against and you can bet there were a few Chelsea players in there. I wasn't amongst them myself because I didn't get up the other end of the pitch much. Personally, I didn't find I needed a black book as I've always had a good memory."

Chopper's defensive partner John Dempsey, though, reckons Leeds' infamous reputation was slightly exaggerated. "People say they were dirty but I found Mick Jones and Allan Clarke up front were okay," he says. "Jones was all arms and elbows and you had to battle him, while Clarke was a skilful player with a touch of the Jimmy Greaves about him. People sometimes criticised him for being lazy but when he had a chance he was deadly. I think Leeds' reputation for being a dirty team came more in midfield and at the back where people like Bremner, Giles, Hunter and Charlton were all very competitive. They could be niggly, too, pulling your shirt and other things like that to put you off."

On the day of the final, Saturday April 11th – the earliest Cup Final date, incidentally, since Aston Villa beat Everton on April 10th in 1897 – the Chelsea squad ate a pre-match meal at the same Gloucester Road hotel they had visited before every Cup tie that season. "Manager Dave Sexton has asked me to keep to the usual menu," the proprietor told *The Mirror*. "It is beef fillets and toast, rice pudding and tea. I call it the Chelsea Special."

By now Sexton had settled on his team. As expected, Tommy Baldwin would fill the gap created by Hudson's absence, playing on the right side of midfield. Moreover, the Sponge was a key element in Sexton's game plan.

"In the team talk, Dave must have spoken to me for about ten minutes," he says. "'Tommy,' he told me, 'whatever happens I want you to make sure Terry Cooper doesn't go on those overlaps. Get to him straightaway. Norman Hunter might come through, so just nip between the two of them to stop them both. If Billy Bremner or Johnny Giles come across to your side just get your foot in . . . and don't forget Eddie Gray, make sure you have a snap at him. So I'm thinking, 'Great, just the five players to pick up . . .' Then Dave turns back to me and says, 'Oh, Tommy, if you get the chance, try to get up there and get us a goal'."

At the time, teams were only allowed to nominate one substitute. As in all the previous rounds, Sexton named versatile defender Marvin Hinton in the role. "Before the final I hadn't got off the bench once," he says. "In those days if a player got a knock he tended to play on rather than come off. Dave was very superstitious so, along with all the stuff about the lucky suit, having me on the bench almost became another superstition. I suppose that worked out well for me – as there were other players who could have been sub – although, obviously, I would rather have been in the starting eleven."

Many of the players were equally superstitious, with a number of them – including David Webb, Ian Hutchinson and Charlie Cooke – having decided that it would be unlucky to have a haircut during the Cup run. By the time of the final the Blues, no doubt to the disgust of the old codgers at the FA, were probably the hairiest team ever to play at Wembley.

When they arrived at the stadium the players went out to inspect the pitch, which they discovered to be in appalling state. This wasn't a surprise. In the previous days the newspapers had been full of stories about the Wembley groundstaff's attempts to prepare a reasonable playing surface for the showpiece occasion. Bad weather was partly to blame but so, too, were the stadium authorities who, in a moment of collective madness, had agreed to the *Horse of the Year Show* being staged at Wembley. The famous hallowed turf had failed to recover from the pounding it received, and in an attempt to even out the bumpy, rutted surface for the Cup Final the groundstaff had resorted to covering the pitch in a hundred tons of sand. The result was an ugly, lumpy, clotted mess quite unsuited to flowing football.

Once the pre-match preliminaries were over, Leeds, wearing unfamiliar red socks so as not to clash with Chelsea's white ones, quickly took control of the match. Much of their threat came down the Chelsea right, where left-winger Eddie Gray had established early dominance over David Webb. Their opening goal, though, came from a corner from the other side. Peter Bonetti failed to reach Gray's inswinger in a crowded six-yard area, Jack Charlton headed goalwards and, although either Eddie McCreadie or Ron Harris appeared well-placed to clear the ball off the line, both were deceived by the lack of bounce off the soft pitch. As the pair kicked thin air, the ball dribbled past the Blues' last defensive barrier and came to a stop a few inches over the line. Chelsea protests that Bonetti had been fouled were ignored by referee Eric Jennings and, after 21 minutes, Leeds had the lead.

The goal knocked Chelsea back and, for a while, only the sure handling of Bonetti and the swift interceptions of Dempsey and Harris prevented Leeds from adding a second. Then, four minutes before half-time the Blues equalised with a goal as soft as Leeds', Peter Houseman's speculative 25-yard shot squirming under Sprake's dive.

Tommy Baldwin hadn't touched the ball in the build up, yet he remains convinced that simply by hovering on the edge of the six-yard box he played a vital role in distracting the Leeds keeper. "I remember talking to Norman Hunter at some stage between the 1967 semi and the 1970 final and I told him, 'If I get the chance I'm going to get Sprakey, I'll just leave my foot in when I go for a bobbling ball,'" he says. "And, funnily enough, in his book Sprake says that when Peter Houseman shot he looked up because I was running in. He took his eye off the ball and it bobbled under his dive. He knew I was out to do him because of what he did to John Boyle in the 1967 semi and that put him off a fraction."

The second half saw good chances fall to both teams, but the two goalkeepers redeemed their earlier errors with some fine saves. Then, ten minutes from the end of normal time, Eddie Gray's fierce shot beat Bonetti but crashed against the crossbar. Three minutes later the Blues were not so fortunate as Allan Clarke's header bounced off a post into the path of Mick Jones, who smashed a left-footer into the opposite corner. Much as it hurt, few Chelsea fans would deny that Leeds deserved their lead.

One of the great qualities of Sexton's side, though, was that they never gave up. Despite being outplayed for much of the game they had hung on and, with four minutes left on the clock, the Blues were awarded a free-kick for a push by Jack Charlton on Peter Osgood. Harris slipped the ball to Hollins who curled the ball to the near post, where Ian Hutchinson flung himself in front of Charlton to send a powerful header past Sprake.

"If you look back over the season, I must have scored eight to ten similar goals," Hutch said later. "Peter Houseman or John Hollins knew it was their job to deliver the ball either to the near or far post. Ossie tended to go far, because he didn't like the studs up his arse, and I normally went near. We scored a hell of a lot of goals that way. It was just sort of programmed into us from the training ground, really."

Minutes later the final whistle blew, signalling half an hour of extra time. Trudging to the sidelines to listen to Dave Sexton's pep talk, Hutchinson was asked by TV reporter Peter Lorenzo for a quick comment on his goal. "I forgot that we were going out live and replied honestly, 'Fuck! Extra time on the sand dunes . . .'"

A few years earlier the flamboyant theatre critic Kenneth Tynan had caused a huge stir when he became the first person to say the word 'fuck' on TV. Fortunately for Hutch, his unwitting slip caused no such outcry – possibly because the entire TV-watching nation had popped into the kitchen to put the kettle on.

At the start of extra time Marvin Hinton came on for Ron Harris, the cloying surface having exacerbated his hamstring injury. Leeds, again, had the clearer opportunities once play resumed: Clarke hitting the crossbar and then Giles shooting beyond Bonetti, only for Webb to stretch out a leg and send the ball spinning over the bar.

"I was just running on instinct when Johnny Giles hit his shot," says Webby of this crucial intervention. "The ball was flying into the roof of the net with Peter Bonetti stranded and I just flung myself up to get my boot on it. If God wasn't smiling on me it would have ended in the back of the net. Instead it went over the bar."

Seconds later Jennings blew the final whistle on the first FA Cup Final at Wembley to end in a draw. The exhausted players, many of whom were feeling the effects of cramp, still managed to drag themselves round the pitch one more time for a joint lap of honour. "Both sides had played so well under the worst possible conditions that it was right to take a bow together," said Eddie McCreadie, who had come up with the idea.

Having been on the back foot for much of the match – the corner count of 12–4 in favour of the Yorshiremen told much of the story – Chelsea were happier with the draw than Leeds. "In the first game we just about survived," admits John Dempsey. "They were on top for most of the match and hit the post and bar a couple of times. I think we missed Alan Hudson because his passing and ability on the ball had been so important for us that season. A lot of the problems for us came in midfield especially down the left where Eddie Gray had a lot of possession and gave David Webb a tough time. They should have won it really, but we hung in there and showed character to hit back again when they scored near the end."

"I think we were the luckiest team ever to come off Wembley with a draw," adds Ron Harris candidly. "I wouldn't say we were totally outplayed but of the two sides they were far better than us."

Back in the Chelsea dressing room, Dave Sexton had already made his mind up to make one important change for the replay which, because of the poor state of the Wembley pitch, the FA had decided would be staged at Old Trafford. David Webb, cruelly exposed at right back by Man of the Match Eddie Gray throughout the afternoon, would move to the centre of defence with Ron Harris switching to the flank.

"Eddie gave me a right royal runaround," Webb admitted

afterwards. "I enjoyed the whole occasion right up until the kick-off, and after that everything I did was about ten minutes too late."

Showing astute management, Sexton bolstered Webb's confidence by quashing any press speculation that the defender might be dropped for the replay. "David showed real grit and character," he told reporters. "He stuck to his job right through to the end and there'll be the replay for him to show who is top man."

"This was a great effort by everybody involved," he continued. "But I must give a merit mention to Peter Bonetti who proved he is the greatest goalkeeper in the world." Indeed, without Bonetti, their best performer on the day, the Blues would surely have been sunk. Peter Osgood was equally admiring of his keeper. "It was like he had glue on his gloves," he said. "Catty can do that at Old Trafford or any time you ask him."

The press reports in the following two days all agreed that Leeds had been unlucky not to win, but neither did they overlook Chelsea's contribution to a thrilling match. "This was the finest Cup Final seen at Wembley since the war, better even than Manchester United and Blackpool of 1948 and lacking only the emotional impact of the last 20 minutes of the Stanley Matthews fiesta of 1953," suggested Geoffrey Green in *The Times*.

In *The Mirror*, meanwhile, reporter Nigel Clarke relived his eventful afternoon in the Chelsea end: "I stood among the Chelsea ranks, high up on the terraces and shared with them an experience that left me emotionally exhausted. Someone spilled a bottle of beer down my neck, a woman with bright blue hair slapped a Chelsea hat on my head. And when Chelsea scored I was pushed crazily, 30 feet down the terraces in a jumble of laughing, leaping people. It was fun."

The post-match comments of the Football Association chairman, Dr Andrew Stephen, featured prominently in all the papers. "This was not a classic," he said. "It was an epic."

The FA, though, was a little concerned that the so-called

'Carry-on Cup Final' might interfere with England's World Cup preparations. Asked what would happen if the replay was also drawn Stephen ruled out the possibility of the Cup being shared. "You would even have to consider tossing a coin for it," he said. Eventually they announced that, if necessary, a third game would be played at Coventry's Highfield Road three days after the replay.

In the 18 days between Wembley and Old Trafford Chelsea played three league games, beating Stoke and Liverpool and losing away to Burnley. The four points won cemented the Blues in third place, their highest finish since 1955. Ron Harris wasn't risked in any of the games but was pronounced fully fit for the replay. Alan Hudson, though, had again failed a fitness test, ending his hopes of making a dramatic return to the team.

As for Leeds, their season was in danger of turning into a disaster of Titanic proportions. Defeats by Manchester City and Ipswich had finally ended their championship ambitions, while Revie's men had also waved goodbye to the European Cup after losing both legs of their semi-final with Celtic. There was further bad news, too: goalkeeper Gary Sprake had been carried off against the Scottish champions with knee ligament damage and was extremely doubtful for the Cup Final replay.

A few hours before kick-off at Old Trafford, Sprake was declared unfit to play and was replaced by 23-year-old Scot David Harvey. Otherwise, the sides were unchanged from Wembley. In another slight change from the original game, Chelsea took to the field wearing yellow socks while Leeds reverted to the pristine all-white strip that Don Revie, inspired by the great Real Madrid side of the time, had chosen for his team a decade earlier.

If the cast was familiar, so too was the script as Leeds began menacingly, putting immediate pressure on the Chelsea goal. Once again Lorimer, Bremner and Giles had gained an early ascendancy in midfield, from where they maintained a steady supply of passes to the dangerous Clarke and Jones. However, left-winger Eddie Gray had not brought his Wembley form with him and looked to be feeling the effects of a wince-inducing Harris tackle which had sent him hurtling off the pitch in the opening minutes.

"I suppose I didn't do a bad tackle on him," says Ron modestly, "and I think that helped us because he didn't do a lot in the game, certainly not compared to Wembley. There were a few vendettas flying around, but we all just got on with it. It's not like today when you get players looking for free-kicks, falling over and rolling around. Personally, I used to thrive in those sort of games."

Softening Gray up wasn't a pre-planned tactic as such, it was just simply what Chopper did in every game. "Ronnie used to sort people out in the first five minutes, just to let them know what was in store for them for the rest of the game," said Peter Osgood. "On the pitch he was a serious man, a very serious man. He led from the front, and he didn't expect anybody else to do what he didn't do. He had a good engine on him, he was a strong boy and people feared him. Quite rightly so. He was the captain. Nobody would try to take the piss out of him on the pitch. Off the field he was a different character. He was one of the jokers, he loved a laugh and a giggle, and he liked a little drink although he wasn't one of the big drinkers. But on the pitch he was just an animal, he really was."

With Gray hobbling rather than flying down the wing, the Blues appeared to have removed one of Leeds' main potential threats. Chelsea, though, soon had a major injury concern of their own as Jones crashed into Bonetti in mid-air while the pair challenged for a cross. The Cat fell to the ground clutching his left knee and required nearly five minutes' treatment from Blues physio Harry Medhurst. These were anxious moments for Chelsea: there were, of course, no substitute keepers in those days, so if Bonetti couldn't continue his green jersey would pass to Dave Webb, the Blues' emergency goalie.

Happily for the Chelsea camp and Webb in particular, Bonetti, although limping heavily, resumed his position in goal with John

Dempsey taking over the goal-kicking duties. "Because they attacked us a quite a bit there were a lot of kicks to take," recalls Demps, "and I remember thinking it was important to reach the halfway line at least. That gave me time to go charging out so as not to leave their forwards onside if they won the ball and played it forward. Fortunately, I didn't skank any and I got good distance on my kicks."

Five minutes after injuring Bonetti, Jones dealt Chelsea an even more painful blow, rifling a shot beyond the Blues keeper after Clarke had skilfully negotiated his way past three tackles and played the ball into his co-striker's path. For the third time in the two games Leeds had the lead, and on this occasion Chelsea would have no quick reply.

Revie's men retained the upper hand until well into the second half when, against a background of constant 'Chel-sea!' chants from the thousands of London-based fans who had made the journey up north to pack out the Stretford End, the Blues at last edged into the game. Baldwin's header prompted Harvey's first proper save of the evening on the hour and, with Cooke and Hollins now gaining more control in central midfield, the chances of a Chelsea equaliser no longer seemed remote.

The goal the Blues fans had been patiently waiting for arrived on 78 minutes. Inevitably, perhaps, it was scored by Osgood, maintaining his record of having notched in every round of the Cup – a feat which no player since has matched.

"I did the crossover with Hutch and then Charlie took it off Hutch," he recalled later. "Charlie went one way, I went the other, he bent it in, and . . . it was a bit like being in a dream or a film. I was just there waiting for it in loads of space. Luckily, Gary Sprake wasn't playing, and David Harvey was in goal. I think if Sprake had been playing he might have come and clattered me, but David stayed on his line and that just gave me time to have a quick look at him and glance it the right way.

"I honestly thought I was offside, but I looked across and the linesman didn't have his flag up. I ran to our fans and I had goose pimples on my skin and the hairs on the back of my neck were standing on end. It was an incredible feeling . . . "

As both sides searched desperately for the winner, the game became increasingly physical. Hutchinson was booked for shoving Bremner in the chest, Leeds hit back with some vicious tackles of their own and then, with just five minutes to go, McCreadie flattened Bremner in the Chelsea area.

"Maybe we were lucky not to give away a penalty," admits John Dempsey. "It wasn't even a normal tackle, it was a chest high lunge which almost cut Bremner in half." However, Eric Jennings, officiating in his last match, was in lenient mood and waved away Leeds' appeals for a spot-kick.

Throughout the season Sexton had drummed into his players the need to keep going for 90 minutes. Now, as at Wembley, tired legs would have to cope with the demands of an additional half-hour. The psychological strain was enormous too, as every player on the pitch knew that just one mistake could settle the match.

Leeds created the first clear opportunity in extra-time, forcing Bonetti, now more mobile but by no means fully recovered, to make a fine save from Lorimer's shot. Osgood's goal, though, had given Chelsea a huge lift which was reflected in the fans' confident chants of 'We're gonna win the Cup!' and, a minute before half-time in extra-time, a Chelsea attack down the left resulted in a throw level with their opponents' 18-yard line. Leeds knew what to expect. At the time, Ian Hutchinson had the longest throw in English football, with his best effort having been measured at 122 ft. "I'm double jointed at both shoulders," Hutchinson once revealed. "It was a flick and then a follow through."

Hutch's long throw wasn't the prettiest or most sophisticated of tactics but it was highly effective. On this occasion, he rubbed the ball on his jersey, stretched back his arms, arched his back and flung the ball through the night air towards the near post. The missile flicked off the back of Jack Charlton's balding pate across the six-yard box to the far post where, in a mad scramble of jostling players, the ball glanced off David Webb and into the net.

"The ball hit me on the cheek," said Webby later. "I went up to head it in, and as I was leaning forward, Leeds players got underneath me to try to put me off. I was determined to connect with the ball, and I knew that if I threw myself in the right spot, I'd score. As I landed in the net I saw the ball in front of me. And, even then, because it was Leeds, the first thing I did was look to see if the linesman was flagging. Then I looked at the referee, and he'd already run to the halfway line. Only after that was I comfortable that I'd scored. Leeds were such a professional side they'd intimidate anybody, you see."

As with Peter Houseman's shot at Wembley, Tommy Baldwin also claims some of the credit for Webb's unconventional goal. "I was at the far post and, when I jumped for Jack Charlton's unintentional flick on, I pushed Terry Cooper into the back of the net and stood on Eddie Gray's thigh," he says. "Webby got the goal, of course, but he might not have scored if I hadn't been in there as well."

Ahead for the first time in 224 minutes of play, Chelsea were determined to protect their lead. Apart from a Hutchinson 'goal' ruled out for offside, the final 16 minutes were largely a rearguard action for the Blues. Finally using his substitute, Sexton replaced Osgood with Marvin Hinton for the last ten minutes to add another body in defence. The plan worked as Leeds, despite a period of relentless pressure towards the end, could find no way through the thicket of blue shirts.

With Blues fans howling for the final whistle, referee Jennings finally took the hint and signalled that Chelsea, for the first time in their 65-history, had won the FA Cup.

Princess Margaret, perhaps not such a big Chelsea fan after all, was not around to present the trophy to Blues skipper Ron Harris. Nor, for that matter, were any other members of the

Royal Family. Instead Dr Andrew Stephen did the honours while cockney-twanged chants of 'Ee-aye-addio, we've won the Cup!" echoed around Old Trafford. Going up to collect their winners' medals, the hairy, mud-splashed and dishevelled Blues, half of whom were now wearing the white shirts of their defeated opponents, were possibly not much of a sight to put before Royalty anyway.

Speaking after the match, Dave Sexton said: "We were very nervous first half, the same as at Wembley. We didn't get into it for a long, long while, but if we're not playing well, we hang on and hang on. That's the quality of our football, and it's paid off. That's why we're a good side.

"When Peter Bonetti went down, it was a really bad moment. If he had not been able to carry on, it would have been very serious. Then came another blow when Leeds scored the first goal again, but I never doubted that we would come back once more.

"David Webb's winner was just typical of him. At Wembley, Leeds had given him the sort of game most players would want to forget, but he could hardly wait for the chance of another go at them. He's bounced back like a rubber ball, hasn't he! I'm terribly pleased for him."

Webb himself spoke of his feelings when his Cup Final almost became a Sunday League player's worst nightmare, with the manager handing him the goalkeeper's gloves. "At half-time, when I looked at Peter Bonetti's left knee and saw it had ballooned right up, I was afraid they'd be sticking me in goal for the second half. I told Harry (Medhurst), 'Do a good job on him, mate – he looks better in the green jersey than I do.'

"Don Revie said earlier in the season something about players down south not being as dedicated as those in the North," he added. "I wonder if he still thinks we're soft. If Leeds are the 'most professional' team in the business, what does that make us? Just too brave for them, we were." Brave, certainly, but also a little lucky.

"Looking at the two games overall, it was daylight robbery that we won it," admits Marvin Hinton. Certainly, the Blues had had their backs to the wall for much of the four hours playing time, and had only shown glimpses of the captivating, smooth-passing football which had characterised their season. Their triumph owed as much, if not more, to single-minded perseverance as pure skill. Still, Chelsea had the Cup and Leeds, for all their efforts, had nothing.

"We dominated them for 70 minutes and still we didn't win," moaned Jack Charlton, who stormed off in a taxi after the match without even bothering to collect his loser's medal. "Peter Bonetti got hurt and we never challenged him again. He's a friend of mine but we ought to have whacked him. Not dirty like, but got stuck in."

While Leeds sulked, Chelsea got on with the serious job of celebrating. "We got absolutely wrecked," says Tommy Baldwin. "We had loads to drink at the formal post-match dinner, then most of us went out to a nightclub in Manchester until about four o'clock. Lots of people were coming up to congratulate us, because everyone hated Leeds at the time. I can remember coming out of the nightclub and there were some railings along the road. For some reason – maybe because it could have been a short cut back to the hotel – Charlie (Cooke) decided to climb over the railings and fell flat on his face. When we got back to the hotel room there were bodies all over the place, all sorts of friends and relatives were crashed out there. Then, coming back on the train to London in the morning loads of fans came into our compartment and the celebrations continued until the buffet ran out of beer."

One of the fans who wangled his way into the players' carriage was the fashion photographer Eric Swayne. "They knew me a bit and invited me and my two mates in," he says. "They had the two middle coaches and we were in with them. John Hollins' wife, Linda, sat on my lap coming back from Manchester. She was a pretty little thing. I can remember getting off at Euston and being kissed by girls who thought I was a member of the team. Everyone was telling me how marvellous I was – it was great!"

Arriving at Euston, Eric and the rest of the Chelsea party were greeted by around 1,000 fans, many of whom had travelled over from the King's Road where they had been celebrating all night. A report by Hugh de Wet in *The Times* that morning suggested the fans' festivities had been at least as wild and unrestrained as the players'. "As the realization gradually sunk in that Chelsea had defeated Leeds 2–1 in the FA Cup Final, the King's Road late last night built up into a state of almost hysterical and disbelieving frenzy as supporters screamed themselves hoarse with pleasure.

"At closing time outside the pubs, clubs and discotheques the long-haired and elegantly velvet clad were, for once, at one with the skinheads as all joined in the chanting and scarf waving. The loud jubilation was echoed from the cars, a solid mass of almost stationary traffic as Lamborghinis and Bentleys hooted repeatedly with stately bravura, to be backed up by the shrill and piercing toots of the minis. The crowds were particularly thick towards the Wandsworth Bridge end of the King's Road, with the gentlemen of the Chelsea Conservative Club standing on the pavement, beer mugs in hand, vociferously urging on the crowds of youths to greater things."

The boisterous celebrations continued as the players climbed aboard an open-top bus, which took them from Euston through Paddington, Kensington and Earl's Court to Stamford Bridge. "All along the route you could see blue and white scarves and flags hanging from office windows and houses," recalls John Dempsey. "It gave you a real tingle along the back of your neck. Then, around the King's Road and Fulham Road, it was just a sea of blue with thousands of people lining the route. It didn't seem to matter that it was a working day. The place was just heaving with people." Nor was the party confined to west London: in Ilford a pub landlord ran out of beer after honouring a 20-year-old promise to serve free drinks when Chelsea finally won the Cup.

In a similarly generous gesture, Eric Swayne invited all the Chelsea squad out to dinner a few days after the Cup Final. "I booked a table at the Meridiana, this lovely posh restaurant I used to go to on the Brompton Road, for the whole team, my wife, Shirley, and four other girls that I brought along. The only players not there were Peter Bonetti and Peter Osgood who had just left for England World Cup duty in Mexico. During the meal I was thinking, 'This is going to set me back a bit, but it's worth it.' It was a wonderful, wonderful meal with marvellous food, lots of champagne and wine plus beer for some of the players.

"After we'd polished off some brandy I was sweating a little, I had slightly moist palms about what the bill was going to be. But at the end of the evening one of the two owners, Walter Mariti, came up and whispered, 'There's no bill, Eric. Tonight's on me.' That was a fantastic gesture, but I think it reflected how proud everyone was about what the boys had done. So we had a marvellous time, and I didn't have to cough up a small fortune."

The Chelsea boys were surely entitled to relax with a glass or two of the finest Courvoisier. According to Dave Sexton, it had taken a "superhuman effort" to beat Leeds. And even if the Blues had enjoyed some luck along the way, nobody could deny that for sheer grit, determination and a cussed refusal to accept defeat they had deserved to become the first Chelsea side ever to get their hands on the world's oldest football trophy.

CHAPTER EIGHT
SEX IN THE CITY

I n the early seventies Raquel Welch was, in every sense, one of the biggest female film stars in the world. An authentic Hollywood sex symbol, the well-endowed actress's movie roles – which, famously, included an extended bout of dinosaur-grappling while wearing a revealing leopard skin loincloth in *One Million Years BC* – were not exactly masterpieces of subtlety or understatement. Not that her many fans cared. "Raquel is raw, unconquerable, antediluvian woman," gushed *Time* magazine in a cover feature. "She is the nubile savage crying out to be bashed on the skull and dragged to some lair by her wild auburn hair."

By 1972, the year in which she made a brief but memorable appearance on the Chelsea scene, Raquel had done a fair bit of skull-bashing and lair-dragging of her own. Aged 32 and with two children by her first husband, she was recently divorced from husband number two, Patrick Curtis, when she turned up at the Blues' home match against Leicester City on November 11th. Although she had appeared in four films in 1972, her visit to the Bridge wasn't simply a promotional stunt.

"I used to work with Raquel Welch all the time and she knew I loved football," says photographer Terry O'Neill, "and one day she said, 'I'd love to see Chelsea and that Peter Osgood', so I took her down there. She was living in Knightsbridge at the time in a mews behind where the Lanesborough Hotel is now.

"Ossie had an agent called Ken Adam who fixed it up for us to go down there, so I walked her round the ground. It was incredible – you never used to see sex symbol movie stars at football and it was quite a thing. Walking with her round the pitch, the shouting and cat calls from the crowd just got louder and louder. I felt totally embarrassed, but Raquel seemed to enjoy it. Then we took her into the dressing room to meet the players, who were all over her, cracking jokes and so on. I don't think Dave Sexton was that pleased but he was very polite. I really didn't mean to create that sort of stir. I just hoped to take her to the game anonymously, but somehow it didn't work out like that."

Playing for Leicester that day was one Alan Birchenall, the former Chelsea striker who had left the Bridge two years earlier. While catching up with his old mates, the Birch was in the home changing room when la Welch made her dramatic entrance. "Dickie Attenborough brought her into the dressing room," he recalls. "When she was introduced to the team she made a beeline for Ossie, so we knew straightaway that she fancied him."

It was by no means the first time that Attenborough had taken a film star into the dressing room to meet the team. On other famous occasion the players had been surprised to see Steve McQueen popping his head round the door. Spotting a fellow smoker, McQueen had sat down for a chat and a fag with Eddie McCreadie. The star of *The Great Escape* was a hard act to top but, at the time, Welch was in the same glittering league – and, as the players couldn't help noticing, she was a damn sight better looking.

"After the game an American guy, her agent or minder, came up to me and said, 'Is Peter Aasgood here?'" continues Alan Birchenall. "I said, 'Get over here, Ossie' and that's when he said, 'Miss Welch would like to invite you and any of the Chelsea boys to a cocktail party at the Dorchester hotel tonight'. Ossie invited me and we went along. We thought we'd stay for an hour or so and we finally got back home on Sunday afternoon. There was a Who's Who of the Swinging Sixties and Seventies there – a couple of Stones, a couple of Beatles, the Animals were there, a smattering of TV personalities. It was a big mixture, a big cocktail party. I lost Ossie for a while and when we surfaced the next morning we thought we'd better get on our bikes. The hour had turned into 12 or more."

Ossie himself had a more distinct memory of the initial meeting than the party afterwards. "We met before the game," he said, "and she was a lovely, beautiful lady. She gave me a little peck on the cheek. Then, with ten, minutes to go, she walked along the side of the pitch, waving at me and saying, 'Bye, Ossie!' So I got a good bollocking from Dave Sexton for that." Certainly, Osgood gave every indication of being slightly distracted, having a quiet game in a disappointing 1–1 draw.

Curiosity in these matters being what it is, Blues fans have long speculated that more than a kiss passed between Ossie and Raquel that day. The Chelsea star, though, maintains that's all that happened. In one sense, it hardly matters what actually took place. The myth of a steamy Osgood-Welch liaison will live on regardless, fuelled in no small way by Alan Birchenall's final, somewhat ambiguous words on the subject:

"Raquel's a tasty woman now but 30 years ago she was absolutely stunning, so if I was Peter Osgood I would certainly claim what happened as being, shall we say, a little more than a peck on the cheek. But I'm sure that Ossie, being the man he is, refrained from taking advantage of the situation. I can say that without a smile on my face – lucky bugger!"

Ossie wasn't the only Chelsea player to get acquainted with 60s celebrity totty. Before George Best claimed a monopoly in the department, it was every footballer's dream to go out with Miss World, and it didn't much matter whether the young lady hailed from America or Zululand. Soon after breaking into the Chelsea team in 1965 John Boyle had a chance to do 'a Bestie' when he ran into the tiara-sporting champion at a charity function. "I didn't know her but we got chatting and swapped phone numbers," he says. "A couple of days later she phoned back and said, 'It's Anne here, you know Anne Sydney, Miss World.' She'd won it the previous year for the United Kingdom. I thought I'd pulled, but I hadn't. She just wanted a chat." Close, Boylers, but no cigar.

Having struck out with Miss World, Boyle had better luck a few years later with Fiona Richmond, one of the original porn stars of the late sixties. "We were on tour in Trinidad and she was over there doing a film shoot. I'd already met her in London at a party and she told me she was going to Trinidad so I laughed and said, 'Oh, we're going there as well! I'll give you a ring and take you out to dinner.' We were staying at the Trinidad Hilton and I managed to track her down and we had dinner at the hotel. She was actually a vicar's daughter and I found her charming company. We had great fun at the dinner and, of course, when I got back it was a typical football scene with all the lads wanting to know how I'd got on. Being a typical man, I probably exaggerated how well the evening had gone, but that's all I'm prepared to say on the subject!"

Although the dinner was a one-off, Miss Richmond retained a strong interest in football, or rather footballers, and a few years later, during Malcolm Allison's reign at Crystal Palace, she was photographed topless in the Selhurst Park team bath surrounded by wide-eyed Palace players. No doubt, if she'd asked, the Chelsea lads would gladly have posed for a similar photo opportunity while she was out in the Caribbean.

In the early seventies the highlight of any edition of *Top of the Pops*, at least for red-blooded males, was the appearance of the dancing troupe Pan's People. Swishing their long hair as they gyrated around the stage, the leggy dancers captivated the studio audience with their energetic routines, only occasionally eliciting giggles for their overly literal interpretations of the hits of the day. As Britain boasted no girl bands at the time – and even solo artists such as Lulu, Sandy Shaw, Dusty Springfield and Mary Hopkin were very much a rarity – the glamorous Pan's People were hot stuff, almost the Spice Girls of their era. At the start of the 1973/74 season a small item in the Chelsea programme revealed that one of the dancers in Pan's People was having treatment at the Bridge for an ankle injury. What the fans probably didn't know was that the connection between the girls and the Blues went a lot further than that.

"I used to go out with the tall dark one, Dee Dee Wilde," says Tommy Baldwin. "I think I met her down the Aretusa club, and we used to go out in the afternoon drinking after I'd finished training. I met all the other Pan's People, too. She wasn't my girlfriend as such, we were just good pals. She was great, she was a good mate and because she lived locally, up on Putney Hill with her brother, I used to see her regularly. We used to drink together and then she started going to games. When she injured her ankle it was my idea to send her down to Stamford Bridge for treatment."

Tommy eventually married another woman in the public eye, Michael Crawford's ex-wife, Gabrielle. "She used to be an actress," says the Sponge. "She was in *Emergency Ward 10* and a few other things. But when she married Michael she gave up her acting. I knew him first. He used to go down to Chelsea with David Webb. In his book he said he was always trying to get Gabrielle to come along to the Bridge. Eventually she went to a game and liked it so much she ran off with the centre forward! I'd split up with my missus and she'd split up with Michael and we just seemed to get it together." The couple had two children before divorcing in 1984.

When not chasing after Miss Worlds, porn stars, actresses or dancers, the Chelsea lads often used to look to the skies for potential girlfriends. "Most of the boys were going out with air hostesses at the time, that was their thing," says Alan Hudson. Peter Osgood's second wife, Pippa, was a stewardess while his strike partner Ian Hutchinson also had a long relationship with a trolley dolly.

"I was married when I signed for Chelsea, but we were young and broke up," Hutch revealed in an interview in 2001. "Then, I was seeing an air hostess called Sally for a while. We actually lived together for three years. But she worked long-haul flights mostly so we were apart a lot. One day she came back earlier than expected and caught me in bed with a young lady. How inconsiderate. She could have phoned me from the airport to warn me at least. So that was the end of that relationship."

For the unmarried Chelsea players, opportunities for casual flings were plentiful, as young women everywhere rejected the strict, almost Victorian morality of their parents' generation. The fear of unwanted pregnancy banished by the new contraceptive pill, they embraced the hippy concept of 'free love'. In the Docherty era George Graham – tall, dark and handsome but with a caddish glint in his eye – in particular took advantage of this happy state of affairs and, amongst the other players, was the acknowledged top 'bird-puller'.

"Gorgeous George we called him," said Peter Osgood. "He used to be immaculate everywhere he went; even in his football kit he was immaculate. He was a good-looking lad. We went to Australia for six weeks in 1965. We flew out of four or five different airports on the tour and there was a bird crying in each and every one over George. I think some of the other lads, especially the ones who'd got married young, were a little bit envious because George was pulling birds left, right and centre and they couldn't do that."

Sometimes, though, the married players did stray from the straight and narrow. One player who succumbed to temptation soon probably wished he hadn't, even though he had managed to keep the affair hidden from his wife. "This player had a little fling and the brother of the girl sent him a note saying he was going to shoot him on the pitch," recalled Ossie. "Anyway, the player was worried, understandably, and took the note to Tommy Docherty. Tom looked at it and said, 'Well, you'd better keep running, then, because a moving target is always harder to hit.'"

The chat up lines used by the players to butter up of their potential conquests could be unconventional. John Boyle, for example, was dubbed 'Trampas' by his team-mates after being heard talking to a girl at some length about the character of that name from the TV series *The Virginian*. Not necessarily a winning routine, you would have thought, but possibly more likely to be successful than a regular chat up line employed by Ron Harris.

"We were down in Bournemouth before an FA Cup tie," remembers Alan Birchenall. "We went to a club in town, brought a couple of birds back to the hotel and I was trying to chat this girl up when Ron Harris came in with a watchstrap round his wendle, and said, 'Have you got the time on you, cock?' This bird just screamed and ran out of the room. I don't think she was that bothered about seeing his knob, she was actually looking at his face."

Another Chelsea player, who even after all these years must remain nameless, and Eric Swayne, a friend of some of the team, found that a slightly more sophisticated approach worked rather better. "We pulled a couple of good-looking girls in the King's Road," remembers Eric. "My favourite trick then was to sit in a restaurant with a mate and if there were two pretty girls at another table we'd just call the wine waiter over and say, 'See the two ladies over there? Please give them a bottle of Dom Perignon with Eric's compliments.' Then you'd join them or they'd join you and you'd take it from there.

"Well, everything went to plan on this occasion and we all went back to my studio in Thurloe Square round the back of South Kensington tube station. My bedroom wasn't a room as such, it was part of the studio, a beautifully made pine gallery. So I was up there with one girl and the Chelsea man, who was married, was downstairs with the other girl. It was a fantastic evening and

I didn't start to fall asleep until about half past three. Even then, I remember I kept being woken up by the Chelsea player and his girl until about six o'clock!"

As now, for many young women the prospect of going out with, or even marrying, a famous footballer was an attractive one in the sixties. Aware of this common fantasy, it was not unknown for some cocky chancers to pretend to be a well-known star to increase their chances of pulling. Of course, it would be absurd to introduce yourself as George Best or Bobby Moore – not even the most gullible, dim-witted 'bird' would fall for that. But, if you looked vaguely sporty and unless the girl was an avid reader of *Shoot!* or a regular viewer of *Match of the Day*, you might well get away with claiming to be a lesser name – say, Chelsea's Alan Birchenall, for example.

"One day Ossie said to me, 'I see you're getting married again'," recalls Birchenall. "I said, 'What do you mean, I've only been married for three months?' Then he told me one of his mum's neighbours in Windsor had heard a woman boasting in the corner shop that her daughter had got engaged to Alan Birchenall, the Chelsea footballer. Ossie had also heard another story about me running up debts at a golf course. This was news to me, too, because I didn't play golf. After much scratching of heads, we came to the conclusion that the only possible explanation was that somebody must be impersonating me."

Determined to unveil the shadowy doppelganger, the two players turned detective and soon tracked down Birch's 'fiancee' to an address in Bracknell. "When we went round to the house the girl who I was 'engaged' to was out but her mother flatly denied that I was Alan Birchenall," says the Birch. "So we got the Chelsea team line up photo out and I told her, 'Look, that's me, Alan Birchenall!' But she just said, 'My daughter's engaged to Alan Birchenall. I think I know what he looks like, thanks'. I kept saying 'But I'm Alan!' and she kept replying 'No, you're not!' We went on for about ten minutes like that, until she started to believe I was the genuine article."

The police were informed and the story was covered extensively in the newspapers at the time. The girl's mother, Mrs Ethel Evans, told reporters: "My daughter, Eileen, met this man in a pub in Bracknell where he was known as Alan Birchenall the footballer. He used to come around here nearly every day and his knowledge of football was exceptional. My husband, who is a keen fan, could not trip him up. He was a smooth talker with lots of charm and nerve. He borrowed £25 off me. I took it out of the rent money I had saved. But he was always making excuses and when I asked about the money he said he had left his cheque book in his flat in Chelsea and was going to fetch it to repay me. He never did. My daughter was crazy about him and believed he was the Chelsea footballer. They were going to be married."

Generously overlooking the fact that the Evans family were unlikely ever to appear on *Brain of Britain*, an outraged Birchenall told *The Sunday Express*, "If I ever catch up with this character he will wish he never started this business. I don't mind a bloke pretending to be me if he just wants to impress a new girlfriend at a dance or something. But this is different and has done my name a lot of harm."

Eventually, police in Birmingham caught the man, who had committed a string of similar scams across the South East, and he was sent to prison.

"It was a bit worrying," admits Alan now. "There wasn't always room in the Chelsea team for one Birch, let alone two."

CHAPTER NINE
KINGS OF EUROPE

I f the Chelsea board of the 1950s had been a little more adventurous, it's just possible that the Blues, rather than Real Madrid, might have dominated the European Cup in its early years. An unlikely scenario, admittedly, but still conceivable in a 'Scotland might have won the World Cup if they'd qualified' kind of way.

What actually happened was this: Chelsea, as league champions in 1955, were invited to take part in the inaugural European Cup the following season. However, the Football Association, concerned about the possible impact on domestic attendances and generally suspicious about 'foreign' initiatives, advised Chelsea not to participate. To the disappointment of the players, Chelsea chairman Joe Mears, an FA councillor, decided to heed this advice. Instead, Manchester United became the first English club to enter the fledgling competition in 1956/57. As it turned out, Chelsea's championship-winning heroes would never have another chance to enter the European pantheon occupied by Real legends Puskas, Di Stefano and Gento.

The Blues finally got their passports out in 1958/59 for the Inter-Cities Fairs Cup, the precursor of the UEFA Cup. The competition was open to teams, other than the reigning league champions, from selected cities around Europe. Normally, the highest placed team from a particular city in the preceding season was invited to take part. On this basis, London's representatives in the Fairs Cup in 1958 should have been Tottenham, who had finished the 1957/58 season in third place, eight places above Chelsea. There was a feeling in UEFA, though, that Chelsea were 'owed' a European invitation from 1955 and so the Blues, rather than Spurs, carried the flag for London. After beating BK Frem of Denmark in the first round, Chelsea went out 4–2 on aggregate to Ville de Belgrade.

Seven years later, in 1965, Tommy Docherty's 'Diamonds' returned to the Fairs Cup on their own merits, as London's top club in the previous season. Despite lacking competitive experience in Europe, the Blues were confident of doing well, after having defeated numerous top continental sides and the West German national team, in a series of high-profile friendly matches.

In the first round Chelsea were handed a tough draw, being paired with former Fairs Cup winners Roma. The Italian side lived up to their nickname, *I Lupi* (the Wolves), in the first leg at the Bridge with some blood-curdling challenges. Roma right back Francesco Carpenetti picked on the wrong man, though, when he took a swipe at Eddie McCreadie.

"I went on an overlap, got my cross in, and this guy came across and kicked me in the shins," Eddie recalled later. "Then he put his hand right round my throat. And I was, well, have some of that, you know. And I decked him." The referee's response was a formality: while the Roma physio administered smelling salts to the befuddled victim, McCreadie was ordered off.

For Peter Osgood, just 18, and playing in only his second ever senior Chelsea match the experience of playing against such cynical opponents was something of an eye-opener. "It was a very hard, physical game," he said. "I didn't really understand it for the first half, to be honest. I just thought, 'What's going on here?' They were pinching and pushing, nudging you and scraping their studs down the back of your leg when the referee wasn't looking. They just tried to intimidate you the whole time, and get you to react

– which Eddie did, unfortunately. He never used to lose his cool, he just used to sort people out but, on this occasion, he turned round and whacked this guy and got sent off."

Despite being down to ten men, the Blues still managed to win the game 4–1, Terry Venables scoring a hat-trick. A bad night for the Italians got worse when the multi-lingual Bridge crowd greeted the final whistle with a rousing chorus of 'Arrivederci, Roma!' Predictably, the newspaper reports the following morning concentrated on the fisticuffs rather than the football.

"At one time, as the first half developed, I felt there would be nothing but a police report or a despatch from the battlefront when the time was over – casualty figures for each headquarters," wrote the man from *The Times*. "The fact is that for almost three-quarters of an hour the match developed into nothing better than a Roman orgy, the roars for blood of the Stamford Bridge Coliseum in one's ears."

If the first leg was a cross between *Gladiator* and *Caligula*, the second leg resembled the famous scene at the end of *Frankenstein* where the pitchfork-wielding peasants storm the castle intent on destroying all those within it. And, while Chelsea might have contributed to the bad-tempered opening act at the Bridge, this time the fault lay entirely with the Italians.

"Roma got the hump," says Marvin Hinton bluntly. "When they got back to Italy they complained that they hadn't been treated properly by Chelsea, that the pitch had been watered by Tommy Docherty and so on. The Italian press blew it all out of proportion and when we went over for the return leg there was a really hostile atmosphere building against us. Roma pulled a bit of a trick by switching the game from their normal stadium to a smaller ground where the fans were right on top of the pitch. That was a surprise for us, but it was nothing compared to the reception we got when we walked out to have a look at the pitch. The crowd pelted us with everything they could lay their hands on: eggs, tomatoes, the lot."

Flying foodstuffs were a minor worry, though, compared to the fans' next choice of weapons. "They chucked everything on the pitch, metal seats and all," recalled Terry Venables. "And then a great big ice block went over the top of the fences. I don't know where they got that from. It must have taken about ten people to carry it."

Once the game started, the Blues had two main aims: first, to protect their first leg lead and second, to avoid any incidents that might incite the frenzied, near hysterical crowd still further.

"We just tried to be as calm as possible," says Hinton, whose famously unflappable temperament was ideally suited to the difficult circumstances. "One of their players punched me after I tackled him, but I just walked away. I think if I had hit him back the crowd would have climbed over the fences."

Apart from the occasional uppercut or left hook, Roma, for whom Carlo Cudicini's father, Fabio, was playing in goal, also tried to unsettle the Chelsea players with the type of sneaky, underhand and downright crooked tactics which were then virtually unknown in the English game.

"They would obstruct you, pinch you or pull the hair under your arms in an attempt to make you lose your cool," says John Boyle. "They also didn't like it when you went in for a full bloodied tackle; if you tackled them they would fall over and writhe on the ground. But we learned to cope with it all and, if you look at the stats, you'll see we rarely got booked in Europe."

With Hinton having a masterful game at sweeper, the match ended in 0–0 draw. "I was the first English sweeper, and it was a role I found very enjoyable," he says. "Tommy Docherty developed the idea when we played in Europe against teams who were technically better than us. He was worried that the quick passing and one-twos these teams played around our box would cut through our defence so he wanted someone in there to cover the central defenders. It suited my style of play to be the sweeper, because one of my strengths was reading the game and I liked to pass the ball out from the back. I wasn't the most physical of players so that free role was perfect for me."

Safely through to the next round, now the only worry for the Blues was how to give the irate Roma supporters the slip on the way back to the airport. "After the game we waited in the dressing room until we thought all the fans would have gone home," says Marvin. "But when we got on the team bus there were loads of Roma fans waiting for us. A lot of them had bricks and they smashed all the windows in. We all threw ourselves on the floor but the chairman's wife was cut by flying glass. It was awful, I'd never seen anything like it before. What made it worse was that there were policemen standing around, but they just stood back and watched us getting attacked."

Thankfully, the second round was an altogether quieter affair, Chelsea beating Wiener Sport-Club of Austria 2–1 on aggregate. The third round, however, saw the Blues involved in another pulsating, edge-of-the seat Italian drama. Drawn against an AC Milan side which included cultured midfielder Gianni Rivera and Paolo Maldini's father, Cesare, Chelsea went down 2–1 in the San Siro before winning the return leg by the same score at the Bridge to the delight of the near 60,000 crowd. In those days tied matches were settled by a play-off and, after Milan had won the toss for choice of venues, the players returned to the San Siro for the decider. That, too, finished level, Barry Bridges scoring Chelsea's goal in a 1–1 draw. The penalty shoot-out had not been invented then; instead, UEFA had devised an altogether simpler though spectator-unfriendly method of settling drawn ties – the toss of a coin.

"I went out on the pitch with Cesare Maldini, Tommy Doc and the referee," recalls Ron Harris, who had replaced Terry Venables as skipper in the aftermath of the 'Blackpool Incident'. "I called right and we went through. I can't remember if I called heads or tails but I know I was the first captain to win a toss of the coin in Europe."

The Blues' luck held in the quarter-finals, when they inched past Munich 1860 3–2 on aggregate, Peter Osgood scoring the all-important winner at the Bridge in the second leg. That victory set up a mouth-watering semi-final with Barcelona, who already had a couple of Fairs Cup trophies to their name. However, the tie arrived at a bad time for Chelsea: dressing-room morale was low after defeat in the FA Cup semi-final four days before the first leg and Blues boss Tommy Docherty had fallen out with several senior players who he had dropped from the team. "We are beset by internal strife," one unnamed player told the press.

Under the circumstances, a 2–0 defeat in front of 70,000 noisy fans in the Nou Camp was hardly surprising. "They were a very good side – it could have been 10–0," admits Ron Harris. Outclassed in Barcelona, Chelsea, with Charlie Cooke making his debut, were gifted two own goals by the Catalans in the return leg to level up the tie. "We were a bit unlucky because I scored a goal in the last few minutes which was disallowed," says Ron. "Then we lost on the draw of straws so we had to go back to Barcelona for the play-off."

In the mid-sixties European club tournaments were still very much in their infancy, and UEFA was uncertain whether the new competitions would appeal to the public. Chelsea fans, though, had responded positively to the Blues' Fairs Cup campaign. More than 200,000 supporters had poured through the Bridge turnstiles for the team's five European home games, but not many of them would be making the long journey to north-east Spain. In an effort to keep the fans involved, the club arranged to show the play-off match live on six large screens erected on the Stamford Bridge pitch – the first time a European game had been transmitted back to England by closed-circuit TV. Chelsea even produced a special souvenir programme to mark the occasion, which turned out to be a forgettable one for the 9,000 fans present as the Blues crashed to a 5–0 defeat.

"It was a disappointing way to go out," says John Boyle, "although just to be out there playing against Barcelona was a great experience. We played them at the end of a long season and it caught up with us a bit. I think by then we were shot."

Chelsea returned to the Fairs Cup three years later in the 1968/69 season, a year after Dave Sexton had replaced Tommy Docherty as manager. After Scottish side Morton had been summarily dismissed 9–3 on aggregate – curiously, Chelsea's goals over the two legs were shared out among eight different players – the Blues were drawn against DWS Amsterdam. The Dutch side had won their country's championship in 1964 but were now beginning the long, slow decline that would eventually see them sink into Sunday League obscurity. Another emphatic Chelsea victory looked likely.

The Blues, though, hadn't reckoned with DWS' goalkeeper Jan Jongbloed who would go on to appear in two World Cup Finals with Holland in the 1970s. Over the two legs he saved everything Chelsea threw at him and was instrumental in keeping the aggregate score at 0–0. Once more, Chelsea's fate depended on the coin-tossing skills of Ron Harris. This time, however, there was no happy ending: Chopper called incorrectly as a Dutch silver guilder spun to the turf, and Chelsea were out.

"We missed some simple chances," said Ron afterwards, "and the DWS goalkeeper played a blinder. Yet, if we had to face the Dutch side again we would have tackled the problem in exactly the same way. Our two 0–0 draws were, to my mind, just one of those things that happen in football."

Maybe, but the Blues had to pay a heavy price for their failure: against all odds, Newcastle, who had finished the previous season four places behind Chelsea in 10th position and had only qualified for the Fairs Cup through a series of unlikely coincidences, went on to win the competition in a two-legged final with Hungary's Ujpest Dozsa. Still, any jealousy Chelsea fans might have felt towards the Geordies would surely have been dissipated had they known that this would be the Magpies last acquaintance with meaningful silverware for decades to come.

The Blues just missed out on a European place at the end of the 1968/69 season after finishing one place behind Arsenal, who claimed London's Fairs Cup slot and went on to win the competition. In 1970, though, Chelsea resumed their continental adventures. By then, of course, the FA Cup was in the Stamford Bridge trophy cabinet and with it came a passport to the European Cup Winners Cup. In terms of prestige this tournament was rated slightly more highly than the Fairs Cup but it was probably easier to win, simply because the leading European football nations only provided one entrant each. In the Fairs Cup, on the other hand, countries with strong domestic leagues like Italy, Germany and Spain usually had three entrants, so the chances of meeting top-quality opposition in any given round were higher.

In the first decade of its existence, British clubs had fared extremely well in the Cup Winners Cup. Tottenham (1963), West Ham (1965) and Manchester City (1970) had all won the competition, while Rangers and Liverpool had been beaten finalists. Unsurprisingly, Chelsea were also expected to do well, being listed among the pre-tournament favourites along with Real Madrid, Benfica, Bologna and Bruges.

Certainly, the Blues' subtle mix of stylishness, resilience and old-fashioned English powerplay looked suited to European football. The likes of Osgood, Cooke and Hudson had the necessary technique, artistry and flair to unlock the tightest of continental defences; Hollins, Baldwin and Boyle would match all comers for effort, perseverance and commitment; and at the back Chopper Harris and co might have struggled to spell *catenaccio* but they still provided as intimidating a barrier as any in *Serie A*. Chelsea, too, had other weapons that could surprise unsuspecting overseas opponents: Ian Hutchinson's jaw-dropping long throws, the aerial threat of Webb and Dempsey at set pieces and, although it was sometimes unappreciated by the fans, Peter Houseman's deadly accurate crossing ability.

Moreover in Dave Sexton Chelsea possessed a manager who

knew how to blend all these disparate elements into an effective unit. "Generally speaking, I tried to get a method of playing that suited the players I had," he said later. "That sounds obvious, but it's not. You have to enable them to produce their best, trying to improve them as you work with them. Some players are very clever, imaginative and creative, but they haven't got much fight or spirit to them, so you try to help them to toughen up. And the other way round. Your hard blokes – your David Webbs, your Ronnie Harrises – you strengthen their passing and their touch. The end result is that you have tough guys who can play football, and vice versa."

In the summer of 1970 Sexton had shuffled his squad, selling strikers Bobby Tambling and Alan Birchenall to Crystal Palace and bringing in Tony Curtis-lookalike Keith Weller from Millwall for £100,000. Weller had mostly played in central midfield at The Den and in his limited appearances for his previous club Tottenham, where his literary-minded team-mates had nicknamed him 'Sammy' after the character Samuel Weller in Dickens' *David Copperfield*. Sexton, though, planned to use Weller as an attacking right-winger, believing that his pace, directness and powerful right-footed shooting would be of more value further up the field.

Along with these personnel changes came a slightly altered playing style, influenced by Sexton's summer trip to watch the 1970 World Cup. "Over in Mexico, I watched Brazil three or four times," he said. "One particular move they did was that somebody on the left-hand side of midfield, instead of playing the ball into the striker's feet, would lift it over the top as the striker came towards him. The forward would then spin off his marker, leaving him completely clean through on goal. I promised I'd pay the bloke who played the pass and the one who scored the goal a fiver each." Sexton's bank manager had no need to worry, though, as Dave admitted, "I never once had to pay out."

The Blues were still struggling to get to grips with the so-called 'fiver ball' when they played their first European game of the season against Aris Salonika. Chelsea's opponents had a reputation as a dirty side and, on a dry, bumpy pitch, it soon became clear that the Greeks were more interested in kicking their English visitors than playing football. Indeed, it seemed only a matter of time before one of their number was given his marching orders by the Hungarian referee, a Mr G. Emsberger. Sure enough, the ref was soon waving a red card – however, the player he was waving it at was John Dempsey.

"It started when their guy tried to kick the ball out of Peter Bonetti's hands while he was clearly holding it," explains John. "I just got myself in between Peter and their striker, there was a bit of pushing and then the guy started rolling on the floor. It was ridiculous, I hadn't done anything. The linesman came rushing on the pitch waving his flag and I was sent off. Ken Jones, who was covering the game for *The Daily Mirror* said it was one of the most ridiculous sendings off he'd seen."

A clear case of a miscarriage of justice, you might think. Yet, according to Dave Sexton, Dempsey was far from being the innocent victim of a combination of Greek play-acting and incompetent refereeing. "Demps was well-known for having a short fuse and players knew they could wind him up," he said. "In the dressing room I took him to one side and said, 'Look, Aris Salonika are going to do everything to get you mad. They'll call your mother names, you names, everybody names. Don't bite at all – ignore it and get on with the game.' John was like, 'Yes, Dave,' and 'Okay, Dave'.

"Five minutes before half-time Aris won a corner and, just as their fella's gone to cross the ball, their centre forward's got hold of Dempsey's bollocks and given them a right old squeeze. John's responded by smashing him with his fist. Down to ten men we did well to hold out for a 1–1 draw." In fact, the result would have been even better if Peter Osgood hadn't missed a penalty after a

ALL PICS PA SPORTS

Above: Manager Tommy Docherty and coach Dave Sexton run through team tactics with the help of a Subbuteo board during pre-season training in July 1963.

Left: Tommy Docherty makes up with the eight Chelsea players he had sent home after the 'Blackpool Incident' of April 1965 when they broke a club curfew.

Above: The Chelsea squad train on Worthing beach in preparation for their FA Cup semi-final against Liverpool in March 1965.

ACTION IMAGES/MIRRORP

PA SPORTS

Top: Teenage prodigy Peter Osgood shoots against Nottingham Forest at Stamford Bridge in August 1966.

Above: Peter Bonetti in action at Villa Park. Spectacular saves like this one earned him the nickname 'the Cat'.

PA SPORTS

PA SPORTS

**Top: Chelsea
captain Ron Harris
shakes hands with
Tottenham skipper
Dave Mackay
before the start of
the 'Cockney Cup
Final' in 1967.**

**Above: Dave Sexton
with Chelsea
chairman Charles
Pratt shortly after
Sexton had replaced
Tommy Docherty as
manager in
October 1967.**

Chelsea line up at the start of the 1969/70 season.
Back row (left to right): Marvin Hinton, Ian Hutchinson, David Webb,
Tommy Hughes, Peter Bonetti, John Dempsey, Eddie McCreadie,
John Hollins. Front row: Alan Birchenall, Charlie Cooke, Alan Hudson,
John Boyle, Ron Harris, Peter Houseman, Peter Osgood,
Tommy Baldwin, Bobby Tambling PHOTO: COLORSPORT

Left: Ron Harris lifts the FA Cup trophy following Chelsea's victory over Leeds. After a number of near misses in previous seasons, victory tasted all the sweeter for the players.

Below left: 'Chopper' poses with the FA Cup in a photo booth at Manchester Piccadilly train station shortly before the team returned to London.

Below: Jubilant Chelsea fans greet the Blues players as they show off the FA Cup along Fulham Broadway the morning after the replay.

PA SPORTS

ACTION IMAGES/MIRRORPIX

ACTION IMAGES / MIRRORP

Above:
Tommy Baldwin,
Ron Harris, and
Charlie Cooke
parade the
European Cup
Winners' Cup
after the Blues
had beaten Real
Madrid in the final
in Athens.

Left:
Alan Hudson,
Peter Bonetti and
John Boyle pose
with the Cup.
The victory
established
Chelsea as one
of the most
successful English
teams of the era.

ALL PICS ACTION IMAGES/MIRRORPIX

Left: Jimmy Hill explains the offside rule to an excited Raquel Welch during the film star's visit to the Bridge in February 1972.

Below: Blue is the Colour: the Chelsea squad record their 1972 League Cup Final anthem. The song reached number five in the charts and is still a much-loved part of pre-match entertainment at Stamford Bridge.

ALL PICS ACTION IMAGES/MIRRORF

foul on Paddy Mulligan, an attack-minded full back signed from Shamrock Rovers, primarily as defensive cover, in December 1969.

In the return at the Bridge Chelsea put on a bravura attacking display, crushing the Greeks 5–1. The pick of the goals came from John Hollins, who powered in a drive from fully 35 yards. For the Blues' anorak brigade the fact that all the home side's goals were scored by players with surnames beginning with 'H' – Hollins (2), Hutchinson (2) and Hinton – was an additional thrill. Despite being humiliated on the pitch, Aris had toned down their roughhouse antics from the first leg and relations between the clubs were further improved when their President told Brian Mears, "If you reach the final in Athens next May you can be assured of our support."

In the second round Chelsea were given a tricky-looking draw against CSKA Sofia, the Bulgarian army side. Regular champions in their country, it was something of a surprise that they were in the Cup Winners Cup at all, rather than the European Cup. Moreover, CSKA had a formidable home record in Europe, never having lost to foreign opposition in 17 European games at their People's Army stadium. A strong all-round team featured five players from Bulgaria's 1970 World Cup squad, including European Golden Boot winner Petar Jenkov. For Chelsea, the trip behind the Iron Curtain for the first leg promised to be a demanding one. And so it proved.

"They were the most impressive side we played in the whole competition," reckons Ron Harris. "We won 1–0 over there, Tommy Baldwin scored and I think that was the only time we got out of our half. They were one of the best club sides I've seen. A really good, technical, well-organised, well-prepared side."

And Peter Osgood added: "It was quite intimidating. All 40,000 of the crowd seemed to be in military uniforms. When you saw that you thought, 'This is serious' but we kept our heads, we did a good job and we came away winners. But they were a bloody good side."

The football may have been of a high standard, but the Blues were less taken with other aspects of Communist life. "You couldn't get Coca Cola or any other mixers," complains Tommy Baldwin, whose winning goal came from a Keith Weller cross just before half-time. "If you went for a drink you got vodka and water. Luckily, we weren't there long. We simply went in and came back out and we didn't really see the city. Most of the time we just stayed in the hotel." Ron Harris, though, maintains that Sofia wasn't really that bad at all. "It was a hell of a lot better than some places I went to with Chelsea: Haiti, El Salvador and so on," he says.

Another disciplined 1–0 win over CSKA at the Bridge, thanks this time to a bizarre David Webb header from a sitting position, sealed Chelsea's passage to the quarter-finals. After the match, the Bulgarians' manager Manol Manolov paid a fulsome tribute to the Blues' star performer over the two legs, goalkeeper Peter Bonetti. "Although Chelsea tackled very hard but very fair, our biggest problem was not their tackling but how to get the ball past Bonetti," he said. "What a magnificent goalkeeper he is!"

By the time the quarter-finals came around, in March 1971, Chelsea's season had taken a turn for the worse. Having already been knocked out of the League Cup in the autumn by Manchester United, the Blues had lost their hold on the FA Cup in January, losing 3–0 at home to Manchester City in the fourth round. Immediately after that game Peter Osgood was suspended for two months by the Football Association, which had just launched a crackdown on player misconduct.

"It was just three bookings," said Ossie, still amazed years later by the severity of the punishment. "What happened was that Bestie had appeared before the FA, and they said the next player who came up was going to be made an example of. That was me. So I was given a six-week suspension. Brian Mears, the chairman, said: 'We're going to fight this, Ossie, we'll take it to appeal.' So I went back and got an extra two weeks plus a £150 fine!"

The suspended Osgood was not the only notable absentee for Chelsea as they headed off to Belgium to meet Bruges in the first leg of the quarter-final. Also missing were the injured Ron Harris and Ian Hutchinson and pneumonia-sufferer Peter Bonetti. Fortunately, Bonetti's deputy, John Phillips, was in fine form, having kept clean sheets in four of the six league games he had played in since taking over in goal. Up front, Sexton was forced to throw in South African centre forward Derek Smethurst for his European debut, alongside Tommy Baldwin.

Already lacking four of his key players, Dave Sexton was confronted with another unwanted problem at the team's hotel. "We were playing cards on the afternoon of the game and somebody lost quite a lot of money," recalls John Boyle. "There was a bit of an argument about that, so Dave banned us from gambling."

All in all, Chelsea's preparations were not ideal for a match which looked like testing the team to the limit. Runners-up in Belgium's Jupiler league the season before, Bruges were gradually emerging as their country's dominant force and would go on to play Liverpool in two European finals in the 1970s. A number of their players, including powerful striker Raoul Lambert, had appeared for Belgium at the World Cup in Mexico the previous year and, like CSKA, they also boasted a good home record in Europe.

In front of their own fans, Bruges gave an under-strength Chelsea a torrid time in the compact, English-style De Klokke stadium. Both goals in the Blues' 2–0 defeat stemmed from in-swinging corners, with Lambert grabbing the first after just four minutes.

"Bruges battered us in the away game," admits Alan Hudson. "How we came out of there still in the tie is incredible. They should have put us away. They had us under us the cosh, but John Phillips was fantastic for us in goal. On the plane coming home that night from Bruges I remember thinking, 'How the hell are we going to get this back?'"

Two weeks later Bonetti and Hutchinson were still out, but Harris was fit to return for the second leg. Osgood, too, had completed his suspension and, banned from the training ground as part of his punishment, had maintained his fitness during his two month-break with regular runs on his own across Epsom Downs. All the same, Sexton was reluctant to pitch his star striker into such an important game without any match practice behind him.

"When we got them back to Stamford Bridge Dave Sexton wasn't sure whether to play Ossie or not because he didn't think he'd be match fit," says Tommy Baldwin. "But, in the end, he did play. We were 2–0 down, but we just went out with the attitude 'let's go for it'. I can remember the team talk quite clearly. Dave kept saying, 'We can do this, but we've got to be patient. We know we can score goals.'" Keeping a clean sheet was just as vital, as a Bruges goal would leave Chelsea requiring four under the away goals rule introduced by UEFA six years earlier.

On a balmy spring evening, the 45,000-plus Bridge crowd was in optimistic mood, generating a raucous atmosphere from the first whistle. For once, even the East and West stands joined in as the Shed went through its full repertoire, while the rickety North Stand almost seemed to sway from side to side as excited fans jumped to their feet to add their voices to the thunderous chants of 'Chel-sea!'

"It was absolutely electric," says Baldwin. "The noise from the fans was constant, they were amazing. Maybe it got to Bruges a bit. Don't forget we were 2–0 down, so you might have thought the fans would be a bit flat, but right from the start they were singing and chanting."

An early goal from Peter Houseman, slotting the ball home from close range after Osgood had headed down Baldwin's cross, intensified the pressure on Bruges. But, with nine minutes left, they were still hanging on to their aggregate lead when Charlie Cooke crossed for Osgood, sporting a magnificent Jackson Five-style 'afro' which he had grown during his suspension, to shoot home the equaliser. It was a vital goal and, typically, Ossie celebrated in flamboyant style, rushing across the greyhound track behind the goal towards the fans in the North Stand terrace.

Quite where he found the energy from for this little display was a mystery. "Ossie definitely wasn't match fit for the second leg," says Alan Hudson. "But it didn't matter with him, because you just needed to get the ball into him in the box. The bigger the game, the better he was." As if to prove this point, Hudson set up Osgood for the crucial third goal, deep into extra-time.

"I got to the byline on the left at the Shed end and looked up, played it across to Ossie and he scored. Me and Ossie used to have this move where he'd run in with the defenders and then pull out to give himself a yard or two yards of space. That would give you the chance to get the ball into him and he'd pick his spot. It was something instinctive we always had between us. It wasn't something we particularly spoke about, even when we were room-mates. Sexton used to hate me for it, but I always used to try to give the ball to Ossie. Football's all about getting your best players in the game, but Sexton had a go at me about it once. He said I was passing too much to Ossie and not getting the ball out to Peter Houseman on the left."

Maybe Sexton had a point, though, because it was the under-employed Houseman who created the fourth, clinching goal for Tommy Baldwin two minutes from the end. "Peter passed it to me, I was about six or seven yards out and just knocked it past the keeper," says Tommy. "That was it, game over. I got mobbed by everyone, they all just jumped on me. That was the best game I've ever been involved in, even including all the cup finals."

On an exhilarating night which would quickly pass into Chelsea folklore, Sexton's gamble in playing Osgood had paid off. "Only an English footballer could have done what Osgood did, playing so brilliantly after eight weeks without a game – not just for 90 minutes but extra-time as well," said Bruges manager Frank de Munck afterwards. "His height gave us real problems."

As for Ossie himself, he admitted that his long lay-off had left him feeling shattered. "It was as well it didn't show, but I felt jiggered after 45 minutes," he told reporters. "I just kept putting one leg in front of the other, but I forgot the tiredness once the goals came."

In the semi-final draw, Chelsea were paired with the holders, Manchester City, with the winners facing either Real Madrid or PSV Eindhoven in the final. City had stuttered in their defence of the trophy, scraping past Linfield on the away goals rule in the first round and then beating Hungarian side Honved in the second. In the quarter-finals they needed a play-off to beat Gornik Zabrze, the Polish side they had also defeated in the previous year's final.

City, though, had gained a win (in the FA Cup) and a draw (in the league) in their two visits to the Bridge that season and in Francis Lee, Mike Summerbee and Colin Bell had three potent attacking threats. Unfortunately for them, only one of that trio, England striker and future toilet roll entrepreneur Lee, was fit for the first leg at the Bridge. Chelsea, too, had injury problems, and lined up without Bonetti, Osgood, McCreadie and Hutchinson. Strangely, Sexton opted for a strike force of Smethurst and Webb, relegating Baldwin and Weller to the bench. At the back, gargantuan 19-year-old defender Micky Droy – a sort of non-green version of The Incredible Hulk – came in for his European debut alongside John Dempsey.

Unsurprisingly, given the cast list of understudies and novices, the match was an uninspiring affair and was decided by a solitary goal shortly after half-time. Weller, on as a substitute for Cooke, started the move with a cross to Webb, he headed down and the alert Smethurst nipped ahead of City defender Tony Towers to slide a shot under goalkeeper Joe Corrigan.

A 1–0 lead was a slender advantage for the away leg, but the Blues were given some encouragement by a 1–1 league draw in a dress rehearsal at Maine Road 10 days before the main event. Again, both teams were, as 'Arry Redknapp might put it, 'down to the bare bones' for the second leg. For Chelsea, Baldwin and Hollins had been added to the casualty list, while City were now without skipper Tony Book and Joe Corrigan. Corrigan's absence proved to be costly for City as his replacement, Ron Healey, literally handed Chelsea their winning goal in the first half. After Hudson won an indirect free-kick for obstruction, Weller bent his shot round the City wall and Healey fumbled the ball into the net.

"I didn't realise the referee had indicated it was an indirect free-kick," said Keith. "So I had a pot and Healey got a touch, but the ball ended up in the net. If he had let it go, the ref would have disallowed it."

"The semi finals weren't good matches, they were scrappy," says Alan Hudson. "It was a relief we got through. They had a lot of players out but so did we, and anyway I think we were a better team than they were. But they had beaten us in the FA Cup that season when Dave Sexton left me out and played Marvin Hinton in midfield. It didn't work. If I'd played I reckon we'd have beaten them. In fact, I'll go as far to say that the two biggest mistakes Dave Sexton made were playing Marvin Hinton in midfield in that game and playing Webby at full back in the 1970 final. He got away with that one, though."

Meanwhile, in the other semi-final, Real Madrid had squeezed past PSV 2–1 on aggregate to set up an enticing final between the kings of the King's Road and the undisputed aristocrats of Spanish football. The stark truth, though, was that this Real side could not be compared to the one which had won five consecutive European Cups between 1956 and 1960, thrilling crowds wherever they played with their extravagant ball skills and incisive passing. Amazingly, Real's team still featured one survivor from that golden era, the clever winger Francisco Gento, nicknamed *El Supersonico*. Nearly 38, Gento was now the elder statesman in a side which also included Spanish internationals Pirri, Zoco and Amancio, the latter a scorer in Real's most recent European Cup triumph in 1966 against Partizan Belgrade.

Real's path to the final had been less than convincing. In the first round the Spaniards had been held 0–0 by the Maltese minnows Hibernians in Valletta before delivering a crushing *coup de grace*, 5–0, in the Bernabeu. A 2–1 aggregate victory over Austria's Wacker Innsbruck put Real in the quarter-finals where they met reigning Welsh Cup holders Cardiff City. To the astonishment of the football world, the Second Division side beat Real 1–0 in the first leg at Ninian Park. A seismic shock was on the cards, but not for long: Real triumphed 2–0 in the return to book their semi-final with PSV.

Real may have been one of the most famous names in European football, but they were still largely an unknown quantity to the Blues. "We didn't know a lot about their players," says John Dempsey. "You didn't have the videos of other teams in those days, so it was more a case of concentrating on your own game rather than thinking about the opposition."

Chelsea arrived in Athens two days before the final, basing themselves in a hotel outside the city. This was a calculated decision by Dave Sexton, who didn't want his players being tempted into a retsina-guzzling, plate-breaking exploration of Athenian nightlife. "The directors were staying at the Athens Hilton," says Tommy Baldwin, "but we were in a hotel right out in the country. Dave Sexton always put us in hotels outside the city, away from all the bars and clubs. If we went out it was always a long, costly taxi ride to get back wherever we stayed."

While the squad prepared for the final with some light training, Sexton agonised over his team selection. The big question was who to play in goal: young John Phillips, who had performed so capably in Bonetti's absence or the ultra-experienced 'Cat', now recovered from his bout of pneumonia. To Phillips' dismay Bonetti, who had returned to the side for the final league game of the season at Ipswich and kept a clean sheet in a 0–0 draw, got the nod. "I thought I'd done enough to replace him," Phillips said later. "We'd conceded very few goals during my spell in the side and I believed I should have played in the final."

Another disappointed player was Tommy Baldwin, although he'd already had an inkling he wouldn't make the starting eleven. "For the game against Real Madrid I was substitute," he says. "I got a notion I wouldn't be in the team when Dave put me in the wall in training while the others were practising free kicks." There was better news for John Boyle, who was chosen ahead of Paddy Mulligan for the full back spot left vacant by the injury to Eddie McCreadie.

The venue for the final, Olympiakos' Karaiskakis Stadium, was situated in one of the less salubrious parts of town, the grubby port area of Piraeus. Four thousand Chelsea fans had made the journey out to Greece and they were joined in their support for the Blues by the majority of locals in the 45,000 crowd. In return, the Chelsea supporters had promised their hosts that English fans would back Panathinaikos, rather than Ajax, in the European Cup Final at Wembley the following month – although quite how they could guarantee this happening was unclear.

Chelsea lined up against Real in a 4–3–3 formation with Cooke, Hudson and Hollins in midfield, and Osgood a lone central striker supported by Houseman and Weller on the flanks. Cooke, mesmerising the Real defence with his intricate footwork, was in wonderful form although Chelsea created few chances until Boyle crossed for Osgood on 55 minutes. His first shot was blocked, but when the ball rebounded to him he buried it in the corner. As the game moved into injury time it was still 1–0. The Cup seemed destined for Stamford Bridge, but disaster was looming.

"There was just a minute to go," recalls John Dempsey. "The trophy, with blue and white ribbons attached, had already been brought to the side of the pitch. Then I miscued a clearance, and the ball skimmed off my boot straight to one of three Real players who would all have been offside if I hadn't touched it. I think it was Zoco who scored. I was really distraught, I was thinking it's my fault we haven't won the Cup. But you just have to try to put those thoughts out of your head and concentrate on the rest of the game, because we had to play extra-time."

In the additional 30 minutes Chelsea came under increasing pressure from Real but, thanks to a combination of stalwart defending and a couple of extraordinary saves from Bonetti, the Blues hung on for a draw.

"That was one of my best ever performances for Chelsea," said David Webb later. "I can't remember putting a foot wrong. Everything I did just seemed to go right. Extra time against Real Madrid was phenomenal. I was clearing the ball away off the line, repelling all their attacks."

Having come so close to winning the Cup, Chelsea might easily have lost it. "I thought we were very fortunate to stay in it the game," says Alan Hudson. "They had a guy called Pirri who was superb for them."

The man from *The Times* took a similar view. "At moments Real seemed to be taunting Chelsea like a matador teasing the bull," he wrote. The *Madristas'* strong finish also seemed to make them slight favourites for the replay, which was scheduled for two days later. "The Spaniards have established a technical and psychological advantage which they could well turn their way in 48 hours time," *The Times'* reporter concluded.

With a day to kill between the matches, Dave Sexton made an unexpected announcement. "After the first game, I got the players together and told them I wasn't going to put any restrictions on them whatsoever," he said. "They'd performed terrifically for me over a long, hard season. I left them to sort out their own arrangements."

Some of the players, including John Dempsey, spent their day off relaxing at the team hotel. Others, Alan Hudson and back-up striker Derek Smethurst amongst them, set off to explore the Athens flea market. A third group, made up of Peter Osgood, Charlie Cooke and Tommy Baldwin, headed to the Athens Hilton where they changed into their swimming gear, settled down by

the pool and set about preparing for the big game in their inimitable fashion. For the Sponge, in particular, this was more like
it. After all, he hadn't come all this way to stand around in a
human wall. "We had some lunch, talked about the following
day's game and got stuck into the rum punches," says Baldwin.
"No, I'm only joking, but we had some beers and we were a bit
pissed when we got back to our hotel rooms."

Ask two people for their recollections of a mega booze-up
and the accounts are likely to be significantly different. Such is
the case here. Peter Osgood fundamentally disagreed with
Baldwin: cocktails, rum punches or otherwise, were definitely
on the pre-match menu . . .

"Tom might have been on beer but me and Charlie were definitely on cocktails," said Ossie. "I had quite a few, I admit. I
remember Alan Hudson going past and saying, 'C'mon lads . . .'
and I said, 'Look, son, don't worry about us, we're on the top of
our form, just worry about your own game.'"

"On the way back from the flea market we called in at the
Athens Hilton and we saw Ossie and co by the pool," remembers Alan Hudson. "A very good friend of mine called Johnny
Fennell was there, and I think he was the instigator of their
drinking session. Ossie said to me, 'You go home and have an
early night because you've got to do my running for me
tomorrow'. They were already pretty pissed."

The mammoth drinking bout, which had begun around 11am,
finally finished some nine hours later. "We were supposed to be
back at the hotel at 7pm for dinner," says Baldwin, "but we didn't
get back until about 8.30pm so I got fined again. Then Dave
said, 'By the way, you're playing tomorrow.' It didn't really bother
me, I probably would have gone out anyway."

Baldwin's unexpected promotion from sub had come about
because of an injury to John Hollins, who was reduced to watching
the replay as an expert summariser for the BBC. This was a big
blow. Although rarely a headline-grabber, Hollins' drive and

stamina made him a vital component of the team. He had a fearsome shot, too, and could be relied on to get his quota of goals. His nine goals in 1970/71 included one against Arsenal at the Bridge – a chip over Gunners goalkeeper Bob Wilson which had struck the bar, only for Hollins to hook the rebound over his shoulder and into the roof of the net from the edge of the penalty area – which had won ITV's 'Goal of the Season' competition. To cap a great year for the midfielder, Chelsea fans had voted him their 'Player of the Season' for the second season running.

Hollins, clearly, would be missed. What Sexton didn't know, though, was that another member of his midfield trio was also far from fit. "In the first game I was clean through on goal and I thought I was going to score, which would have been fantastic," recalls Alan Hudson. "But I got a whack and was brought down. The tackle gave me a dead leg and with the replay being on the Friday I thought, 'Here we go, I'm going to miss another final'. Sexton asked me how I was, and I said, 'Fine', but I wasn't really. If it had been a league game I definitely wouldn't have played."

There were also doubts about the fitness of Peter Osgood, who was suffering from a knee ligament injury and had only managed to play in the first game after having a cortisone injection. "I didn't think I was going to play because I could hardly walk," he said. "In the first game the injection wore off and I had to come off. On the Thursday I thought I had no chance of making Friday. I'd resigned myself to missing it, so that was the reason I had a good bender down by the pool. I didn't think I'd be playing. But on the Friday morning the doctor stuck the needle in again. He said we could do it again and, fortunately, it worked out for us."

With Baldwin joining Osgood up front, Chelsea reverted to a more orthodox 4–4–2 formation for the replay. Without the missing Hollins, always a dynamic presence, a lot would depend on whether Cooke and Hudson could establish supremacy in midfield. Fortunately, Madrid had injury concerns of their own in this area.

"As luck would have it Pirri, their top midfielder, sprained his arm and wasn't as mobile in the replay," says Huddy. "I actually think that turned the game our way. I was feeling the dead leg but as the game went on I was more or less able to run it off."

"If we stop Cooke, we will win," Real's Amancio was quoted as saying after the first match. That, though, was easier said than done. Again, Charlie was in sparkling form and, on the half hour, sent over the corner from which Chelsea took the lead.

"I headed the ball towards goal," says John Dempsey, "their goalie punched it in the air and I just hit it on the volley into the top of the net. It flew in. It was a wonderful feeling to score. I just felt I'd made up for my mistake in the first game. It was not only the most important goal I'd scored but also the best."

It was indeed a stunning goal, so good in fact that many Chelsea fans couldn't quite believe that Dempsey had scored it. What they didn't know was that the confidence with which Demps struck his shot probably stemmed from a successful run he'd enjoyed as a striker with his previous club, Fulham.

"A few years before the final I'd scored a hat-trick for Fulham as an emergency centre forward against Northampton in the League Cup," he smiles. "I'd played there as a schoolboy and the manager, Vic Buckingham, put me up front when we were short of forwards. I scored a couple more in the next few games, too, and there was an article in one of the papers saying, 'Fulham have found a new striker'. But the next week they signed Allan Clarke and I was back in defence."

Not to be outdone, Osgood soon scored an equally brilliant second. "Tommy Baldwin had the ball, he gave it to me and made a run forward," recalled Ossie. "As he went he was screaming for me to knock it through, but all of a sudden a big gap opened up because he'd taken two of their defenders with him. I just bent it, the ball hit the post and went right in the corner. So, really, Tommy had done a lot of the work for me. He would always do that for you. He probably saw me score more goals than him but he wasn't worried about that. His contribution was great for the team: he'd hold the ball up, lay the ball off, make chances for you and he took chances himself, obviously. He was one of the lads who worked really hard for the team."

For the second time in three days the Cup was within Chelsea's grasp. However, with 15 minutes to go Fleitas pulled one back for the Spaniards and the pressure grew on the Chelsea goal. Bonetti dived to save a Zoco header, Webb blocked Amancio almost on the goal line and then, suddenly, it was all over – the Blues had won their first ever European trophy. As Chelsea players embraced each other and were mobbed by the ecstatic Blues fans who stormed onto the pitch, John Boyle made a beeline for the Real substitute who had made a fleeting appearance towards the end.

"The great thing for me was that in both games I had marked Gento, who had played for Real in the best game that I ever saw, the 1960 European Cup Final between them and Eintracht Frankfurt. Thank goodness, he was slower by the time of our final – probably about my pace. I made sure I got his shirt at the end, too, and Keith Weller reckons that when I ran over to swap shirts at the final whistle that was the fastest I ran all night! Unfortunately, I lent the shirt to someone when I was out playing in America and never saw it again."

Later Peter Osgood paid tribute to Boyle's performances in the two games. "He was a Ray Parlour-type player, the sort who doesn't get the recognition he deserves," said Ossie. "Dave Sexton put him at right-back against Gento and he marked him out of the game. John wasn't the quickest and he was up against a very tricky player but he did a good job on him."

Dave Sexton's tactical switch, bringing in Tommy Baldwin to support Peter Osgood in attack, had also paid dividends. "We set out to take the initiative," the Chelsea boss said afterwards, "and here we are with the Cup. Yes, we had to fight for it, but in the end we fought harder than Real. They were much better in the second half because they were more attack-minded. But the way our boys never faltered made me feel proud of them."

Booked in at the Athens Hilton for the last night, the celebrating players were able to properly sample the delights of the Greek capital for the first time. "Me, Charlie Cooke and a reporter Charlie knew went to a restaurant where there were belly dancers," says Tommy Baldwin. "When we got there the reporter guy said, 'Have what you want, it's on me'. So, we ate our food and at the end the waiters were throwing plates as they do in Greece. As we were leaving the manager came over and said, 'Excuse me, you haven't paid your bill'. I said, 'He's paying', pointing to the reporter, but he said, 'Sorry, I haven't got any money on me, I've lost my wallet'. There was a massive doorman there who wouldn't have let us out, so we decided the best thing was to pay up."

"Everywhere you turned there were players celebrating with fans," adds Alan Hudson. "All round the hotel, there were loads of people there. When you think that the fans stayed over there when they had no money, they'd missed their flights home after the first match, it was amazing. It was the first thing we'd ever won in Europe, so it was quite something."

Despite Sexton's alcohol ban, the champagne was out on the flight home the following morning. "I mean, how could he stop us? We'd just won the Cup," says Hudson. Hundreds of jubilant fans were waiting for the team at Heathrow and, from the airport, the players boarded an open-top bus which took them all the way to Stamford Bridge. A year earlier the team had paraded the FA Cup in their dull club suits. This time, reflecting the laid back 'anything goes' philosophy of the times, they were allowed to wear their civvies and took full advantage, donning a variety of flowery shirts that wouldn't have looked out of place on a King's Road dance floor.

"It was a Saturday morning so people were out shopping," says John Boyle, who had grabbed a prime spot with Keith Weller, Alan Hudson and the trophy at the front of the bus, "but they'd all put their bags down and wave to us. By the time we got to Hammersmith there were fans lining the streets and when we got to Fulham Broadway there was just a massive party going on. I was pretty tired but I had some friends to catch up with after the parade and they were all ready to celebrate as well. We had another party at home in South London on Saturday evening – in fact, there were parties going on all over the place – and I didn't get to bed until about two in the morning."

For Alan Hudson, who had missed out on the FA Cup celebrations the previous year, the joyous homecoming was particularly emotional. "I went to the Adelaide pub, next door to the Imperial on the King's Road, had a couple of drinks with my family there and then I almost collapsed. Partly, it was because I was knackered by then – I hadn't got any sleep – but it was also the euphoria. And we'd been drinking champagne all through the flight home!"

As Cup Winners Cup holders, Chelsea automatically received an entry to the competition the following season. Naturally, the Blues were among the favourites again, with Barcelona, Bayern Munich, Torino and Glasgow Rangers their most likely challengers. But they avoided the big guns in the first round, and the medium-sized ones too. In fact, their opponents, Jeunesse Hautcharage from Luxembourg, were more like krill than minnows, hailing from a village with a population of just 704. Their domestic Cup triumph the previous season, against Jeunesse Esch, had been a major surprise as Hautcharage were then in the Third Division.

The first leg, switched from the club's 1,500-capacity ground to the 13,000 national stadium was, as expected, a rout. Chelsea won 8–0, with Peter Osgood helping himself to a hat-trick. "It was easier than training," was Ron Harris' verdict afterwards. Worryingly, for Jeunesse at least, the Blues seemed intent on hitting their opponents' net even more frequently in the return.

"I've backed myself to score," Chopper told *The Sun* the day before the teams met at the Bridge. "All sorts of bets have been struck by the lads and we are definitely trying for the biggest score in Chelsea history − ten!"

Among the many wagers was one for £5 between Peter Osgood and Peter Bonetti that the striker would score a double hat-trick, a feat previously recorded only once in Chelsea history, by prolific striker George 'Gatling Gun' Hilsdon in 1908. Tommy Baldwin, too, had an incentive to get among the goals. "Mike D'Abo, who was in the pop group Manfred Mann, had a restaurant on the King's Road and after the game in Luxembourg he said he'd give me a free meal for two if I scored a hat-trick in the second leg."

On the night, the 5p Chelsea programme had some intriguing information about the Jeunesse players. Five of them were steel workers, four of them were from one family, one wore glasses on the pitch and the inside left, a student, only had one arm. The rest of the team included a station-master, a car mechanic, a butcher, a blacksmith and − no doubt, to the great amusement of the Chelsea dressing room − a hairdresser.

At half-time it was 6−0. Harris had got the goal he wanted, but Osgood had been stuck on two since the 6th minute and Baldwin hadn't scored at all. "I'd forgotten all about my bet with Mike and I'd just been trying to set up Ossie," says Tommy. "Suddenly, a steward came into the dressing room at half-time and said, 'There's a note here for Tommy Baldwin'. It was from Mike and it said, 'Don't forget you've got a free meal if you score a hat-trick.' So I went out for the second half thinking, 'Sod Ossie, I'm going for it!'"

Suitably fired up, Baldwin clinched his hat-trick with the last kick of the match. Osgood, though, had to settle for 'just' five of the Blues' 13 goals. Needless to say, Jeunesse didn't manage a goal of their own. "I don't think Peter Bonetti had a shot to save," says Tommy. "He could easily have popped out of his goal for a chat with the Shed end." The 21−0 aggregate set a new record for European football which, although equalled by Feyenoord the following season, remains intact today.

Summing up one of the strangest matches ever played at the

Bridge, Peter Osgood said: "No disrespect to their lads – I mean, they were lovely people – but they were useless. The guy with one arm even went to take a quick throw and he had to put the ball down. And then there was the guy in glasses – it was like *Dad's Army*. It was unbelievable."

In their own way, the events of the second round were equally unlikely. Drawn against Swedish part-timers Atvidaberg, the Blues' strikers envisaged another scoring spree. But, in blustery conditions on a slippery pitch, Chelsea failed to find the net once in Sweden. "We should have beaten Atvidaberg by ten over at their place but we just couldn't score," says Alan Hudson.

Still, a 0–0 draw was no disaster and, back at the Bridge, Huddy settled the crowd's nerves with a sumptuous volley shortly after the break. Fifteen minutes later the tie seemed to be over as Ron Harris, in search of another rare goal, was hacked down in the penalty area. John Hollins, normally so reliable from the spot, stepped up to take the penalty and struck his shot against a post. Despite continuous Chelsea pressure the second goal wouldn't come and then, to the horror of the home fans, Atvidaberg equalised. In a frenzied finish, John Dempsey hit the bar and other chances went begging before the final whistle signalled the holders' exit from the competition on the away goals rule.

"If we'd have got through that round I'm convinced we would have won it again," says Hudson.

Maybe, but the history books show that they didn't get through. What's more, they also show that, incredibly, it would be another 23 years before Chelsea would appear again on the European stage.

CHAPTER TEN
THE SHED

O n Wednesday 7th September 1966, Chelsea maintained their unbeaten start to the 1966/67 season with a 2–2 draw at home to Leicester City. Of more long-term importance than the result, though, was a letter which appeared in the match programme. Signed C. Webb of South Ockoden, Essex, it read: "From now on we wish the Fulham Road End to be called 'the Shed'. That is the section where the fanatics stand – and, while we are on fanatics, why don't more people come in the Shed and join in the singing and chanting, instead of just at big matches like last season's Fairs Cup? If we could have had that support all through the league and Cup, we would have won them both. This year we must have this attitude at every game, so please help us make the Shed as fanatical as the Kop."

The reference to Liverpool's Kop was significant. The Merseysiders had been the first fans in England to generate a fiercely partisan atmosphere at their team's home games, creating a wall of sound from the terraces. The Kop's repertoire wasn't huge – apart from chants for the team, it largely consisted of sing-a-longs to Beatles and Gerry and the Pacemakers hits, with the lyrics unchanged – but the constant noise helped turn Anfield into an intimidating fortress.

The 1965 FA Cup semi-final between Chelsea and Liverpool at Villa Park was a turning point for Blues fans, who realised how poor their support for the team was compared to that of the vocal Reds. "They outsung us, outchanted us, and they were just more passionate than we were," remembers Tony Easter, a Chelsea fan from west London, who had just started following the team. "We simply weren't organised like we became later to sing the songs."

The Kop had been a singing end since 1963, an *annus mirabalis* on Merseyside which saw both the start of Beatlemania and Liverpool's re-emergence as a football power after nearly a decade in the Second Division. At the same time, Chelsea were returning to the First Division in an altogether more genteel environment. Polite applause, the occasional witty remark shouted from the terraces and a spot of banter with the away fans were the order of the day.

The Bridge, as Tommy Docherty had already mentioned in a newspaper interview, was far from being a daunting venue for opposition teams. The bowl-like design of the stadium, with the greyhound track circling the pitch and the terraces pushed back some way behind the goal, meant that fans were distanced from the action – in contrast to other London grounds, such as Upton Park or White Hart Lane, where it felt like the crowd was almost spilling out from the stands and terraces onto the field.

"We had a good home record but it didn't help us that the fans were pushed back from the pitch," says Alan Hudson. "It cost us a few times, and I couldn't help thinking when I first saw the completed new stadium that we'd have won the league if we could have played there. The Bridge would have been our fortress. The only time the atmosphere became really electric was for the big night games – against Roma, Bruges and Spurs in the League Cup, for instance. Because it was dark you couldn't see how far away the fans were and the noise seemed to carry more at night. But even then you couldn't compare it to the atmosphere the fans created at Old Trafford in the Cup Final replay when they were right on top of the pitch at the Stretford End. They really pulled us through that night."

The longstanding Bridge tradition of swapping ends, which continued into the late sixties, also contributed to the lack of atmosphere. "At half-time we always used to change ends," recalls Fred Roll, who attended his first game at the Bridge as a 14-year-old in 1966. "You could walk under the tunnel of the old East Stand – where the traps for the greyhounds were – and you'd meet the opposing supporters halfway down the tunnel. Obviously, Chelsea still kept the area under the Shed but you wanted to stand behind the goal where your team was going to score. You didn't want to see defenders, you wanted to see goalscorers. So there would be home and away supporters at both ends as some of them would stay where they were."

Occasionally, Chelsea fans couldn't even get into the Shed at all, especially when Manchester United were the opponents. In the early 1960s the United fans had the habit of turning up a few hours before the game to stand en masse at the Fulham Road End. The fact, of course, that virtually all of them were glory-hunting 'Cockney Reds' rather than residents of Salford made arriving at the Bridge at 11am somewhat easier.

"They would completely take over the Shed three hours before the start," says Jim Luck, a Chelsea fan from East London, who began going to games with a schoolmate at the age of 10. "You'd turn up to go in your usual place and the turnstiles would be shut and you'd have to get in somewhere else in the ground. There wasn't the segregation of fans you got later."

Fortunately the Bridge's enormous capacity – around 70,000, dropping to 62,000 after the West Stand sprung up on the West terrace in 1966 – meant that most fans could usually squeeze in somewhere or other even for the biggest matches. But outsung by Liverpool and outmanoeuvred by Manchester United, Chelsea's support was lacking in direction. One fan, in particular, realised this and set about giving Blues fans some leadership. Mick Greenaway, a 20-year-old Chelsea nut from Grove Park, south-east London, had been impressed by the backing Liverpool's followers gave their team and, with a group of equally passionate Blues fans, began thinking up some songs and chants for the hardcore supporters in the Shed to sing.

Early efforts included The Beatles-inspired 'Blue Submarine', and a homage to Docherty's 'Chelsea Aces' sung to the tune of *The Blaydon Races*. The famous 'Zigger Zagger' chant, which Greenaway adopted as his own personal rallying cry, also became a matchday regular, with the whole of the Shed joining in the finger-jabbing 'Oi, oi, oi!' response. There were songs, too, for the most popular members of the team, including this one for Peter Osgood, set to the tune of *The First Noel*:

The Shed looked up
And they saw a great star
Shooting goals past Pat Jennings
From near and far
And Chelsea won, as we all knew they would
And the star of that team
Was Peter Osgood.
Osgood, Osgood, Osgood, Osgood,
Born is the King of Stamford Bridge

Not surprisingly, Ossie loved that one and even subtitled his recent autobiography, *King of Stamford Bridge*. After making an instant impact for the Blues following his arrival at the Bridge in September 1966, Osgood's strike partner Tommy Baldwin was also soon being serenaded by the Shed, this time to the tune of *McNamara's Band*:

His name is Tommy Baldwin
He's the leader of the team – *what team?*

The finest football team
That the world has ever seen
We-e-e-e-e
Ar-r-r-r-e
The Fulham Road supporters
And we're louder than the Kop
If anyone wants to argue
We'll kill the fucking lot

"I remember the fans singing my song just a few weeks after I joined," recalls Tommy. "I think they liked me because I would always battle for everything and I never used to give up. I could play a bit, too, but they loved my tenacity and aggression." Even today, the Baldwin song can still be heard on matchdays, sometimes in the stands but, more often, in the bars around the Bridge. "It's brilliant, I love it," he says. "I get embarrassed when fans recognise me in a pub and start singing it, but I'm still proud of it. I always had a good rapport with the fans."

The same couldn't be said for Peter Houseman who, over the years, became something of a scapegoat for Chelsea fans when the team wasn't performing well. He even got stick when the Blues were winning, most famously when Chelsea thrashed Luxembourg minnows Jeunesse Hautcharage 13–0 at the Bridge in 1971. Usually fans don't bother creating a song for an unpopular player; in Houseman's case, however, the Shed made an exception, although the player probably wished they hadn't. To the tune of The Scaffold mega-hit *Lily the Pink*, it went:

Peter Houseman, played terrible football
And the Shed all called him names
So they gave him
A kick in the bollocks
And now he plays in all our games

This cruel ditty then segued into a tribute to Shed idol Charlie Cooke:

We'll drink a drink a drink
To Charlie the king the king the king
The saviour of our football team
For he invented professional football
And now we're gonna win the league

Poor Houseman must have been devastated – not only was his song merely the warm up act for Cooke's, it was downright hurtful to boot. Some supporters, though, felt that by openly criticising the fans in the Shed in a letter to the programme, Houseman had encouraged the mickey takers. The letter, which appeared in October 1966, was signed 'Peter House, Battersea', but Houseman, a Battersea resident, was widely believed to be the author:

"In reply to C. Webb, who wishes the Fulham Road End to be named 'the Shed', I would like to rename it 'the Foulmouthed End'. I find myself – and probably many more supporters are, too – sick and tired of hearing these so-called 'fanatics' finding any excuse to call players and officials of opposing clubs any filth which comes into their heads. These 'supporters' are a bad advert for the club and, in time, will only make the good name of Chelsea FC a bad one."

The letter, whoever had written it, had absolutely no effect. If anything, the four letter word count only increased as chants like 'Who the fucking hell are you?' (directed at the visiting team as they ran out of the tunnel), 'You're going home in a fucking ambulance' (directed at visiting supporters after their team had scored), and 'What the fucking hell was that?' (directed at opposition players who had shot miles over the bar) made their Bridge debuts in the late sixties.

The away fans or players weren't the only targets, either, as

Robert Holliday, a fan from Uxbridge, recalls. "The first time I went in the Shed the TV cameras were there. The game was obviously going to be on *The Big Match* because we all spotted Brian Moore walking in front of the Shed before the match. The fans started waving at him and singing his name – 'Brian, Brian, Brian Moore, Brian Moore, Brian Moore, Brian, Brian, Brian Moore, Brian, Brian Moore' – to a sort of can-can tune, and he waved back. He really looked delighted to be recognised. Then came the 'second verse' to the same tune: "Oh, wank, wank, wank, wank, wank, wank, wank, wank, wank, wank . . ." complete with 'wanker' hand signs. It was a lot cleverer than 'Brian Moore is a wanker' but I think he got a dose of that as well as he scuttled off. Poor bloke, he looked completely crestfallen. But it was very funny."

Along with the 'foul-mouthed' lyrics came an increase in 'aggro' on the terraces. Football hooliganism was not a new phenomenon in the 1960s – Millwall's home ground, The Den, had been closed four times between 1920 and 1950 after outbreaks of crowd trouble, for example – but it did became more widespread, thanks in part to cheap 'football special' train services which encouraged greater numbers of over-excitable young fans to travel to away matches. From the mid-sixties onwards Stamford Bridge probably witnessed as many incidents of fan violence as any other ground, while Chelsea's massive away following became so notorious the Government tried – and failed – to ban Blues fans from travelling in 1977.

"The first hooligans came from Liverpool," says Andy Jackson, who started going to the Bridge in the early sixties when he was still at primary school. "The first time I saw fighting was at Easter 1965 when the Liverpool fans caused a lot of trouble at the Shed end. Loads of fans climbed over onto the dog track from the Shed and then it spilled all round the ground."

Liverpool fans may have started the trend, but soon it became a matter of honour for all large away followings to attempt to 'take' the home end. Even increasing segregation of rival fans at matches didn't stop the violence, as Fred Roll remembers.

"I was in the Shed once, around 1967/68, when all these fans came in wearing blue and white scarves. I thought it was a bit strange because there were so many of them in a big group. Then, all of a sudden, I got a whack on the side of my head. They were Arsenal fans in disguise and, of course, once everyone realised what was happening there was a huge fight.

"We used to establish ourselves more at away games," he adds, "because you'd get the high terracing and the tactic was to start at the top and force yourselves down. There was violence, but it wasn't violence as we know it today. It was more scuffling, a bit of pushing and shoving. It was territorial, more than violent. You might get the occasional slap round the back of the head, but that was it.

"I remember going to Burnley one year and it was all Chelsea – no Burnley supporters would come near us. This one copper came over with a big black stick with a brass bit on the end and he said, 'Any trouble from you lot and I'll have yer', so one wag at the back shouted out 'Quick, hide the shotgun!' One copper for the whole ground, it was unbelievable."

Around the same time, Andy Jackson attended his first Chelsea away game outside London, taking a football special up to Coventry. "In those days we used to only take 300-400 away fans," he says. "By the mid seventies it was more like 7,000-9,000, depending on who we were playing. All the same, there was a lot of trouble, with kids running around like idiots. There was a lot of damage to the town centre. Coventry was still being rebuilt after the war and I remember in the next day's papers the local chief of police said, 'Chelsea did more damage in 90 minutes than the Luftwaffe did in five years.' It was vandalism more than anything. Some fans went into a carpet shop on a street on a hill, stole some carpets and then started rolling them down the hill. That was a strange sight.

"When we got back to Coventry station the Chelsea chairman, Charles Pratt, was there. He had just cut the half-price concession for kids because some of them had been running on the pitch to celebrate goals or to mob the players at the end of games. So eventually, after a number of warnings, the concession was cut and all the youngsters had to pay full price. Obviously that wasn't popular, so while he was waiting for the train everyone was chanting, 'Our chairman is a prat!' I was quite naïve at the time and I didn't even know what 'a prat' was."

Throughout the 1960s the various youth cults of the decade – mods, rockers and hippies – had been well represented on the terraces at Chelsea. The newspapers had got themselves into a right old tizz about all three groups, but never specifically about their connection with football violence. It was a different matter, though, when the skinhead look swept through the Shed in 1969.

The skinheads had borrowed heavily from 'hard' mods and West Indian 'rude boys' to create their own unique style: typically, Ben Sherman shirts, Sta-press Levi's, Doc Martens boots, often worn a size or two too big for added effect, and a half-soldier, half-convict shaved head. To many the new look was both alarming and threatening, and the tabloid press was not slow to exploit these fears by making little or no distinction between 'football hooligans' and 'skinheads'.

Eventually, too, in the popular imagination, 'skinheads' would be synonymous with 'racist thugs', which rather overlooked the fact that the original skinheads were into black music in a big way, particularly ska and reggae. Ska stars like Laurel Aitken and Prince Buster returned the favour by writing affectionate songs about skinheads. It was, though, an instrumental reggae track which was to be adopted by the skins in the Shed as their own anthem.

Reaching number nine in the charts in November 1969, *The Liquidator* was a one-hit wonder for Harry J Allstars, the house band of Jamaican producer Harry Johnson. Featuring the swirling organ of Winston Wright, the record had an instantly catchy hook and, crucially, a series of pauses into which a staccato chant of 'Chel-sea!' could be inserted before the hypnotic riff re-started. Around the country fans of other clubs whose names contained two syllables – West Brom, West Ham and 'The Wolves', for instance – also latched onto *The Liquidator* but none could match the passion, intensity and sheer volume of the Shed's rendition. In the days before *Blue is the Colour*, which didn't come out until 1972, *The Liquidator* was *the* Chelsea song, and its airing ten minutes or so before kick-off would crank up the atmosphere in an already packed and expectant Shed to near fever pitch.

By the mid-seventies the skinhead cult had largely died out on the terraces. Hairstyles, influenced by bands like Sweet, Slade and T Rex, grew long and feathery; silk scarves, worn around the wrist à la Bay City Rollers became a necessary fashion accessory; wide flared trousers which could have doubled as curtains flapped around the lower leg; and huge platform soles, inspired by the stilt-like monstrosities worn on stage by Gary Glitter, David Bowie and Elton John, replaced the infamous skinhead 'bovver boot'.

Unfortunately, the new gear, especially the footwear, was totally unsuitable for football 'aggro': balancing was difficult during hand-to-hand combat and running away was virtually impossible when the police snatch squads moved in. As one vogue supplanted another, even the preferred style of terrace fighting changed: thanks to the popularity of the TV show *Kung Fu*, martial arts-style drop kicks and hand chops were favoured over old-fashioned punches to the face or knees to the groin. By the time Chelsea and Tottenham fans clashed on the pitch before a vital relegation decider in April 1975 fans watching from the stands could easily have imagined they were watching a surreal glam rock version of a Bruce Lee movie.

"The hooligan element got worse as the seventies went on," says John Dempsey, who was on Chelsea's books for most of the decade. "But in the early seventies it wasn't a big issue among the players. Yes, kids ran on the pitch when a goal went in and the re-start would be delayed a minute or two. Other than those occasions, I can't remember being involved in a game which was held up for any length of time because of pitch invasions or crowd trouble.

"At away games we would be escorted to the ground by the police and when we got off the coach there would often by lots of home fans hanging around the players' entrance. You'd get a lot of insults, but most of them seemed to be directed at Ossie – 'Osgood, you're rubbish!', that sort of thing. Then, when we got out on the pitch you'd see our fans packed together in an end or a corner. If we were playing in London – at Tottenham, Arsenal or West Ham – they would completely fill an end, and even up at places like Old Trafford or Anfield the fans would be there in large numbers. Coming from Fulham as I had, I wasn't used to seeing so many fans at away games. The Chelsea away following really was fantastic."

Cheap train travel and inexpensive, pay-at-the-turnstile entry on the day encouraged increasing numbers of Chelsea fans to go to away games. The prospect of 'aggro' was an added attraction for some. "There was always an element who would try to 'take' the home supporters' end," says Robert Holliday. "If you were in the away end you would suddenly see them waving Chelsea scarves about, usually a few minutes after kick-off. Then, the home fans would either back away, creating a gap around our mob, or they'd steam in and a fight would break out. After a few minutes the police would pile in and escort our fans to the away end, where they'd get a heroes' reception.

"The first time I joined up with a Chelsea crew was for a game at Arsenal in the mid-seventies and, bizarrely, we weren't even playing. We were supposed to be playing at home in the FA Cup, but as the tube train I was on pulled into Earl's Court there was an announcement that the match had been called off because of a waterlogged pitch. Everyone groaned and then somebody said,

'Let's go to Highbury, Arsenal are playing Wolves!' A few people got off at this point but most of them stayed put. Everyone was very excited, banging the windows and singing 'We hate Arsenal!' and 'We're gonna take the North Bank!'

"As we got nearer the Arsenal tube stop, word went around that we should stop singing and hide our Chelsea scarves – we didn't want the Arsenal fans knowing who we were. When we left the station there were so many people milling around outside Highbury that it was impossible to say how many Chelsea fans were in our mob, but it must have been a few hundred. We all went in together at the North Bank end, which was absolutely heaving. Suddenly our gang seemed pitifully small and the idea of 'taking' the North Bank, where there were about 20,000 home fans, simply ludicrous.

"I was only 14 and rather small for my age. I didn't really fancy getting beaten up by irate Arsenal fans, so I decided the best thing to do would be just to melt into the crowd. As I was doing that, a huge 'Chel-sea!' chant went up and I could see dozens of blue and white scarves coming out. The Arsenal fans around me were genuinely surprised, they hadn't seen us coming. There was a lot of movement around me, people were either trying to get away from the Chelsea fans or were barging their way through to try to get nearer. The game was just about to start, but everyone's attention in the North Bank seemed to be on this one corner of the ground. Scuffles were breaking out and there was a lot of shouting – 'Fuck off, Chelsea!' 'You're gonna get your fuckin' heads kicked in!' and so on.

"By now, the police had realised something was happening and started to move in. Eventually they managed to herd the Chelsea fans into a corner and gradually shove them down the terracing towards the pitch. The Arsenal fans around them were absolutely livid. One guy spat at our fans but missed, and gobbed on a policeman's chest instead. He was quickly hauled off and I thought the police would chuck all our fans out, too, but instead they escorted about 200 of them down to the Clock End where all the Wolves fans were. The whole of Highbury seemed to explode with anti-Chelsea venom – even in the posh seats people were standing up and shaking their fists – but our mob just waltzed down to the other end waving their scarves triumphantly.

"The game was on *Match of the Day* that evening. At one point the camera showed a group of Chelsea fans twirling their scarves among the Wolves supporters. John Motson was commentating and he said something like: 'Oh I say, Chelsea fans there giving their support to Wolves after their match was postponed. They could have gone shopping or gone to the cinema but they chose to come to Highbury. In a way, that sums up the universal appeal of the FA Cup.' No mention of the big fight earlier – he must have been having a pre-match cup of tea!

"Of course, the next week back in the Shed, the chants were 'Arsenal run from Chelsea!' and 'We took the North Bank, the North Bank, the North Bank, Highbury!' Word had got around what happened and everyone joined in, even those who weren't there or, like me, had played a rather limited role on the day. It really felt like we'd got one over them, turning up like that when they weren't expecting us."

Despite the undercurrent of latent violence which existed at virtually every Chelsea match in the late sixties and throughout the seventies, for many young fans being part of the boisterous crowd massed in the Shed or on an away terrace was an incredibly exciting experience. No trip to the Bridge, though, could possibly match the thrill of seeing the Blues play in a cup final. Between 1967 and 1972 Chelsea reached four finals, providing the fans who attended the games with some of their most vivid football memories.

Like all Chelsea fans at the time, Tony Easter was desperate to go to the 1967 FA Cup Final against Tottenham, the first all-London final at Wembley. True, the fact that he hadn't got a ticket was a slight problem, but not by any means an insurmountable one.

"I was apprenticed at a garage in west London and, luckily, the senior mechanic's father worked at Wembley as a senior turnstile attendant. He wasn't going to be on the turnstiles on the day of the final, but he told me he could get me in to the game if I turned up at Wembley at around 12.30. I arrived on time with my father and we joined a queue of about 30 or 40 outside a door. We were on the list as St John's Ambulance workers and when the door was opened we both went in. We just had to pay the guy the going rate for a terrace ticket, although he didn't actually have any tickets on him. I knew the score because we'd got into Wembley for the England-Argentina match at the 1966 World Cup in exactly the same way.

"After about half an hour in the outer ring of Wembley we were shepherded to the next entrance where another guy was checking the tickets – and, of course, we didn't have any. But our contact just said, 'OK, Fred, these are the St John's Ambulance people', and we were in the ground at about 1pm. The only trouble was as the fans with tickets arrived we realised we were in the Tottenham end. We didn't fancy spending the match with the Spurs fans but we knew you could walk round Wembley and get to the other end. So we went down the Chelsea end, waited until one of the attendants was busy checking fans in with their tickets and ducked in to watch the game. It was a total scam, but I've always promised I'll learn how to take a pulse one day!"

In 1970 he didn't need to pull the same trick, having obtained a ticket through legitimate means for the FA Cup Final with Leeds. "I went to Wembley and the replay at Old Trafford," says Tony, one of 20,000 Blues fans who made the midweek trip up north. "Up in Manchester my mate and I were with two Manchester City supporters. They took us to a club in the city after the game, and we didn't leave until about 4am. Then I drove back to London, we arrived about 7am and came straight down the King's Road. We had breakfast in a café in the area, and waited for the boys to come along on the open-top bus. It was just fantastic, everyone was going crazy. We even got our pictures in the *Evening News*, which was a bit of a worry because I was supposed to be working and I'd phoned in sick."

Eric Swayne, who travelled back down to London with the team on the train from Manchester, had also enjoyed his night at Old Trafford – unlike the Leeds fans. "There was a huge Leeds supporter behind us and he kept going, 'That's it, stroke it around, that's beautiful, you're makin' 'em look silly.' This went on for ages until Ossie scored the equaliser and this guy was literally sick – he puked! At the end of the match he was crying his eyes out."

The following year, around 4,000 Chelsea fans travelled out to Athens for the European Cup Winners' Cup Final against Real Madrid. Unfortunately, most of them were booked on a short two-day package which didn't take into account the possibility of the final going to a replay which, of course, it did. Reluctantly, some fans took their scheduled flights back to England. Others, meanwhile, were determined to see the climax of Chelsea's European adventure and altered their travel arrangements. Short of funds, they relied on the generosity of other fans, donations from the players and the hospitality of the locals to provide them with bed, breakfast, beer and kebabs for the extra couple of days.

Concerned that there might be a replay, Jim Luck had erred on the side of safety and arranged a week's holiday in Greece. "Lots of fans who were supposed to go back after the first match stayed on in the rooms which the others had booked up," he says. "We ended up with about six fans in our room. The hotel staff must have realised what was going on. They can't have been too thrilled but there were so many people coming and going they probably couldn't tell who was a paying guest and who wasn't. We were staying outside Athens in a separate resort. After our victory in the replay we went over to a higher standard hotel where the better-off fans were staying. They'd put money behind the bar and we stayed up most of the night drinking and singing. In the morning there were loads of bodies crashed out all over the place surrounded by empty bottles. It was a great night. Then in the morning we got on the coach to the airport."

For stay-at-home fans, meanwhile, there was intense disappointment when they discovered the first match with Real Madrid would not be shown on television. From the perspective of today – when Sky will quite happily screen a mid-table Conference clash as part of its saturation coverage of the game – it seems extraordinary that no TV channel in 1971 was prepared to broadcast a major European final involving a British club. However, the fact is that very few games were shown live in the early seventies. In football circles there was a widespread belief that live coverage would adversely affect attendances, so fans had to make do with highlights of two matches on *Match of the Day* on Saturday night and three games the following afternoon on *The Big Match*. Unbelievably, Chelsea fans couldn't even look forward to highlights of the game with Real on *Sportsnight* as the Beeb had chosen instead to show snippets of England's Home International fixture with Wales at Wembley.

The only way for Blues fans to keep in touch with events in Athens was through the commentary on the radio. "I ended up on the King's Road in the Stanley Arms opposite the World's End," recalls Andy Jackson. "I went round there with a couple of friends to listen to the game on the radio. It wasn't that busy, I suppose most fans just stayed at home. I felt very deflated when Real Madrid equalised with the last kick of the game, but at least they carried on with the commentary in extra-time rather than switching to some other programme that had been originally scheduled."

As it turned out, Real's last-ditch equaliser, while disrupting the travel plans of thousands of fans in Greece, proved to be a bit of a boon for the supporters back home as the BBC announced it would be showing the replay live on Friday evening. Hooray! Some bright spark had even recruited the injured John Hollins to act as expert summariser. This was more like it. The only question for Chelsea fans was where to watch the game – home or pub?

Andy Jackson chose the pub. "We went back to the Stanley for the replay and this time the place was absolutely heaving," he remembers. "I think the World's End and all the other local pubs were the same. It was so packed, we were literally swaying in the pub shoulder to shoulder. I used to wear glasses and when John Dempsey scored the first goal I jumped up to celebrate. I went one way and my glasses went the other way. I never saw them again. We were 2–0 up when Fleitas scored for Madrid, and I needed a leak so I battled my way to the toilet. It was just as packed in the bog because there were fans who were so tense they daren't come out. They were almost praying in there. At the final whistle the whole place erupted, tables and beer glasses went flying everywhere. It was sheer jubilation. Everybody spilled out on the King's Road and the party carried on in the street. The next day the estimates in the newspapers were that 5,000 people were still out on the street celebrating at two in the morning.

"In the early hours a group of us decided to go down to Trafalgar Square. The replay was the day before the England–Scotland match at Wembley and, of course, all the Scots were in the square. I don't think they were quite sure what to make of us. Some of our fans went in the fountains and splashed around for a while. Then we went straight back to Chelsea – we didn't bother going home – to see the victory parade. I was standing in the doorway of a dry cleaner's next to the old Supporters' Club on Fulham Broadway. There was an enormous crush and one of the shop windows went in just through the pressure of bodies. By this stage I'd had no sleep, little to eat, too much to drink but it was great – it wasn't like the recent victory parades at Chelsea which have all been very organised. There was no organisation, no crush barriers, nobody selling flags or T-shirts. It was just spontaneous mayhem. People were going right up to the open-top coach to scream and wave at the players and the police couldn't stop them."

The following year Chelsea reached a third consecutive final, this time in the League Cup. The competition couldn't really match the FA Cup or Cup Winners' Cup in the glamour stakes but, nonetheless, a ticket for the Wembley final against Stoke was still highly prized.

"I'd been to all the games and sent away for my tickets through the voucher system," remembers Ray Taylor, a fan from Fulham who had been supporting Chelsea since 1965. "The final was in March and in February I got married at Fulham Town Hall. I had a reception afterwards, a local family thing, and I was opening the telegrams and cards of congratulations when I came across a letter with writing I recognised. Of course, it was my writing and the letter contained the two tickets I'd applied for. I was over the moon – more so for having the tickets than for getting married. My euphoria completely overtook me; but what a disappointment in the end – the final and, as it turned out, the marriage as well."

While Ray Taylor, Andy Jackson and thousands of other Chelsea fans were slumming it on the terraces a handful of lucky supporters had VIP passes for the best seats in the house in the new East Stand. "I used to go in the directors' box on a 'comp' ticket provided by Brian Mears," says Mark Colby, who is now a season-ticket holder at the Bridge but admits to not being much of a fan at the time. "I had a mate at my school, a minor public school in Leatherhead, and his dad knew Brian Mears and some of the Chelsea players.

"We'd go up to games and, obviously, we got a very good view from the directors' box. Then, after the game, the players would come up in the lift and you could help yourself to sandwiches and drinks. It was all very safe and contained and you felt a huge discrepancy between the experience of being in the directors' box and, say, going in the Shed. Later I started going in the Shed and I preferred it there, really, being with the real supporters.

"I remember Henry Kissinger, who was American Secretary of State at the time, came to one game when I was there and he was surrounded by his secret service people. Every time Chelsea went close to scoring the secret service people would jump up and when we did score they were totally surrounding him. I think they got nervous because the fans kept shouting 'Shoot!'"

Thanks to his connections, the young Colby wasn't only rubbing shoulders with the players and other well-known faces on match-days – he was bumping into them in the school holidays as well. "I'd go over to my mate's house in Cobham, Surrey and there would be all these young Chelsea players – people like Ian Britton and Steve Finnieston – hanging around the swimming pool," he remembers. "Michael Crawford's ex-wife, who was married to Tommy Baldwin by then, would quite often be there, too."

Another fan who became friendly with some of the players was Ron Hockings, the chairman of the original Chelsea Supporters Club which was founded in 1948. Ron, who sadly died in 2006, was also the author of *90 Years of the Blues*, a massive reference work which has helped settle many an argument between statistically-inclined Chelsea supporters.

Although slightly older than most members of Tommy Docherty's young team, Ron got to know the players fairly well during the sixties. "It started by accident, really," he recalls. "I used to drive a motorbike and in 1959 I had a smash and broke my leg. I was in plaster for five months and from January to the end of the season I used to go to the training ground at Welsh Harp, Hendon nearly every day. Peter Bonetti, Bobby Tambling and all those were there, so I knew them right from when they were kids. The youth system then was superb, it really was. We had so many good young players compared to other clubs. Jimmy Greaves, Ron Harris, a whole team came through from Chelsea youth. I used to go up there on crutches and the players used to bring me cups of tea after training. I was in a really privileged position and all because of my broken leg. I was married with kids but I used to get out of the house to see them train, it was a sort of therapy. That's what I told my wife anyway. So I got to know the players, although a lot of them never made it at Chelsea and had careers elsewhere.

"It was around that time I went up on the train to Newcastle for an FA Cup tie. I was still on crutches, we got all the way to Newcastle only to find the game was postponed because of the bad weather. So we went to another match, between Bishop Auckland and Whitley Bay. I was walking along in the snow with one leg in plaster covered by a blue sock. But I didn't need the blue sock because my toes were blue beneath it!"

Ron's relationship with the players grew as the youngsters were swiftly promoted by Docherty from the youth ranks. "Having known them as kids, the players became used to seeing me and a few other regular fans once they got in the first team. We'd see them at away games and they'd come out of the dressing room to chat to the supporters. Often we'd be coming back from away games and be on the same train as the team. They'd be on the platform waiting with us and then invite us in to their compartment to chat to them. It was great – you got to know the players as friends. We'd play cards with them sometimes. Eventually they got a bit selective about who they'd let in there because some fans would take liberties with players, smothering them basically. Tommy Docherty didn't like that very much. I was alright, luckily, because I was always there – that's the way to get known. By the late sixties, though, they started going by coach. I think they found the train too public. Another factor was that they were tied to the train timetables which weren't always necessarily the most convenient for them."

However, before the Blues swapped British Rail for National Express Ron had managed to have a few frank heart-to-hearts with the Doc, mostly while returning to London after away games up north. "I liked Tommy Docherty. He was very open. He told the fans things he perhaps shouldn't have been telling you. He'd say things about players after a game – 'what a lazy little sod' so and so was, for instance. He was brash, but friendly. You could talk to him, have your own say. I liked Dave Sexton too, but I thought he was a crap manager. He was a bloody good coach, mind you. But he couldn't manage a flea circus."

When he wasn't acting as an informal advisor to the Chelsea manager of the day Ron had an altogether less glamorous role at the Bridge – as a matchday steward. "In the sixties I was a steward in the enclosure in front of the old East stand. We just had to pack them in – 'Could you move along a little bit?' was our catchphrase. We didn't have uniforms or bibs, we just wore an armband and badge with 'steward' on it. We picked up ten bob (50p) a game, which was more than they got later. When the match started we just disappeared up to the back of the stands and watched the game from there. It wasn't like now where the stewards can't even watch the game. It was a cushy number, basically. Eventually they brought in another guy to organise the stewarding and he stuck me behind the gate in the old North Stand, the small stand on stilts above the terracing. The first game of the season, I think it was in 1970 or 1971, I was standing behind a door looking through a bloody window at the game. I said to him 'No way, mate' so I chucked it in and got Mick Mears in the ticket office to get me a season ticket up in the North Stand."

Ron and the other supporters interviewed in this chapter all agree that the late sixties and early seventies were a great time to follow the Blues. Apart from the team's successes on the pitch, the fans began to develop a strong collective identity through chants and songs – many of which, incidentally, remain essential components of the Chelsea canon. Meanwhile, cheap admission prices and bargain 'Soccer Special' train fares kept costs down for the dedicated travelling fan. On the down side, hooliganism was rampant, ground facilities were poor and club merchandise was virtually non-existent. For most supporters, though, these were minor inconveniences compared to the thrill of being part of the Blue army which roared on Ossie, Huddy and the rest.

Even today, a surprisingly large percentage of Chelsea's regular fans can date their support for the club back three decades to the double cup-winning side. The 1970 FA Cup Final was particularly important in this respect, acting as a highly effective recruiting sergeant of youngsters all around the country who were just beginning to become interested in the game. They didn't know it then, but for many of those kids glued to the TV that April night the Blues would become a central part of their lives in the years to come.

CHAPTER ELEVEN
TRAINING BLUES

xciting trips abroad, invitations to parties attended by the rich and famous, assignations with beautiful women, the adulation of thousands packed on the terraces: from a fan's point of view it must have seemed that the Chelsea players of the time were living the lives of gods rather than mere mortals.

Probably few supporters, though, fully appreciated the hard work which underlaid these trappings of success. If anything, the players' everyday experience, away from the snapping cameras of the sports photographers and society *paparazzi*, was just about as unglamorous as it can get. After all, most people would agree that the prospect of running around a field in south London, in weather conditions ranging from blisteringly hot to bone chillingly cold, is not in itself particularly alluring. Yet come rain, wind or raging blizzard, the Chelsea players would be out jogging on the club's training ground in Mitcham, no doubt uttering a few oaths under their breath when out of earshot of Dave Sexton.

Now the site of Tooting and Mitcham's Imperial Fields stadium, the complex contained three pitches – one, by the river Wandle, used to get very heavy in winter – and a pavilion where the players changed. It was here that Tommy Docherty and Dave Sexton would hone the players' fitness, develop tactics and create some of the defensive and attacking ploys which would be used in future games. Sexton is widely regarded as one of the best coaches this country has produced and in his two spells at Chelsea, first as Docherty's assistant then as manager, he did much to build his reputation as one of the game's great thinkers.

"Tommy, or 'Boss' as we called him, would do his bits but when I got into the first team squad Dave Sexton was already there as the coach," said Peter Osgood. "He was a brilliant, fantastic coach. He made everything interesting, different and new. One day we went in and he took us to Twickenham to watch a rugby match and then for three or four days we trained with a rugby ball – we didn't see a football. The reason for that was you couldn't pass the ball forward, you had to pass it back. What he was trying to get you to do was to get to the by-line and get crosses over for people coming in. It worked out brilliantly. Peter Houseman and Charlie Cooke would whip in the crosses and me and Hutch went flying in to get them. We got loads of goals that way."

And Alan Birchenall adds: "I was his first signing and whenever I bump into him I always say, 'After me, Dave, it all went downhill', but it didn't really. His coaching was superb. With all due respect to the other managers I played under, Dave Sexton was far and away the most innovative coach. He was years in front of his time, and some of the stuff we did on the training pitch was great.

"One of my first training sessions was at Winchester College on the Embankment. He wouldn't let me go until I'd bent two balls out of ten into the goal from the corner flag. I'd never done anything like that before and, at first, I couldn't see the point of it. I said, 'What am I doing this for? I'm the centre forward, not a winger.' Dave said, 'It doesn't matter, there are other aspects of your game I want to develop.' And, credit to Dave, I felt my all-round game really came on at Chelsea."

Skipper Ron Harris, too, has nothing but praise for Sexton's coaching skills. "He'd been there as the coach under Tommy Docherty a few years before so lots of the lads related to him straight away," he says. "One thing he did was to bring in zonal marking, which nobody did before. In the past, if I was playing right-back and Eddie McCreadie was playing left-back and my winger went over to Eddie's side we used to swap over. Dave changed all that. He brought these bollards in to training to mark out different zones on the pitch, then if a player moved into your zone you had to pick him up. So in training he'd say, for example, 'Hey, Webby, he's in your zone now' and that's how we switched to zonal marking. The training changed how we played, but he also made it enjoyable."

As well as working on the defence as a unit, Sexton was also determined to improve his defenders' individual skills. In the passing game that was Chelsea's hallmark at the time there was no use for the aimless long punt from the back which, dispiritingly, became all too common a feature of British football in the 1980s.

"Dave taught me a lot of stuff," says Micky Droy, who played his first games for Chelsea under Sexton as a teenager before eventually going on to become the Blues' skipper. "He was way ahead of his time, too. For example, he was the first manager to go abroad in the summer and study continental sides' methods – that was unheard of then. He used to have me and Gary Locke back for training in the afternoon at Mitcham and we'd spend hours whacking balls at each other and bringing them down – from 20, 30, then 40 yards. That made me comfortable on the ball. A lot of defenders just used to whack it, they didn't care where it went, but I did. That all came from Dave."

After the serious technical and tactical work the players would often be rewarded with a five-a-side game at the end of the session. On Fridays, the day before matches, the team trained at Stamford Bridge and these mini-matches were played in full view of the passing public in the ground's forecourt. "We used to play games between 'The Goodies' and The Baddies'," says Ron Harris. "The Baddies were me, Ossie, Hutch, Huddy and a couple of others. That was good fun, and fans would stop to watch as they walked past."

And Micky Droy adds: "It could get a bit tasty because the games always had an edge to them: North v South or England v Scotland. It was really competitive because we usually had the same teams each week and nobody liked to lose. There were a few tackles flying in – Ronnie Harris used to do slide tackles on the gravel – but I used to play up front out of the way. Looking back, it was unbelievable; but it was good for the spirit of the team and the players used to look forward all week to those games."

Droy wasn't the only defender to switch to an attacking role in these games. Indeed, David Webb claims that his scoring feats in training were instrumental in persuading Dave Sexton to try him out as an auxiliary or emergency striker in first team matches. "I was always the most prolific goalscorer in five-a-side games," he boasts, "so in league and cup games they'd throw me up front if we were behind. That old buccaneering spirit would turn matches. I threw so much effort and enthusiasm into it that it just sparked off everybody else off."

For new signings arriving at the club, the five-a-side game would generally be their initial taste of competitive action as a Chelsea player. Naturally, they would be eager to do well but, as Alan Birchenall recalls, a test of character rather than skill would often be the first challenge.

"I was introduced to the boys and we started off with a five-a-side game on the concrete forecourt outside. I got the ball for the first time and then, wallop, Ron Harris whacked me right up in the air and knocked me out. When I came round he was standing right over me, snarling, 'Welcome to Chelsea. You may have cost a hundred grand but you're still not earning more than me.' Ossie picked me up and said, 'Chopper runs things round here. That was your initiation and you reacted well; you didn't jump up and retaliate.' Well, the only reason I didn't jump up was because I was bloody concussed!"

Harris, though, denies that this incident was in any sense a formal 'initiation'. "Alan Birchenall says he got larruped and I said, 'Welcome to Chelsea Football Club'," he muses. "Well, put it this way, I used to play the same way in training as I did in a match. I could only play one way."

All the same, the idea that Chopper liked to test the mettle of new players – and the strength of their shinpads – certainly gained currency around the Bridge. "When I joined Chelsea, one of the players warned me to watch out for Harris in training," said Keith Weller who signed for the Blues three years after Birchenall in 1970. "I was told he topped all the new players to put them in their place. I'd never heard anything like it. I thought that was ridiculous. But nothing happened, until one day down at Mitcham when we had a very long training session.

"Ron didn't drive at the time and his wife used to come and pick him up. One day we were still playing when I saw her parking her car and casually remarked that we must be training late if old Chopper's missus had turned up. For some reason he took offence, I don't know why as I didn't mean anything by it, and soon after in our five-a-side game there was a 50–50 ball between the two of us. He went over the top and left me in a crumpled heap on the ground. He'd done my knee in and I missed the next game because of it. Dave Sexton was worried that I'd seek retribution. I told him he had nothing to worry about. I wasn't like that. If it had happened during a proper game, I might have but I was prepared to let the matter drop."

It went largely unnoticed by his terrified opponents, but Ron Harris did possess a sense of humour. Again, the new signings would often be the victims. "We were down the training ground at Mitcham and John Dempsey, who had just joined us from Fulham, was kicking lumps out of me," recalled Peter Osgood. "I said, 'Demps, listen, you're not playing for Fulham now, I'm your team-mate, what's going on?' But he kept kicking me so I said, 'Demps, if you do it again, I'm going to deck yer! What's the problem?' And he told me, 'Chopper Harris says you told him I put hair lacquer on my hair!' That was typical of Ronnie, winding somebody up, which is why we called him 'Buller' – because he was full of bullshit."

Ron Harris wasn't the only player with an eye on the new boys in training. Charlie Cooke, too, liked to set them a challenge which invariably resulted in the recent addition to the squad handing over the contents of his wallet to the canny Scotsman. "On the first day of training Cookie said, 'Bet you a tenner I can walk down the middle of Stamford Bridge with the ball on my head, turn round and come back'," recalls Alan Birchenall. "I'd never seen anybody do anything like that, so I said, 'Go on then, you won't be able to do it'. I was set up. I gave him the tenner, which was the equivalent of about £50 nowadays, and he just walked down to the bottom of the pitch and back again with the ball perfectly balanced on his head the whole way. I learnt a lesson that day!"

Such moments provided light relief for the players from the serious side of training. Since the abolition of the maximum wage in 1961 football clubs had required greater professionalism from their players, and this new ethic was reflected in training programmes which were much more gruelling and taxing than ever before. Certainly, by the mid-sixties the training regime at Chelsea was nothing like the relaxed and relatively undemanding one it had been under Ted Drake just a few years previously.

"A lot of what we did was tough – 100 yard sprints, 220s, 440s, 880s and cross countries," said Peter Osgood. Famously, Ossie wasn't so keen on the last of these exercises. "No, I fucking wasn't," he confirmed. "I thought that football is to be played with a ball and if I didn't see a ball for two days I thought it was ridiculous. I think I should have been a Brazilian, to be honest. They play with the ball all the time and that would have suited me.

"Peter Bonetti was the best trainer at the club," he continued. "Chopper wasn't far behind. Johnny Hollins and John Boyle were good runners, too. Only me and Marvin Hinton were useless. When we went running on Epsom Downs Dave used to take his car to collect us because the minibus would have been gone about 20 minutes before me and Marvin finished."

Osgood particularly disliked pre-season training, which included regular cross-country runs around Epsom Downs in an attempt to build up stamina levels for the campaign ahead. "Ossie was a lazy so and so," says Alan Birchenall. "Every day, Ena (John Hollins) would come in first, I'd finish somewhere in the middle and Ossie would always come in last after we'd been sat in the van for 20 minutes. Dave Sexton had enough of this so he says to Ossie, 'Right, if you come in last tomorrow, everyone will have to go round again in the afternoon.'

"So, on the way home, I'm nagging Ossie to pull his finger out and he just says, 'Don't worry about me, there's no way I'll be last tomorrow.' Next day, exactly the same thing happens. Ena goes off in front, I'm in the middle of the pack, and Ossie's right at the back. We're coming into the final straight and there's no sign of Ossie. He's not even with the stragglers at the back. Just as we're cursing him and preparing to go round again, we hear the sound of galloping hooves. I turn round and there's Ossie riding this racehorse flat out and he comes charging past us giving it all the 'hi ho silvers!' and shouting, 'Come on, you lazy bastards, who's going to be last, then?' He'd only got his mate to bring a racehorse up, hidden the horsebox in the woods then nipped in the saddle when we were all sweating it out."

The club's pre-season tours abroad provided more opportunity for fun and games. Unlike the summer tours, which were essentially exotic holidays with a few exhibition games thrown in, these trips tended to be short haul rather than long haul, with Germany, Spain and Scandinavia among the favoured destinations. For Dave Sexton, the pre-season tour was a chance to whip his men into shape after the long summer break. Punishing training schedules would be drawn up; tough local opposition would be arranged;

and, knowing his fun-loving players as he did, Sexton would be careful to find a training base which was miles away from the nearest bar or nightclub.

Both Sexton and his predecessor Tommy Docherty liked taking the team to Germany in the summer as the local training facilities were good and the longstanding rivalry between English and German teams added a competitive edge to otherwise inconsequential friendly fixtures. For the players, too, Germany provided the added attraction of first-rate lager served in *uber*-sized glasses by buxom, lederhosen-clad *frauleins*. Certainly, more than a few *steins* of the local brew were downed on the Blues' trip to the Rhineland in July 1968, as Alan Birchenall recalls.

"We were on a team night out in Kaiserslautern. Dave Sexton had told us the bus was leaving the town square at eleven but, of course, me, Ossie, Marvin Hinton and Joe Fascione missed it and we got a lift back along the motorway from a German guy we'd met in a bar. I told him it was about 30 miles back to hotel, but he said it wasn't a problem so off we went. Marvin was in the back and was rapidly turning a pale green colour. Suddenly, he shouted out, 'I've got to be sick!' so the guy stopped his Merc and Marvin puked up in the middle of the *autobahn*.

"He got back in the car, we carried on driving for another four or five miles and then Marvin cried out, 'Turn back, I've lost my tooth'. He told us he had a single false tooth on a dental plate and it had fallen out while he was throwing up. 'You're never going to see that pile of puke, it'll be squashed!' we told him, but he insisted we turn back. Luckily for Marvin it was about three o'clock in the morning and there was no traffic, so we managed to spot the place where he'd been sick.

"Marv poked around in the sick in the headlights of the Merc and after a few minutes he triumphantly waved something in his hand. 'I've got it!' he yelled. Anyway, we got back to the hotel – a baronial German mansion in the middle of nowhere, which we dubbed Stalag 14 – and we couldn't get back in because it was all locked up. We didn't fancy waking Dave Sexton up by ringing the bell so, after looking around for a while, we found a skylight above the back entrance and we decided to shove the smallest one of us, Joe Fascione, through it. Small he may have been but he had a big arse, and although he got his upper body through his arse and legs got trapped. Well, we pushed him and he went like a blooming Exocet through the skylight, straight into the kitchen, knocking over a pile of saucepans in the process.

"Of course, the hotel security was alerted by the noise, as was Dave Sexton who came rushing down in his dressing gown. He was furious when he saw us and we all got hit with a big fine. I was upset about losing two weeks' wages but Ossie didn't seem that bothered and I soon saw why. When we got back to Heathrow he phoned up the *Daily Express* from a telephone kiosk. 'Do you want a hot one? Yes? Chelsea boys get fined after night out . . .' I couldn't believe it, I thought it would get us into more trouble. But Ossie just said, 'Don't worry, the money we get for the story will pay off the fine'. Fortunately for Marvin, Ossie left out the bit about his teeth." Needless to say, although Sexton took the Blues back to Germany in later years, he always gave Kaiserslautern a wide berth.

Three years later, in 1971, Sexton's meticulous pre-season arrangements came unstuck again when he booked the team into a remote Swedish hotel that turned out to be altogether livelier than he anticipated. "I got married on the Saturday and we went to Sweden on the Monday, so I had my honeymoon with the lads," remembers Alan Hudson. "We came from the airport and on the coach we were travelling down these country lanes and we didn't see any life anywhere. Finally, we pulled up outside this big hotel – a gigantic gaff – and all the boys were saying, 'What's he brought us to?' It looked like a concentration camp in the middle of nowhere. There was no sign of a bar, or any life whatsoever.

"We took up our gear to our rooms and then we walked up the back stairs to the restaurant for dinner. We opened the door and the place was packed with Swedish birds dancing, there was a band on the stage, and in the corner Dave Sexton was sitting at a table with his head in his hands. It was so funny. We all got there and went 'Great!' and, what's more, they had a nightclub downstairs. The hotel was the local entertainment centre and everybody would go there for a night out. I've never seen so many beautiful girls in one place at one time. What our boys got up to was unbelievable – we'd be out on the beach with the girls we'd met until five in the morning."

Which sounds fun, except the Chelsea boys were expected to be back out on the beach an hour later for the start of an arduous day's training. "We'd train at six o'clock in the morning, when half of us hadn't been to bed," says Huddy. "We'd just have time to go back to the hotel to get our kit on. After training, we'd come back to the hotel to have breakfast, train again at eleven o'clock, two o'clock and four o'clock.

"The first session was running along the beach, back and forth. Dave Sexton and Ron Suart had done their homework. They'd walked along the beach, and marked it all out. There were about five or six canoes or little boats, 50 yards apart as you went up the beach. So on the first morning they said, 'This morning you run to the first boat and back, second morning you run to the second boat and back and so on.'

"We went off in fours, the four quickest followed by the next four, down to the fourth group of four. I was in the front group with Peter Bonetti, Eddie McCeadie and Johnny Hollins. The worst runners were the last ones to go – Peter Osgood, David Webb, Tommy Baldwin and John Dempsey. We'd reached the last boat and turned back to see the others still coming. They were trotting along and chatting to each other and they said to us, 'Oi, slow down a bit'. But on the fourth day we didn't see them at all. We thought, 'What's happened to them?' Then we got back to the first boat and they were all lying in it with their feet up. It was a bit misty that morning so Dave and Ron couldn't see them and as the third group went by they all jumped out of the boat and ran in just behind them. When they got back Sexton and Ron Suart were really impressed. 'Well done boys,' they were saying, 'you boys at the back have done absolutely terrific'."

The management team were less impressed later that afternoon when the unusual seaside setting diverted Charlie Cooke's attention from the serious business of a five-a-side game. "We were playing at the waters' edge," Huddy remembers. "Someone got the ball and passed it out to Charlie, who was looking out to sea in a bit of a daze. Sexton went mad, he picked the ball up, and said, 'Charlie, if you don't want to play, we won't play. We'll run instead.' Charlie said, 'I'm only looking out to sea!' and everyone cracked up. We got back from pre-season in pretty poor shape and I don't think we won until about eight games into the season."

Significantly, Sexton switched the squad's training base to Holland the following season — staying well clear of the fleshpots of Amsterdam, of course — and the Blues never returned to Sweden while he was in charge.

CHAPTER TWELVE
OVER LAND AND SEA

aiti, Iran, El Salvador, Mozambique: four countries where war, violent revolution, natural disasters and abject poverty have been pretty much the norm over recent decades. Despite the best efforts of their respective tourism ministries, none of the quartet is what you would call holiday brochure material yet, bizarrely, Chelsea went on summer tours to all four places during the 1960s and 1970s.

The decidedly oddball destinations, however, seem a little less unusual when viewed in a historical context. Over the years, the Blues have specialised in travelling to the sort of exotic locations normally favoured by the likes of Alan Whicker and Michael Palin. Africa, Asia, Australasia, Europe and America – Chelsea really have 'been, there, done that and got the T-shirt'. Way back in 1929, for example, the Londoners were one of the first teams from Britain to tour South America, playing games in Argentina, Brazil and Uruguay. Newspaper accounts from the period suggest the expedition wasn't an unqualified success.

"A Chelsea player was assaulted with a brutality that was the more regrettable because one of the principal assailants wore the uniform of a public service," reported *All Sports Weekly* of a match in Argentina, while the *Estado de Sao Paulo* correspondent appeared shocked by the spectacle he witnessed in Brazil. "The shouting and booing of the spectators and the violence of the game made it look like a bullfight," he wrote.

More recently, in 1986, the Blues accepted an invitation to play a match against the Iraqi national team in Baghdad – despite the fact that the Iran-Iraq war was still raging. Saddam Hussein was expected to attend the match and kick-off was delayed for over an hour as the two teams waited for him to appear. In the event, he didn't show up but, presumably, the Iraqi dictator would have been reasonably satisfied with his side's 1–1 draw.

As one of the most successful and well-known English clubs of the 1960s and early 1970s, the Blues wouldn't have had any shortage of tour offers from overseas clubs and national associations. In many cases, the tours would be sponsored by major international companies, allowing Chelsea to collect a handsome cheque for their participation as well as having all their costs covered.

The size of the financial inducement which enticed Chelsea to play two games in Mozambique in May 1969, both against the national team, is anyone's guess. What is certain is that the Blues pitched up in southern Africa at a time when the country, then still a Portuguese colony, was wracked by civil war between govern-ment forces and the anti-colonial resistance movement, Frelimo. Most of the fighting, though, was in the countryside and Chelsea were assured that the visiting party would be safe in the capital Maputo, then known as Lourenco Marques. Having toured the millionaire's playground of Bermuda on their previous summer club outing, the news that they'd be heading this year to a war-torn, fly-blown African outpost didn't have the Chelsea players exactly whistling with joy as they packed their suitcases – 'football boots, check . . . mosquito repellent, check . . . flak jacket, check.'

"With all due respect, Mozambique's not Trinidad and Tobago and 30 years ago it certainly wasn't," says Alan Birchenall, who had just missed out on the Bermuda trip, having signed for Chelsea from Sheffield United a couple of months later. "If you had a straw poll and had to choose between Bermuda and Mozambique

OVER LAND AND SEA

I don't think there'd be a contest. I think we landed in a field, and the local airport was a hut. It was unbelievable. I thought, 'Of all the places in the world, what the hell are we doing here?' I'd like to know if Sir Dickie Attenborough was planning to do a film out there and our visit was supposed to spread a bit of goodwill."

Ian Hutchinson, another player on his first Chelsea summer tour, was at least prepared to give the place a chance. "I'd never been to another continent before and, naturally, I was excited about going," he recalled. "But when we arrived, it was the pits, starting with the hotel. Huddy was my room-mate at the time, and when we got upstairs there were lizards in the bedroom. We chased them round the room and swatted them. We woke the next morning covered in bites, and went down to reception to be told the lizards were there to catch the mosquitoes. You could just see their logic – but we really didn't fancy lizards crawling all over us."

First impressions may have been disappointing, but the Chelsea lads were still determined to search out the best in nightlife the Mozambique capital had to offer. "We did manage to find the only nightclub in Lourenco Marques," says Alan Birchenall. "Wherever you put the Chelsea boys we'd find a place with a bit of music and serving late beers. I've frequented most night-clubs throughout the world as a player and a businessman. I've seen the best and the worst, and this one was certainly one of the worst. The roof was just a corrugated iron sheet. But, on the other hand, music's music and a beer's a beer.

"Mozambique was a very sinister place back then, there was a civil war going on, you saw soldiers and tanks on the streets and it was quite scary. We'd been warned to stick together and not to go wandering off. Some of the single lads wanted to go off with the local ladies we met in the club but we'd been advised not to travel back to the hotel on our own, so in the end they didn't. It was that frightening you could have had Naomi Campbell on your arm and still not taken a chance by going off with her."

All very sensible. However, John Boyle has a different version of events altogether, in which a trio of players ignored the advice they'd been given – and almost paid a heavy price for their reck-lessness. "We were in this club and the young lady we'd been talking to invited us back to a party at her place," he recalls. "I went along with a couple of the other lads. It turned out to be back in a township, a very basic place – just a shack really. We arrived there at about two o'clock in the morning. It was just the four of us; there was no party as such. After a while, two of us went outside, leaving the other guy inside with the girl. While we waited, we could hear the bed springs squeaking. Then, the other one went in, and the same thing happened. When it came to my turn I said I wasn't bothered, but this young woman suddenly started shouting, 'Escudos! Money!' We shook our heads, but then she pulled out a knife. Well, of course, that changed the situation – we flung down some money and just ran. We didn't have a clue where we were going but eventually we managed to make it back to the hotel."

As for the two games, Chelsea won them both – the first by a ridiculous Sunday League-style scoreline, 9–3, and the second by two goals to one. "In the first match one of their guys played in bare feet," remembers Tommy Baldwin, who admits to feeling somewhat the worse for wear after the previous night's drinking session.

"It was a baking hot day. In the first few minutes I made a couple of runs and threw up on the pitch on the edge of their penalty area. Ah, it was terrible and I felt awful. At half-time I came into the dressing room, ran some water in the sink and just sprawled out under the tap. All I could think of was getting loads of water on me. Dave Sexton came in and said, 'Where's that Tommy Baldwin? I want him off.' I just wailed, 'I'm over here'. He subbed me off and fined me."

Oh dear. The Blues had successfully avoided the worst Mozambique could throw at them – repugnant reptiles, bloodthirsty rebels and knife-wielding locals – only for one of their number to be felled by a raging hangover.

If Costa Rica is the Switzerland of Central America, then El Salvador is more like the Balkans. Government-backed 'death squads', moustachioed dictators and gun-toting guerrillas are all familiar features of the political scene in El Salvador, a country which on more than one occasion, rightly or wrongly, has been described as a 'banana republic'. Colourful and exciting it may be, but it's hardly somewhere you'd choose to go on holiday. Unless, of course, you're the players and staff of Chelsea FC.

Quite why the club decided to head off on a summer tour to El Salvador in May 1971 is a bit of a mystery. There are suggestions that a multi-national tobacco company wrote out a big cheque in front of the directors and this suddenly persuaded them, despite all the available evidence to the contrary, that San Salvador, the capital, would be a pleasant spot to spend a few days. Certainly tobacco – like bananas, coffee and state-sanctioned torture – is big business in El Salvador so this explanation sounds plausible.

Football, too, is hugely popular in this small, earthquake-afflicted country although passions can easily get out of control. Two years earlier, in 1969, El Salvador's World Cup qualifier play-off with neighbouring Honduras had ignited the so-called 'Soccer War' between the countries – a four-day conflict which left 2,000 dead. True, the nations had been squabbling for some time over various non-sporting issues, including those arising from the presence of hundreds of thousands of Salvadoran 'squatters' in Honduras, but the fact that a football match could spark such bloodshed and misery must have been a little worrying for the visiting Chelsea players. That unease could only have been increased on the first night the squad stayed in San Salvador.

"I could hear shots being fired outside the hotel," recalls Alan Hudson. "We really were in the middle of it." Quite what 'it' was – soldiers firing on demonstrators, possibly, although it could just as easily have been the other way round – remains unclear and, understandably, Huddy wasn't particularly keen to find out. "We just kept our heads down indoors, wondering what the hell we were doing there," he adds.

Fortunately, perhaps, the Blues' itinerary was a short one. First up was a game against Southampton, who were also in town, followed by a match two days later against the El Salvador national team. That promised to be a tough encounter as the El Salvadoreans, having won their local spat with Honduras, had made a first ever appearance at the World Cup finals in Mexico in 1970.

English pride would be at stake in the second game so the last thing the Blues needed was to be involved in a bruising fixture with the Saints, who were known as one of the most physical, if not downright dirty, teams in England at the time. Not that the boys from the Dell were looking for a fight – for them, like Chelsea, the game was primarily a bit of fun between boozing sessions.

Chatting away in a local bar together the night before the game, the two sets of players got stuck into a drinking contest. While lager followed lager, talk turned to the two matches the teams would be playing against each other, first in San Salvador the following day, then in the altogether more agreeable Caribbean island surroundings of Trinidad a week later. As the beers took hold, Tommy Baldwin and Southampton's Jimmy Gabriel struck a £100 bet on which player would score the most goals in the double-header. It was a bold wager by Gabriel, as he played in midfield, while the Sponge, of course, was a striker. The bet was discussed for a few minutes – then, as the night wore on, somebody came up with what seemed like a bright idea.

"We were in the bar all evening and along the way we sorted out what was going to happen when we played them the following day," remembers Alan Hudson. "We decided to have a high-scoring, friendly game, but to keep it a draw. So it would go 'you score, we score' and so on." Needless to say, neither Dave Sexton nor the Southampton manager, Ted Bates, were to be informed of the pact.

"The next day everything was going to plan on the field and it was something like 2–2 or 3–3 at half-time," continues Huddy. "The fans seemed happy, we were happy, but Dave Sexton wasn't. He came in the dressing room at half-time and we could tell he was angry. 'I fucking know what's going on,' he screamed, 'don't think I fucking don't know. I know where you all were last night, drinking with the Southampton mob. People have paid good money to see this game, the club have been paid good money to come out here and you're playing like this, thinking it's a joke. Now get out there and you show people how you can play.'

"We went out for the second half and tried to tell the Southampton players that the agreement was cancelled, but they thought we were joking. Pretty soon we scored, then straight away we scored again. The Southampton players were furious and it turned into a kicking match, a right war. They thought we'd turned them over on purpose." By the final whistle, a Sexton-energised Chelsea had banged in eight goals to Southampton's three, with Baldwin taking a seemingly unassailable four-one lead in the first leg of his personal duel with Gabriel.

The following day Baldwin, Gabriel, Charlie Cooke and Eddie McCreadie took a tour of the city. "The army was out on the streets and everywhere you looked there were people carrying guns," remembers the Sponge. "At one point Eddie asked a policeman if he could have a look at his gun. The guy gave it to him, but he quickly took it back when Eddie started waving it around like a cowboy in a western."

In a San Salvador nightclub the Scot managed to go one better – or should that be one worse. "There was a bloke at the end of the bar in an army sergeant's uniform," says David Webb. "Eddie proceeded to remove this guy's gun from his holster and started firing it as a joke. But the gun had real bullets in it and people started diving for cover."

Little wonder, then, that by now the locals were viewing the Chelsea players with some suspicion. "We took a taxi back to the hotel one night and I could tell we were going in the wrong direction," says Tommy Baldwin. "I tapped the driver on the shoulder and said, 'Hey, where are we going?' Immediately, he reached for the glove compartment and I could see there was in a gun in there. I just put my hands up and said, 'Carry on, señor!'"

Unaffected by that scare, Baldwin scored the winner as Chelsea beat El Salvador 1–0 in front of 18,000 fans and hundreds of gum-chewing, tooled-up soldiers. He continued his hot streak in Trinidad, grabbing another two goals as Chelsea thrashed Southampton again, 6–2 this time. With Gabriel only managing one for the Saints in reply, the Baldwin bet was in the bag. Three straight wins, a wager won and nobody hit by a stray McCreadie bullet – the tour had been a rousing success. Which is more than you can say for the Blues' trip to Haiti although, given the country's reputation, perhaps that was no surprise.

The western half of the Caribbean island of Hispaniola, Haiti is the home of voodoo, a strange blend of Roman Catholicism and west African religion which apparently makes perfect sense to the locals but, thanks to numerous B-movies featuring pin-sticking witch doctors and sleep-walking zombies, has dark and sinister connotations elsewhere. Politically, the country is what is some-times known in diplomatic circles as 'a basket case'. Democracy has the most tenuous of footholds here, and few eyebrows were raised when the Haitian leader President Aristide was overthrown in an armed rebellion in March 2004. His abrupt flight into exile led to scenes of mass looting and general chaos on the streets of the capital, Port-au-Prince, with order eventually being restored thanks to the intervention of a UN security force.

Happily, when Chelsea called in on the last stage of a three-week long Caribbean tour sponsored by the British/American Tobacco Company in June 1964, Haiti was more stable – if only because the notorious dictator 'Papa Doc' Duvalier had made himself

President for life and crushed any dissenting voices by creating a terrifying civilian militia, the Tonton Macoute. Overall, it seems, the Blues players would have preferred to have been somewhere else.

"Haiti was a horrible, dirty, stinking place," is Ron Harris' terse summary. "When we got off the plane it was absolutely chucking it down and you could see cars floating down the street. I wouldn't fancy going out there at night – and we didn't. We were pleased to get out of there."

Chelsea were lined up to play two matches in Haiti, the first against fellow tourists Wolves – who they had already played four times in Barbados, Trinidad and Jamaica – and the second against the country's national team. The game against the Midlanders went off without incident, the Blues winning 2–0 to claim a 3–2 match aggregate victory. It was a different story, though, the following day when Chelsea met their hosts in Port-au-Prince.

"We were losing 2–1 against the Haiti national team at the time," recalls Chopper, "and it got a little bit physical. It's possible that Tommy Docherty come on and played. I know he came on in Malta in 1963 and we had a big ruck because he topped one of their players. I'm not sure whether he got involved in something in Haiti but the game definitely got abandoned. It wasn't because of the rain, either, it was because so much was going on, either in the dug outs or on the pitch. I can't remember whether the referee was a bit biased and that kicked it off or whether there was a bit of a schemozzle between the players. But the ref took the teams off and that was the end of the game."

Tommy Docherty, however, is certain that it *was* the weather and nothing he or any of his players did which caused the abandonment. "There was absolutely no trouble between the players," he says. "What happened was that we were hit by a tropical storm – well, it was more like a hurricane – and the ref called the game off. The rain was lashing down, the wind was howling and it was quite frightening. When they get a storm like that there it's quite something. There were spectators on bicycles trying to get home by cycling across the pitch, but they weren't getting very far. It was a shame because the stadium was packed and Haiti, who had some good players, were giving us a decent game."

Whether the match was prematurely ended by torrential rain or violent scenes on the pitch, the upshot was the same: the abandonment allowed the Chelsea players to get out of Haiti a full half hour earlier than scheduled, so it's unlikely there were too many glum faces in the away dressing room.

Roman Abramovich may have more money than a double rollover lottery winner, but he is far from being the first multi-billionaire to take an interest Chelsea FC. That honour goes to the Shah of Iran who, before his overthrow in the 1979 revolution, was an occasional visitor to the Bridge. The Shah was also a big fan of Real Madrid and, in November 1966, sponsored a charity game between his two favourite teams at the Bridge.

"He was at the game and presented us all with a gift on the pitch," says Tommy Baldwin. "Real also gave us all a gold watch with the club crest on it. It was a really beautiful watch, but unfortunately I don't know what's happened to mine. The most interesting thing about the game was that Puskas, the great Hungarian player, was still playing for Real. He must have been in his late thirties by then and he was carrying a bit of weight. He couldn't get around the pitch very well, but he still had some lovely touches."

Chelsea won that game 2–0 but, more importantly for our story, the evening helped cement ties between the Shah and the club. And although the Iranian leader didn't invest any of his untold wealth in the Blues – "a shame," says Baldwin, "because he wasn't short of a few quid at the time" – he did invite the Londoners to tour Iran whenever they fancied. Seven years later, in 1973, Chelsea accepted the offer and headed off to Tehran.

Iran in the early 1970s was a very different place to the hardline Islamic society it is today. The Shah, Mohammed Reza Pahlavi, had ascended to the Peacock Throne in 1941 determined to exploit the country's huge oil reserves and transform Iran into a modern, westernised, economically successful Middle East power. With support from the West his dream soon became a reality but, by the 1970s, the Shah's authoritarian regime was facing increasing opposition. Before the decade was out he and his family would have to flee for their lives as popular discontent turned into full-scale revolution.

"It was a weird place," remembers Tommy Baldwin. "It was more decadent than it is today. You saw girls wearing make up and short skirts, and they didn't cover their faces with a veil. You could get Coca Cola and other western products. It wasn't the culture shock it would be today, but it was still very different. Again, we couldn't go out alone at night. Instead, we went to some big dinners every evening where English-speaking women would come along and sit between us – one player, one girl, one player and so on. Afterwards we went to a couple of shows, one with belly dancers and the other was a more western thing, with can-can dancers."

During the ten days they were in Iran the Blues played three matches against local opposition, including a game against a Tehran Combined XI – effectively, the national team. Then, as now, Iran had a useful side and were reigning Asian champions. Many of the players in the side that faced Chelsea would also go on to play in the 1978 World Cup in Argentina, where they famously held Scotland to a 1–1 draw. The Blues knew they would be in for a difficult match, especially as the conditions were so unlike the ones they were used to back in England.

"The biggest problem was the altitude," recalls Tommy. "Tehran is 5,000 ft above sea level and it was really hot as well. It was a very tight, hard, bumpy pitch, too. There was a big, noisy crowd in the stadium. We were told not go near the terraces, not to incite the crowd and not even to celebrate if we scored a goal – because the fans would throw anything they had at us. Anyway, there were a couple of controversial incidents in the game and when we came off there was stuff raining down from the stands and bouncing off the cover over the tunnel. And that was just a friendly!" Fortunately, perhaps, the Blues didn't score, losing the match 1–0.

To mark their visit the Shah presented the Chelsea players with a magnificent gift, a big tub each of beluga caviar – the world's best. Most people would have been thrilled to receive such a present but, it seems, the Chelsea boys were distinctly unimpressed. "Coming back on the flight home everyone was going 'Yuk, what's this?' and flicking it around the plane," says Tommy. "I opened my tub, which contained about a pint and a half of caviar, took a taste and flicked it around like the others. The stuff was all over the place. When we got back to London we found out that top-quality caviar costs something like 10 guineas an ounce, so the amount we each had was worth about five hundred quid. Shame we'd left it all over the plane, really. But I'm sure Peter Bonetti kept his because he was astute like that."

Wars, revolutions and hostile crowds may get the adrenaline running but, given the choice, most players' ideal summer tour would involve a spot of footy and a lot of chilling out on a beautiful sandy beach, preferably one with ready access to a cocktail bar staffed by stunning bikini-clad waitresses. A clear case, you might say, of hot spots winning out over hotspots every time.

During the sixties and seventies, much to the players' delight no doubt, Chelsea made a good number of post-season tours to the sort of glamorous, palm-fringed locations you used to see in *Bounty* chocolate bar ads. Australia, Bermuda, Barbados, Jamaica, Trinidad, Venezuela . . . the list goes on. Trips like these – at a time when most ordinary people went on holiday in Britain or, if they were a bit better off, somewhere in France or Spain – represented a substantial perk of the job. No wonder so many of the players stayed so long at the club.

Only the most dogmatic of trade unionists could possibly describe these trips as 'work', as the players readily admit. "It was like a six-week holiday, to be honest," says John Boyle of a 1965 club tour to Australia. "There was a bit of training, we played a few games, but most of the time we were on the beach, relaxing or having parties.

"Coming back from Australia we stopped off in Hawaii for a while. George Graham met this girl on the beach and obviously thought it would be fun to grab her hand and run into the sea like they do in the films. But he tripped as he ran into the water and we could all hear him shouting, 'Help, I can't swim, I'm going to drown!' In a matter of seconds he'd gone from being a big superstar figure to a helpless bloke flapping around in the water in a state of panic." Luckily, Graham's female companion came to his rescue – or, remembering his yawn-inducing reign as Arsenal manager some 25 years later, maybe that should be 'unluckily'. "Usually, though, George was the smoothest operator you could ever hope to see," adds Boyle.

Nine years later Australia was again the Blues' destination, with Dave Sexton's men playing half a dozen matches against State teams. The Chelsea party consisted of a mix of seasoned pros and promising youngsters, among them rookie striker Steve Finnieston.

"It was basically a holiday," he says, echoing Boyle. "Although the games were a big thing for me as I hadn't yet made my debut, I was still out drinking and partying with the rest of the lads. Anyway, before the last game against New South Wales in Sydney, most of us went out till around three in the morning. I was thinking, 'Well, at least we don't have to report for the game until half past one so I'll get eight hours sleep.' Then, at 7am, the phone goes in my bedroom, and it's Dave Sexton. 'Get up, you're coming to church!' he said. I was surprised he even knew I was a Catholic as I was very lapsed. In church with Dave and Peter Bonetti I could hardly keep my eyes open, but I was trying to pretend I wasn't dog-tired. I felt shattered in the afternoon and, to make matters worse, Dave picked me in midfield. We lost 2–1, which was the first time a Chelsea team had been beaten in Australia."

Football may not top the list of popular sports Down Under, but at least the Aussies show some enthusiasm for the game. The same, alas, can't be said of our American cousins who even now still generally view 'soccer' as an unfathomable past-time for 'sissies', girls and Latino immigrants. So, when the Blues headed across the pond on a North American tour in May 1967, they must have been wondering about what sort of reception was awaiting them.

As it turned out, Chelsea went down a storm – not so much with the American public, only a handful of whom actually attended the games, but with the local women. "The team we were playing in New York asked us all along to a party," recalls Tommy Baldwin. "Me, Johnny Boyle and a couple of others went along. We walked into this house, got a drink, sat down and it seemed a bit strange because everyone was watching the television. So I glanced at the screen, and was a bit surprised to see a blue movie.

"Then some skimpily dressed girls came into the room and sat next to us. It was beginning to click that this wasn't quite a normal party, but we all took full advantage. I think maybe the Americans thought this is the sort of thing soccer teams like to do. It seemed that they were laying it all on for us and it was all part of their hospitality. That was pretty much a one-off: I hadn't known anything like it before and nothing similar to that happened afterwards."

John Boyle has an altogether different recollection of the event – for a start, he says, it took place in Los Angeles rather than the Big Apple. "Yes, it was definitely Hollywood, not New York. And the other team didn't invite us to a party, either. What happened was that two wise guys from Glasgow – two jack the lads – were hanging around the team because of the Scottish connection with Tommy Docherty. These two guys told us that there was a party on that evening. A group of about six of us went along and when the door of this big flat opened we saw an old-fashioned cine film showing a blue movie. There were about five or six stunning girls there and within a few minutes one of them said, 'Hey, do you want to come to bed with me?' I was 20 at the time, she was very attractive, so I didn't need any further encouragement. We came back down, had a drink and left. It was a brothel! When we got outside someone was collecting money, and they said, 'Right, all the greedy bastards who went twice owe me 20 dollars!'"

Bizarrely, Boyle ran into one of the girls he'd, er, become acquainted with over a year later when Chelsea played a Fairs Cup match at Morton. "One of the girls in America was Scottish," he says. "My parents were with me in the players' bar at Morton after the match and this girl came over to us and said, 'Oh, Mrs Boyle, your son's a really nice boy!' At first I didn't recognise her but once she'd spoken I remembered her as being the girl from Hollywood. I was in a bit of a panic what with my parents being there, but she didn't give away any details. I think she just wanted to say 'hello'."

'*Woh, We're Going to Barbados!*' Remember Typically Tropical's one hit wonder? Shame, really, that it didn't hit the charts until 1975 otherwise the Chelsea boys could have belted it out on the plane as they flew off to the sun-kissed Caribbean island in May 1970. On the other hand, maybe they didn't feel much like singing as most of the squad were nursing brain-splitting hangovers.

"We'd won the FA Cup, we were going to take the trophy out with us to Barbados and the night before we left Eric Swayne fixed up a party for us at the Meridiana restaurant," remembers Alan Birchenall. "When we walked down the stairs into the restaurant every other chair was filled with one of his Page Three models – all fully clothed, in case you're wondering. Afterwards we went to a club before finally staggering home. It was a brilliant night. One player, who shall remain nameless, got off with one of the girls and ended up with four false fingernails stuck in his arse. He wandered around for three days out in Barbados without even noticing they were there. It was only when another player drew his attention to the marks in the showers that he realised the nails were still embedded in his bum cheek!"

A salutary lesson, you might have thought. But did this poor player's misadventure have any effect on his team-mates' crumpet-chasing antics in Barbados? In a word, no. "While we were staying at the hotel in Barbados some of the lads made a play for one of the girls behind the bar," continues Birch. "But although she was attractive, she was a stuck-up bird and gave them all the cold shoulder. In an attempt to warm up this ice maiden, Eddie McCreadie told her that I had suffered a terrible accident and was paralysed from the waist down.

"I played along with the scam, telling her that I feared my career was over. At this point, the lads turned up with a wheelchair they'd found in the hotel foyer to ferry me off to the club we'd been to the previous evening, Alexandria's Nightclub in Bridgetown. While the other lads went to check out the action the girl stayed with me in the VIP lounge, telling me that she hoped we would be able to dance together one day.

"After three hours the joke was beginning to run out of control, and I decided to end it when my favourite Rolling Stones record, *Satisfaction*, came on. I told her I could feel some sensation in my legs and, as she screamed with delight, I tottered to my feet. She supported me to the dance floor where I suddenly burst into my best Mick Jagger strut. The look on her face went through all the emotions – from disbelief to anger, to finally seeing the funny side.

"Some people might think it was a bit sick, but you have to have a footballer's mentality to appreciate it. You've got to look at it in the context. You do these things when you're a young bloke. It was a classic. You wouldn't think a woman would fall for a stunt like that, but she did."

For the most part, the games Chelsea played on their various tours were uncompetitive affairs. Even at half pace and after a night spent sampling the local tipple the Blues were usually way too good for their enthusiastic but technically limited opponents. Indeed, some of the scorelines in the history books suggest mismatches of almost David and Goliath proportions: 15–0 v St James Montego Bay in 1964, 12–0 v Tasmania in 1965, 10–0 v Barbados in 1972 and so on. Just occasionally, though, Chelsea would face opposition who were a genuine match for them.

In February 1971 the Blues flew out to Jamaica to play Santos of Brazil in a prestigious friendly. The Brazilians' star player was none other than the legendary Pele, then at the height of his formidable powers. Four other members of Brazil's wonderful 1970 World Cup-winning squad were also in the Santos team – the great Carlos Alberto, defensive midfielder Clodoaldo and reserves Joel and Edu. Little wonder, then, that for the Chelsea players this was a friendly with a difference – and, what's more, it was a game they desperately wanted to win.

"It was a tough match," says Tommy Baldwin. "At one point Pele was playing down the right hand side when Eddie McCreadie came in and brought him down pretty hard. Ten minutes later Pele had the ball in the centre circle and he just made a beeline for Eddie in the left back position. He ran at him, knocked the ball past him and as Eddie tried to get back, Pele knocked him spark out with his elbow. Pele was the most complete player I ever played against. He had everything: pace, control, heading and shooting ability, he scored goals, but he could handle himself physically too as Eddie found out."

On the Chelsea bench, John Boyle saw McCreadie's dazed state as his big chance. "I remember really hoping at the time that Dave would bring me on, just so that I could say that I'd played against Pele," he says. Unfortunately for Boylers, Eddie recovered and Sexton, clearly treating the match very seriously, chose not to use any of his substitutes. Santos won the game 1–0, their late goal sparking a good-natured pitch invasion which held up play for six minutes until the Jamaican police cleared the crowd with a baton charge.

After the game some of the Chelsea players went to a Kingston nightclub where they bumped into a familiar face. "When we walked through the door there was Pele with a nice-looking blonde on his arm," recalls Tommy Baldwin. "We went up to him and he seemed pleased to see us. He was drinking gallons of vodka and orange, smoking a few fags and he had this blonde lady with him. I thought, 'Brilliant, this is the greatest player in the world and he can still enjoy himself!'

"We had a good night, and had a few drinks with him. He was a lovely bloke, not big-headed or anything. He wanted to talk about football all the time, about different games, training programmes and the game in England. I'd actually met him once before. In 1966, when I was still at Arsenal, I was living in digs with John Radford in north London. The landlady went on holiday for a while so Arsenal put us both up in a hotel in Finsbury Park. It just so happened that Santos were staying in the same hotel. Some guy came in to our room and introduced us both to Pele. We said 'hello' and Pele signed a card for me which I've still got."

Whether rubbing shoulders with the world's greatest player, relaxing in their own inimitable way in some of the planet's most exotic locations or getting embroiled in some unlikely far-flung adventures, the Chelsea lads had some of their most memorable experiences while on tour. Footballers plus sun plus beer is always likely to be an explosive mixture but Alan Birchenall, for one, has a theory why the Blues' overseas antics were wilder than most.

"We lived all over the place in London and the Home Counties so unless there was a club function you never saw us all out together," he points out. "That's probably why when we got together on tour it was twice as mad."

CHAPTER THIRTEEN
BLUE IS THE COLOUR

By the summer of 1971 Chelsea were firmly established as London's most glamorous side. The club's location just off the fashionable King's Road, the epicentre of 'Swinging London' throughout the 1960s, had added a sprinkling of stardust during the previous decade. But now, with the FA Cup and European Cup Winners' Cup safely locked away in the Stamford Bridge trophy cabinet, substance had been added to the Blues' hip image. Their triumphs had even led to a subtle change in the team kit, with two gold 'victory' stars proudly sitting either side of the club badge.

Despite their recent achievements, however, Chelsea couldn't claim to be the capital's most successful team. That accolade had to go to Arsenal, winners of the Double in season 1970/71 – only the second time the feat had been accomplished in the twentieth century. The Gunners' triumphs, though, had been based on solid defending, a flair-free midfield and a series of ultra-functional 1–0 victories. Their pragmatic, results-obsessed and, at times, downright dreary football failed to captivate neutrals in the way that Chelsea's free-flowing game did. Only ex-Blue George Graham and Charlie George, the long-haired Islington teenager who had scored Arsenal's winner in the FA Cup Final against Liverpool, possessed a fraction of the charisma which oozed through the Chelsea team. Otherwise, there was simply no comparison in the glamour stakes.

Take the two goalkeepers, for instance. In goal for the Gunners, Bob Wilson's hallmark was his bravery: he specialised in diving at forwards' feet and quite often ended up with a kick in the head for his troubles. Peter Bonetti, on the other hand, was a much more spectacular keeper, probably the most acrobatic in the league at the time. He also had a brilliant nickname, an exotic-sounding surname and was the first keeper to bring out his own gloves – all important factors in the school playground, where the Cat was the role model for countless aspiring young goalies.

In the battle of the destroyers, meanwhile, Ron Harris had a much larger public profile than Arsenal's hatchet man, midfielder Peter Storey. Again, the nickname issue was crucial – every football fan in the country knew who Chopper was and many enjoyed his no-nonsense approach to defending.

With the exception of Charlie George (who, in any case, was often on the bench), Arsenal's attack lacked a genuinely exciting superstar along the lines of an Osgood, Cooke or Hudson. The Gunners' two main strikers, John Radford and Ray Kennedy, were a pair of hard-working performers who complimented each other well and regularly appeared on the scoresheet, but they didn't set pulses racing in the way, say, that an extravagant Cooke dribble or outrageous Osgood dummy could. Of course, Arsenal's highly organised, well-drilled and effective team play couldn't be lightly dismissed but, as far as Blues fans were concerned, there was no question of envious glances being cast towards Highbury.

Moreover, there was a general feeling that Chelsea could build on their Cup triumphs, even perhaps finally emulating the heroes of 1955 by lifting the title. This, after all, was an era when the championship was extremely open, with six different clubs – Arsenal, Everton, Leeds, Manchester City, Manchester United and Liverpool – having won the title in the preceding six seasons. There was no reason at all, it seemed, why Chelsea, who had finished in sixth place the previous season, couldn't add a new name to that list. The talent was undoubtedly there; just a little more consistency and, possibly, application was required.

It was all the more disappointing for Chelsea fans, then, that the Blues got off to such a poor start to the 1971/72 season. A 3–0 defeat at Arsenal on the opening day was bad enough, but worse was to come four days later when the they lost 3–2 at home to Manchester United, who managed to claim the points despite having George Best sent off for swearing at a linesman just before half-time. Immediately after the game Dave Sexton dropped a bombshell by announcing that Peter Osgood was being placed on the transfer list for "lack of effort and doing less and less".

Asked by a reporter how much Chelsea wanted for their star striker, Sexton replied: "Although a firm figure has not been fixed, it will be something around £250,000. If anybody wants to pay that or exchange a player, that is okay. He has done great things for Chelsea and I should be sorry to see him go. I hope it does not come to that."

The fans reacted to this shock news with fury. Outside the Bridge the following day blue-scarfed demonstrators paraded with placards reading 'Ossie must stay', 'Don't leave Ossie' and 'Sexton must relent'. The campaign was successful: Sexton did relent and Osgood was taken off the transfer list. However, the whole episode suggested that the manager was altogether less enamoured of the England forward than were Osgood's adoring fans in the Shed. "It was completely out of the blue," recalled Peter Osgood. "I wasn't happy."

The fact that Ian Hutchinson, in his comeback game after a cartilage operation, had broken his leg in a reserve match at Swindon made it all the more surprising that Sexton was prepared to sell Osgood. If anything, Chelsea needed to buy a striker rather than sell one. Despite his apparent willingness to offload Osgood, Sexton knew that his attack required strengthening and was keen on Chris Garland, Bristol City's poodle-permed centre forward. The Robins, though, weren't prepared to sell their top asset for less than £100,000, a fee the Chelsea board were reluctant to meet unless they could raise some cash from elsewhere.

"I couldn't get any money from the board," Sexton said later, "so the only way of funding a deal was to sell somebody." But who? David Webb, for one, was dismayed when he discovered the identity of the player Sexton was prepared to sacrifice in order to bring Garland to Chelsea.

"Coming out of a League Cup game we'd won 2–0 against Plymouth at the Bridge, I bumped into Jimmy Bloomfield, the Leicester manager," he recalled. "He asked me if I'd seen Keith Weller. I answered in the affirmative and enquired if he wanted me to pass on his regards. When Bloomfield told me that Chelsea had agreed to sell Weller to City, I went numb. I couldn't believe it. Keith was a key player. He gave the team balance. To me, that was the beginning of the end. That made me stop believing in Chelsea as a force that was going onwards and upwards."

Sexton now maintains that selling Weller was "the biggest mistake I ever made", giving credence to Webb's view that the transfer was something of a turning point in the Blues' fortunes. "He was one of my signings and I liked him as a player," Sexton said a few years ago. "But then at the beginning of that season we'd got some injuries to our strikers. In came Chris Garland from Bristol City and out went Keith to Leicester. But I don't know what else I could have done: my hands were tied. I could hardly have come up with the money myself."

True, but maybe Sexton could have exerted more pressure on the board. Money *was* available for new players as, later that month, the £170,000 purchase of Steve Kember from Crystal Palace proved. On the other hand, Sexton had been tracking Kember for some time so it's possible the board gave him a stark choice: Kember or Garland, but not both without funds being raised through a sale.

An industrious midfielder with three England Under-23 caps to his name, Kember was initially reluctant to leave the club he had supported as a boy. Perhaps, though, he felt he would be safer playing for the Blues rather than against them.

"We played Chelsea in the FA Cup when I was still at Palace in 1971," he recalls. "I went to close Ron Harris down and as he cleared the ball he's gone bosh and he's done me, shattered all my teeth. One tooth came out completely and the other split in two. So they put a peg in and attached the other tooth to it and they were alright. Then playing for Chelsea against Leeds, I went round Paul Madeley one side and Ossie went round him the other. As I've gone to tackle Madeley, Ossie accidentally kicked me in the face and knocked my teeth out again."

The unfortunate Kember was also in the wars on his Chelsea debut, away to Sheffield United. "After about 10 minutes of play, United were awarded a free-kick," he says. "Geoff Salmons, who used to be able to smash a ball in those days, whacked the ball straight into my face. I was seeing double for the rest of the game. I suppose I should have come off but it was my debut and I had this thing in the back of my mind that I had to stay on."

The game at Bramall Lane ended in a 1–0 defeat for the Blues, leaving them with a dismal record of just two wins in their first ten league games. With a championship challenge appearing distinctly unlikely, the season would depend yet again on Chelsea's performances in the cups.

Since winning the trophy in 1965, the League Cup had become a depressing black hole for Chelsea. Not once had the Blues got past the fourth round and on three occasions they had been dumped out of the competition by lower league opposition. A run in the League Cup was very much overdue, especially as the competition now boasted a prestigious Wembley final and a passage to the UEFA Cup for the winners. Having disposed of Plymouth comfortably enough, Chelsea were drawn away to Nottingham Forest. In a tempestuous 1–1 draw at The City Ground, Chris

Garland was clattered by Forest defender Barry Lyons and limped off. Lyons didn't know it, but he would very soon be following Garland into the treatment room.

"Chris got done by a bad tackle and there was a big ruck," recalled Peter Osgood. "Suddenly, I felt a tap on my shoulder, so I turned round and it was Ron Harris. He was squinting because the game was under floodlights and Ron's eyesight wasn't good at the best of times. 'Who was it, Os, what number?' he whispered. I told him, 'Number six' and ten minutes later Forest's number six was carried off on a stretcher."

Maybe Chopper was in a generous mood, though, because Lyons was back for the replay a week later – unlike Garland, who was out of action for over a month. Chelsea won the game 2–1, thanks to goals by Baldwin and Osgood, setting up a fourth round tie with Bolton Wanderers, then chasing promotion from the old Third Division.

As he always did in the League Cup, Sexton fielded a strong side against the Trotters. Weak line-ups had never been a factor in the Blues' early exits from the competition and unfamiliar faces could not be blamed for the disappointing 1–1 draw with Bolton, either. Chelsea simply weren't playing well.

By the time of the replay at Burnden Park in early November, confidence in the Blues' camp had been dealt a further shattering blow by their unexpected failure to overcome Swedish part-timers Atvidaberg in the European Cup Winners Cup. Sensing another upset, the press pack headed north to Lancashire with sharpened pencils. The journos didn't get the story they wanted: instead, the back page headlines heaped praise on the Blues as they crushed Bolton 6–0, Tommy Baldwin claiming a hat-trick.

The result seemed to kick-start Chelsea's season. A Peter Osgood goal was enough to clinch victory at Norwich in the fifth round and by the time the Blues lined up at the Bridge for the first leg of the semi-final against Tottenham, the holders of the League Cup, they were undefeated in 14 matches in all competitions.

Despite being played just three days before Christmas, the match against Spurs attracted Chelsea's largest ever crowd for a home League Cup tie, 43,330. The fans were rewarded with a breathtaking London derby, which had more twists and turns than a John Le Carré novel. Osgood's cleverly angled shot gave Chelsea a first-half lead, but two quick-fire second half goals by Terry Naylor and Martin Chivers appeared to have changed the course of the match. Almost immediately, though, Garland levelled with a header from Houseman's corner and then, with just five minutes left, Naylor handled in the box. Hollins blasted the penalty high past Pat Jennings at the Shed end to give Chelsea a slender first-leg lead.

Two weeks later the teams met again at White Hart Lane in front of another enormous crowd. Chivers gave Tottenham the lead with a powerful volley just before half-time, but an equally thunderous shot from Garland deservedly restored Chelsea's aggregate advantage in the second half. With the clock ticking down, Spurs increased the pressure on the Blues' goal in a desperate bid to force extra-time. Like Chelsea, Tottenham had their own long throw expert, centre forward Martin Chivers, and his airborne missiles were causing panic in the Blues' defence.

"Chivers threw the ball in, it came off the ground and hit me on the chest and the upper arm," recalls Alan Hudson. "With the pitch being muddy the ball made a mark on my chest which I tried to show the referee, but he wasn't interested. He gave Spurs a penalty and Martin Peters scored. I was thinking, 'Oh dear, I thought we'd be at Wembley in ten minutes' time'. But with just a minute left we got a free-kick on the left-hand side near the corner flag. Johnny Hollins went after the ball to take it but I got in front of him and pushed him aside. I could see all our big lads running forward and I thought, 'Don't put it in the air, that's what they're expecting.' So I drove it in low instead. It worked. Big Pat Jennings missed it at the near post and it went through Cyril Knowles' legs and bobbled into the far corner. For me, it was a massive relief because I'd given the penalty away a few minutes earlier. Now, I'd got us the goal to take us to a major final. Looking back, I'd say that was my most important goal for Chelsea."

Hudson's slightly fortunate goal, which gave Chelsea a 5–4 aggregate victory over two tumultuous games, sent the Blues fans in the 52,755 crowd into raptures. The players were in celebratory mood, too, and – decent restaurants being thin on the ground around White Hart Lane – headed back en masse to their King's Road 'manor' for something to eat and drink.

"A group of about five of us had a meal in Alexander's," remembers Huddy. "There was me, Ossie, Chris Garland – who'd played terrifically in the two games against Spurs and had scored a great goal at White Hart Lane – and a couple of others. We had some champagne – in fact, we pretty much drank everything that night – and we were laughing and joking all evening; we were in great spirits because one thing is winning, another thing is winning and playing the way we had played that night. We were brilliant, we really played some fantastic football. And it wasn't just me who thought so. I went back to Alexander's the next day for lunch and Terry Venables was there. We sat down and had a chat and Venables said to me, 'I was there last night and that was the best performance I've ever seen from a Chelsea team'."

The Chelsea party finally left Alexander's in the early hours of the morning. Intoxicated by the heady mix of post-victory euphoria and copious amounts of champers, Ossie, Huddy and co couldn't resist breaking into song. "All we were singing was 'We're on our way to Wembley' and 'we shall not be moved' on our way to our cars," said Peter Osgood.

"Suddenly, the Old Bill turned up out of nowhere. There were loads of them, three or four vans. At first I thought there must have been a shooting or something, but they came over to us. 'Have you been drinking?' they asked. I said, 'Yes, we've just got through to the League Cup Final and we've been celebrating.

We've just been singing a Chelsea song, that's all, we're not upsetting anybody.'

"One of the policemen said, 'Well, there have been complaints. Get in your car and drive off.' My mate Danny Gillen, a big lad who became Phil Collins' minder, heard this and said, 'That's exactly what you want him to do because you'll nick him for drink-driving.' All of a sudden he was having a ruck with the copper and, when I went over to calm the situation, a policeman put my arm up behind my back and said, 'You're nicked as well, Osgood!' They took us in the meat wagon down to the police station and locked us in the cells. Then, around four o'clock in the morning, a policeman came in and said, 'Hoppit, here are you car keys.'

"When I got to Magistrates' court the next day my brief asked the copper what happened.

'Well,' he said, 'Osgood had to be restrained, and he staggered when he got into the Black Maria'.

So my brief asked him, 'Was he drunk?'

'Oh, yes. He was drunk,' the copper replied.

'And what time was this?'

'About half past one.'

'And what time did you give him back his car keys?'

'Four o'clock.'

'So, you gave a drunk man his car keys back did you?'

The magistrate listened to this exchange and banged his hammer – case dismissed. He just threw the case out. My brief did a brilliant job. I thought he was on their side to begin with, but he just led the copper right into it."

A good day for British justice then and, more importantly, for Ossie, who was now free to concentrate on the build-up to the final with the rest of the team. As now, the League Cup was very much secondary to the FA Cup but, since all Football League clubs had become obliged to enter and a Wembley final had replaced the old two-legged format in 1967, the competition had been growing in stature. Reaching the final was definitely a big deal, and the Blues decided to mark their achievement by cutting a record.

In the early seventies football records were still something of a novelty and, to the music critics' exasperation, occasionally struck a chord with the record-buying public. In 1970, for instance, the England World Cup squad had topped the charts with *Back Home* prior to heading off to Mexico to defend the Jules Rimet trophy. Then, the following year, Arsenal reached Number 16 with their FA Cup Final record, *Good Old Arsenal*, an uninspiring dirge set to the tune of *Rule Britannia* and with lyrics by football pundit Jimmy Hill.

Wisely, Chelsea preferred to commission a couple of professional songwriters, Peter Lee Stirling and Daniel Boone, and they came up with a jaunty little number called *Blue is the Colour*. The idea, as with all football records before and since, was that the players would sing the song themselves. Meanwhile, the Larry Page Orchestra, who specialised in instrumental versions of pop songs and had recently released an album of Kinks covers entitled *Kinky Music*, were signed up to provide the backing music.

"We recorded it at a studio in Islington," remembers Tommy Baldwin. "We knocked it out first or second go and we did an LP at the same time. In the morning we took about 10 cases of lager in and a couple of cases of vodka and by the evening we were pretty drunk. But it came out okay. A lot of the lads did a solo vocal for the album tracks – I remember Ossie did a version of *Chirpy Chirpy Cheep Cheep* – but I just stayed in the chorus. After the amount of vodka I'd drunk that was all I could manage."

The album, perhaps inevitably, quickly found its way into the remainder section but the single did well, rising to number five in the charts. "*Blue is the Colour* was a very catchy tune but I was still surprised it sold so well," says John Dempsey. "It wasn't just Chelsea fans who were buying it, obviously." With the Blues rubbing shoulders in the top five alongside the likes of T Rex's

Telegram Sam, Nilsson's *Without You* and Chicory Tip's *Son of My Father* the call went out for the squad to appear on *Top of the Pops*.

"When we turned up at the studio at BBC Television centre at White City we were all wearing our ordinary clothes – leather jackets and whatever – and the producer wasn't very impressed," recalls Dempsey. "He said we didn't look like a proper group so somebody had to rush out to Marks and Spencers and come back with 14 identical jumpers. I can't remember what colour they were, they may have been blue. There was a fan with us, a friend of Ian Hutchinson, and for a laugh we sneaked him into the group at the back. People watching at home must have wondered who he was.

"We had a rehearsal which went okay and then we went on stage. Gilbert O'Sullivan was on the other stage and the Sweet were also on that night. It went fine, they were a bit worried we wouldn't remember the words so off screen above the stage they had huge boards with the lyrics on them; I didn't really need them as the words were fairly easy to remember."

John Boyle, though, has a different memory of the event, in which the rehearsal went far from 'okay'. "When we got there, a guy told us to sing along to the music – but we made an awful racket, just terrible," he says. "So, Eddie McCreadie said to him, 'Look, do you want a good song? Well, what we need are four bottles of vodka and a couple of crates of lager – then come back later on." So we went back on stage quite a bit later, and suddenly it was like having 16 Frank Sinatras!"

"We were outrageous," adds Alan Hudson. "We were running amok in the BBC studios. We had a lot of beer in our dressing room and we'd been drinking all day by the time we got on. We ended up down at Alexander's that night, and three of the boys had a trio of Pan's People with them. Dee Dee Wilde was with Tommy Baldwin, and a couple of others were there. I think it was someone like John Phillips or Hutch who got lucky."

Despite its crossover appeal and 12–week stay in the charts, *Blue is the Colour* didn't make the players rich. They each made around £300 from the record, the rough equivalent then of a couple of weeks' wages before bonuses. More importantly, though, the song – like *The Liquidator* – was to become an essential and much-loved part of the pre-match build up at Stamford Bridge. Even today, *Blue is the Colour* still gets the crowd going at the Bridge, although it has to be said most fans would benefit from a short refresher course in the lyrics.

Blue is the Colour's climb up the charts mirrored Chelsea's increasingly good form as the League Cup Final with Stoke City approached. Two weeks before Wembley, on February 19th, Dave Sexton was presented with a gallon of Bell's whisky on the Stamford Bridge pitch after being voted Manager of the Month for January. Later that afternoon he saw two goals from Peter Osgood help the Blues to a 2–1 victory over Leicester, a result that extended their impressive recent record to one defeat in 24 games.

Two of those games had come in the FA Cup. In the third round Chelsea had won 1–0 at Blackpool, thanks to a John Dempsey header, and in the fourth round Bolton were seen off with the minimum of fuss; Hollins, Cooke and Houseman netting in a 3–0 victory at the Bridge. A fifth round draw away to Second Division Orient appeared far from daunting and only increased the feeling that the in-form Blues could make a return trip to Wembley later in the season.

On paper, Orient had few players to worry Chelsea. Ian Bowyer, a busy midfielder who would go on to win the league and European Cup with Nottingham Forest, was their most accomplished performer, but otherwise the O's, – who also had future Blues flop Dennis Rofe at left-back – were almost entirely made up of unknown journeymen. At first, the gap in class looked more like a chasm as Chelsea strolled into a two–goal lead through Webb and Osgood. But with a minute left of the first half the course of the match, Chelsea's season and, some might argue, the Blues' future over the next few years was changed by a single dramatic moment.

"We were cruising at Orient and then they scored right before half-time," remembers Alan Hudson. "I was standing near their centre half Phil Hoadley when he shot, he hit this ball from at least 35 yards and it kind of bobbled up just right for him. On another day it would have gone miles wide but this thing flew in the net."

Worse was to follow three minutes into the second half when indecision in the Chelsea defence allowed Micky Bullock to equalise. As the game neared the end with the scores level, a replay at the Bridge – which, surely, would be a formality for the home side – looked on the cards. But, in the 89th minute, bearded Orient striker Barrie Fairbrother took advantage of some more sloppy Blues play – "a horrendous defensive balls up by us", is Alan Hudson's description – to score the winner.

The mood in the Chelsea camp after the defeat was one of complete deflation, mixed with anger at the basic errors which had cost them the match. "It's disgraceful – leading 2–0 then losing 3–2 to a team like that," Blues full back Paddy Mulligan said afterwards. "If I were running a schoolboy team and they allowed the same thing to happen, I would really murder them." What was all the more galling was that the defence had been playing so well up to the Orient game, conceding just that one goal to Leicester in the previous five matches.

Still, at least there was the League Cup Final to look forward to the following Saturday. Stoke, Chelsea's opponents, were a lower mid-table First Division side who relied heavily on a core of veteran players, including England goalkeeper Gordon Banks, pipe-smoking captain Peter Dobing and former Arsenal and Newcastle star George Eastham. The game with Chelsea would be the Potters' first ever visit to Wembley and they had got there the hard way, needing two replays to get past West Ham in the semi-final.

In the hour before the Final kicked off the 100,000 crowd was entertained by the band of the Royal Artillery and the final of ITV's *On the Ball* Penalty Prize competition, hosted by – who else? – Jimmy Hill. The teams then emerged from the tunnel to a thunderous reception to be presented to the guest of honour, UEFA President Gustav Wiederkehr.

In selecting his team, Dave Sexton had ignored the Brisbane Road debacle and made just one enforced change from the previous week, Chris Garland replacing the cup-tied Steve Kember. Sexton named Tommy Baldwin as substitute, even though the forward had only just returned from an unauthorised holiday in Spain.

"I went AWOL after being dropped so often and I disappeared off to Benidorm," says the Sponge. "But I came back the week before we got beat by Orient in the FA Cup and Dave asked me to come in for training in the week before the final. He fined me again – I think it went up to about £50 that time – and then said I'd be sub."

Baldwin came on for the injured Paddy Mulligan at half-time, with Peter Houseman retreating to left-back. By that time, the score was 1–1, Peter Osgood having cancelled out Terry Conroy's early header. The Blues' goal was an unusual one: lying on the ground after challenging for Cooke's cross, Osgood reacted instantly when the ball rebounded to him and, despite being surrounded by Stoke defenders, hooked his shot past Banks from near the penalty spot. It was an audacious finish, and one a less quick-witted player would probably not even have attempted.

The stage looked set, then, for the Blues to go on and claim a third different cup in three seasons but, to the joy of their fans and most neutrals, it was Stoke who lifted their first ever trophy thanks to a late goal by the oldest of their old stagers, 35-year-old George Eastham.

"Had we won the game against Orient we'd have been flying but I think the defeat had a knock-on effect; we were feeling a little bit flat," says Alan Hudson. "Another factor was that Dave Sexton didn't learn his lesson from the 1970 Final and he played Webby at right back. Terry Conroy tore him apart and Stoke's winning goal came from the left wing. Conroy took it up to Webby, he dived in again and Conroy went by him. He crossed it to John Ritchie, who headed down, Jimmy Greenhoff smashed it and George Eastham knocked in the rebound."

Sexton himself, though, looked for scapegoats elsewhere, notably Ron Harris who was replaced as captain, first by John Hollins then, at the start of the following season, by Eddie McCreadie. Publicly, however, the Chelsea boss remained upbeat, saying afterwards, "Our season is by no means over – there is still much to play for. We have bounced back before. We shall do so again."

Indeed, for a while, the Blues performed a passable imitation of a yo-yo, winning five straight games at the end of March and the beginning of April to give themselves a decent chance of a UEFA Cup place. This sequence was remarkable for a four-goal burst from David Webb in two of the victories, while Sexton employed the defender as a makeshift striker during an injury crisis.

Yet Webb's success as a striker was nothing compared to his most unlikely alter ego as an emergency goalkeeper. Earlier in the season, a few days before the first leg of the League Cup semi-final, Webb had replaced the injured Peter Bonetti in goal after 30 minutes of the Blues' match at Coventry. In those days there were no substitute goalkeepers, so Webb's hour between the sticks – during which he conceded just one goal in a 1–1 draw – was not, in itself, particularly unusual.

Ten days later, though, and it was a different story altogether. "Peter was still out injured," recalls Webby. "Then John Phillips had stayed overnight at John Hollins' house and as he got out of bed in the morning he slipped a disc. The club had already allowed Steve Sherwood to go home to Yorkshire. So they sent a police escort to get him back. In the meantime, we submitted two team sheets, one with Steve Sherwood in goal and another one with me in the net. The referee said he'd give it till quarter to three. Steve Sherwood came running through the door at ten to three, but the ref wouldn't budge."

To the amazement of the crowd, Chelsea took to the field with Webb in the goalkeeper's kit. Ever the showman, the Blues' new custodian knelt down in his penalty area in front of the Shed and pretended to pray. Who knows, maybe he really did appeal for divine intervention. He would certainly need all the help he could get. Not only were Ipswich a useful mid-table team, they also came to the Bridge fired by a sense of injustice from the corresponding fixture the previous season when an Alan Hudson shot which had struck the outside of a stanchion had been incorrectly given as a goal.

John Dempsey, for one, didn't have a great deal of confidence in Webb's goalkeeping abilities. "It was brave of him to volunteer to go in goal but I looked at him and thought, 'Blimey, we could let in five or six today.' Surprisingly, though, he had very little to do. If I'd been Bobby Robson, who was the manager of Ipswich then, I'd have told my players to test him out from all over the pitch but they hardly had a shot. It was nerve-wracking but we got through it without conceding a goal."

"Webb has played so many roles that he has become the Alec Guinness of Stamford Bridge," wrote Laurie Pignon in *The Daily Mail* after the Blues' 2–0 victory. At the end of the season the versatile Webb was voted the club's 'Player of the Year', although nobody was quite sure whether he'd won the award for his resolute defending, his goal-poaching striker's instincts or, indeed, his eye-catching stint as a stand-in keeper. Probably, the recognition was for his whole-hearted approach to whichever role he was asked to perform.

"Webby was 150 per cent every time," said Peter Osgood. "I remember playing against Blackpool once. We were 3–0 down with 20 minutes to go and, all of a sudden, this ball's come over and – boom! – Webby's knocked it in. I said, 'What are you doing up here?' He said, 'Fuck tactics, I'm staying up here with you' and it worked, we won 4–3! The nice thing about Webby was that he'd go for everything. If there was a 60:40 ball in their favour he'd make it 50:50, and he'd get the knock downs so for me it was perfect when he went up front. Like Hutch, he'd play the battering ram role."

Webb was equally committed off the pitch, putting his surplus energies into a variety of business interests. These included, at various times, a wig shop, a Sunday league kit-cleaning scheme and a car lot. "Webby was a romancer," said Ossie. "He used to come in to training and we'd say, 'What have you bought today?' Some of the business interests he had in his playing days weren't so successful but they've put him in good stead for later on. He's done some good deals and he's become a millionaire."

A poor run of just one win in their last six games meant the Blues finished the 1971/72 season in seventh position, a couple of places short of a UEFA Cup slot. Overall, despite the excitement generated by the League Cup run, it had been a disappointing season. The expected title challenge had not materialised, neither of the two expensive new signings, Chris Garland and Steve Kember, had made a great impact and, more worryingly, there were signs of discontent among the established players.

Osgood was still unhappy about being transfer-listed at the start of the season. Alan Hudson, too, was upset after being reposi-tioned from the centre to the right side of midfield to make way for Sexton's new signing, Steve Kember. "That's when it all started to go wrong. That was the writing on the wall. I didn't mind going out wide now and again, but I didn't like being stuck out there. You're only going to get the ball when other people give it to you. If you play in the middle, you can go and get it for yourself. It makes you a better player, because you're always involved. Playing me on the right wing was like asking a marathon runner to become a sprinter, really. It just wasn't me. It wasn't that I was being selfish or anything like that – I thought I wasn't helping the team. Sexton was getting me to play wing back, effectively – to track back and pick up a full back, and then get forward to join in the play."

Another malcontent was Tommy Baldwin, who was becoming increasingly fed up with being left off the team sheet. "Dave played me all the time to start with but later he decided he didn't like my lifestyle and I was often left out," he says. "He played me in the finals, though. Dave was completely different to Tommy Docherty. Much quieter, he was the sort of manager who wanted to organise your lifestyle. He wanted everyone to be an upright citizen, non-smoking, no dirty women sort of guy. Be regular and improve every day on the football pitch. He was fighting a losing battle with that team, though."

For the time being, however, the players' grumblings were only a minor blot on the Bridge landscape. Overall, there was an optimistic mood about the place, no more so than on 5th June 1972 when chairman Brian Mears announced plans for the total redevelopment of the ground, a project which had first been discussed three years earlier.

Mears' vision, he told journalists at a press conference, was to create a new 60,000 capacity stadium, costing around £5.5 million, by the end of the seventies. The first stage of the redevelopment would see a massive three-tier, 12,000 capacity stand built in place of the existing 5,000 capacity East Stand. Once completed, the stand would be the largest in Britain. Quite possibly, the warmest, too, as the design by architects Darbourne and Darke provided an option to pipe hot air through small holes underneath each seat. Other elements in the grandiose scheme included 156 private viewing boxes, bars, restaurants, new offices and leisure facilities. "We will make the home of Chelsea FC second to none in Europe," predicted Mears. "And Dave Sexton will still have all the money he needs to buy new players."

Coming a year after Mears had, apparently, ended speculation about Chelsea's future at the Bridge by announcing the purchase of the ground freehold from the JT Mears estate for £475,000, this latest news seemed to indicate a bright future for the club.

Press reaction was overwhelmingly positive. "It is a breathtaking venture," wrote Danny Blanchflower in *The Sunday Express*. "Brian Mears, you have given Chelsea fans a cause to be proud of. We hope you make it and that we are around at the end of the seventies to help you celebrate the big opening." J.L. Manning in the *Evening Standard* was equally enthusiastic: "Not in my lifetime has a British football club set out to rebuild itself completely. For 70 years there has been sporadic patching up, but nothing to compare with what Chelsea have decided to do."

In the short term, however, the redevelopment of the East Stand was an inconvenience for players and supporters. As bulldozers and wrecking balls piled into the old stand with the force of a Chopper Harris tackle it was, quite literally, a case of having the builders in for the whole season. The home and away dressing rooms had been located in the East Stand; with these no longer operational, the players would have to change in temporary Portakabins which were more Sunday League than First Division. There was change, too, on the North Terrace as the 1,000-capacity North Stand – that bizarre-looking structure on wooden stilts which loomed over the away fans – was demolished following reports that it had rocked alarmingly during a recent match.

For the first game of the 1972/73 season against Leeds, 51,000 fans packed into the three remaining stands while another 9,000 were locked out. The crush was so great hundreds of youngsters spilled over from the terraces and watched the game cross-legged on the grass behind the greyhound track. Leeds, FA Cup winners and runners-up in the league the previous season, and now sporting numbered tags on their socks, promised to be stiff opposition. Yet, thanks in part to an injury to David Harvey which forced Peter Lorimer to go in goal, the Blues thumped their deadly rivals 4–0. The second goal was probably the best: Cooke collecting Hudson's superb defence-splitting long pass and angling a left-foot shot past Leeds' stand-in keeper at the Shed end. Few Blues fans could have imagined a better start to the campaign, although the hyper-critical Brian Glanville remained under-whelmed in *The Sunday Times*. "The immense skill in the [Chelsea] team still does not yet find full expression, while tactically we saw nothing new from either side," he complained.

The news was not all good, though. Eight supporters had been taken to hospital after a crash-barrier had collapsed under the weight of the crowd. As a result, the Stamford Bridge capacity was cut by around 30% to 36,000 for the remainder of the season. A series of pitch invasions by jubilant fans during the Leeds game also led to the club becoming the first in Britain to erect wire fences behind both goals.

As it turned out, there wasn't a great deal for the fans to get excited about after that opening day win as the gaping hole where the East Stand once stood seemed to drain both players and fans of their energies. "There was a morbid atmosphere and it became like two cemeteries in one," says Alan Hudson, referring to the now visible expanse of Brompton Cemetery beyond the cranes and digging machines.

"Without the East Stand there was an eerie feeling about the place," agrees John Dempsey. "Instead of dug-outs on the side of the pitch, there were benches which was very odd. It wasn't the best atmosphere and teams were no longer intimidated about coming to the Bridge."

One fan went further, describing the home support as "a disgrace" in a letter to 'In Off The Post', the programme's letters column. "It's no wonder visiting sides settle in so quickly; they feel as much at home as our lads," wrote Mrs Elaine Walker from Surrey. "Is any other team greeted with such apathy? It's not surprising Chelsea play so well away from home."

In fact, Chelsea's away form wasn't any better, either, and the Blues' final position of 12th was their lowest since they were promoted back to the First Division a decade earlier. Yet again, the fans looked to the cups for some cheer and, for a while at least, another Wembley appearance seemed possible.

In the League Cup, the Blues saw off Southend, Derby, Bury and Notts County on their way to a semi-final with newly-promoted Norwich City. Chelsea, hot favourites to reach the final against Tottenham or Wolves, appeared to have warmed up in the best possible way for the tie when, just four days before the first leg, they crushed the Canaries 3–1 at the Bridge. This game was notable for two goals by Shed hero Ian Hutchinson, in his come-back match after almost two years' absence through injury. This, though, was very much a case of a dress rehearsal being more successful than the first night as, back at the Bridge, Norwich surprisingly won 2–0 in the first leg of the semi. A week later in the return leg at Carrow Road, Norwich led 3–2 on the night when a thick East Anglian mist descended on the stadium, making visibility virtually impossible for players, fans and the referee.

"With six minutes to go one of the Norwich players was running through the centre of the pitch and Eddie McCreadie just punched him," recalls John Phillips. "The referee, Gordon Hill, came running up to see the City player lying on the floor. The fog had obscured his view and he asked what had happened. When the Norwich guy told him he'd been hit, Gordon Hill just said, 'I've had enough of this', and called the match off." The reprieve was short-lived as Norwich won the rescheduled game 1–0 to go through to the final against Tottenham.

Chelsea enjoyed no better luck in the FA Cup. After knocking out Brighton, Ipswich and Sheffield Wednesday the Blues met Double-chasing Arsenal in a sell-out London derby at the Bridge in the quarter-final. The match finished 2–2 with all the goals, including a stunning 20-yard left-foot Osgood volley which went on to win BBC's 'Goal of the Season' competition, coming in the first half. "We should have beaten them," says Steve Kember. "For one of their goals 'Sticks', John Phillips, dived past the post to make a save. The ball wasn't going in but he somehow pushed it into the back of the net."

Three days later a crowd of nearly 63,000 poured into Highbury for the replay, with an estimated 10,000 locked outside. London pride as well as Cup glory was at stake – just as it had been in the Chelsea-Tottenham League Cup clashes the previous year – and for fans of both teams this was the 'must see' game of the season. With Second Division Sunderland lined up as semi-final opponents whichever side emerged victorious on a mild spring evening would be firm favourites to reach Wembley.

Playing some of their best football of the campaign, Chelsea took the lead when John Hollins crossed for Peter Houseman to score with a rare header. The Blues were still on top when, right on half-time, Arsenal were awarded a controversial penalty after Steve Kember brought down George Armstrong.

"It was just inside the box," admits Steve. "What annoyed me about it was that I'd chased George Armstrong all the way back from their 18-yard box. I was convinced I'd made the tackle but at the last moment he toed the ball on and I caught him. It wasn't intentional. The ref gave it outside. Then Frank McLintock and Alan Ball virtually manhandled him over to the lino and the lino said it was inside."

Ball scored from the spot and, in the second half, Ray Kennedy hit the winner for the Gunners. The only consolation for Blues fans was that Arsenal surprisingly lost to Sunderland in the semi-final.

In terms of playing staff, Sexton had stayed broadly loyal to his double Cup winners throughout the 1972/73 season. The one exception was Charlie Cooke who, to the disappointment of his many fans on the Shed, was sold in a job-lot with Paddy Mulligan to Crystal Palace in September 1972. New faces, meanwhile, included Bill Garner, a powerful centre forward whose heading ability had impressed when the Blues met his previous club, Southend, in the League Cup; Gary Locke, an athletic, pacy right-back who had come through the youth system; and Ian

Britton, a tiny, Scottish terrier of a midfielder who had a run in the side in the second half of the season. The fresh faces were welcome as a number of the established players were starting to look stale, jaded and unmotivated. In his autobiography Alan Hudson admits, "I stopped caring around then", and he was far from alone in appearing a listless shadow of his former self.

Chelsea were beginning to look like a side in transition. But transition to what? A dismal run of three league wins in 25 games between late October and April clearly suggested that the road ahead could be rocky. Three straight home victories at the very end of the season, including one over Manchester United in Bobby Charlton's last match for the Reds, raised spirits slightly but by then the fans had voted with their feet. Attendances at the Bridge had dropped to below 20,000 for some run-of-the-mill fixtures, although more than 40,000 crammed in for Charlton's emotional farewell.

For the bean-counters at the club, declining gates had come at the worst possible time. Building costs for the new East Stand were increasing by the day thanks to roaring inflation and the 1973 oil crisis. Meanwhile, pay strikes on the site and the Conservative government's imposition of a national three-day working week to conserve fuel usage had combined to put the scheduled completion date of the stand back a full year, to the summer of 1974.

You didn't need to be a latter-day Nostradamus to sense that storm clouds were forming above the Bridge. Very soon those clouds would open with drastic consequences.

CHAPTER FOURTEEN
END OF THE DREAM

Chelsea went into the 1973/74 season, a campaign which was to be remembered as one of the most troubled in the club's history, in reasonable shape. Two pre-season tours, the first to Germany and Holland and the second to Spain, had proved successful exercises, with the Blues emerging unbeaten from five matches against tough local opposition, including Werder Bremen and Celta Vigo. Even the fact that three Chelsea players – Peter Osgood, Eddie McCreadie and Steve Kember – had been sent off in two matches in Spain was open to a positive interpretation, suggesting that the trio's competitive instincts were well and truly intact.

For the first game of the season away to Derby County, Dave Sexton was able to call on eight of the players who had won the FA Cup three years earlier. The exceptions were Charlie Cooke, who was no longer at the club; John Dempsey, who was to miss the whole season with Achilles tendon and ankle injuries; and Tommy Baldwin, who, once again, had not been selected. Steve Kember, Chris Garland and John Boyle, playing his last ever game for Chelsea before moving to Orient via a loan spell at Brighton, took their places. Alan Hudson, annoyed at being played on the right of midfield, had seen his pre-season request for a transfer turned down by Dave Sexton and was relegated to the substitute's bench.

The trip to the Baseball Ground did not turn out to be a happy one. Chelsea lost the match 1–0, while clashes between rival groups of fans on the pitch resulted in eight arrests. Following further defeats at newly-promoted Burnley and at home to Sheffield United, the Blues found themselves planted firmly at the bottom of the First Division after three games.

The pre-season optimism had already evaporated before August was out. In the summer, inspired by the 'Magical Magyars' who had thrashed England at Wembley in 1953, Dave Sexton had requested a new change kit in Hungary's colours of red, white and green. The team looked great, but their performances on the road remained largely disappointing.

The picture appeared a little rosier by mid-December when, after better results in the late autumn, the Blues had risen to the heady heights of 13th. The chief factor in the steady improvement was the rich goalscoring vein struck by Peter Osgood, now back in the England squad after a gap of three years, and the recalled Tommy Baldwin – 17 goals between them in 14 matches. If the duo could keep up that sort of return maybe something could be salvaged from the season after all.

In the event, they weren't given much chance to add to their combined tally. Shortly before Christmas 1974, Chelsea's revival came to a shuddering halt as they lost 2–1 at the Bridge to unbeaten leaders Leeds and 2–0 away to Wolves the following week. Still, a Boxing Day encounter at home to struggling West Ham looked to be the ideal fixture to launch another good run.

"The West Ham game was the catalyst of everything that happened next," says Alan Hudson. "I scored a goal and we were 2–0 up at half-time. We were all over them, it should have been a few a more. Then, all of a sudden, they seemed to score every time they attacked in the second half. It wasn't as though they outplayed us. There was no build up to their goals. They came from goal kicks from their keeper and mess ups by our centre halves, that sort of thing." Nonetheless, the 4–2 final score to the Hammers – for whom Frank Lampard (senior) got the all-important first goal – represented a stunning turnaround and left Dave Sexton fuming.

"We came in after the game and Dave gave me and Peter Osgood hell," continues Huddy. "We had a meeting the next day and Dave said, 'It's you two, you're letting down the team.' It was an unbelievable thing to say, but I think it had been boiling up inside him." Hudson had good reason to be bewildered by Sexton's outburst as he had been Chelsea's best player against West Ham, setting up the Blues' first goal with a pass to Ian Britton, then scoring a superb second himself after beating three defenders.

Sexton's scathing criticism of Osgood, meanwhile, was nothing new. Earlier in the season, after a League Cup defeat at Stoke, the Blues' boss had blamed his star striker for the loss. The row which ensued ended with Osgood swearing at Sexton and storming off to a Stoke nightclub. Yet, despite these run ins, Sexton was seriously considering making Osgood the new Chelsea captain.

"Dave came to see me and said, 'How do you fancy being captain?' said Ossie. "I told him I'd think about it, although I wasn't that keen on the idea because Chopper was our skipper." In fact, at the time John Hollins was wearing the armband, having taken over the captaincy from Eddie McCreadie in September.

Three days after the West Ham debacle Chelsea lost for the fourth consecutive game, going down 1–0 at home to second-placed Liverpool. The result saw the Blues drop to 18th in the league table, just two places clear of the relegation zone. Losing to the high-flying Scousers was no disgrace in itself, but for Sexton it was the last straw. For the next match, away to Sheffield United on New Year's Day, he decided to drop four senior players: Peter Bonetti, Peter Osgood, Alan Hudson and Tommy Baldwin, although the Sponge did make the bench. "I have no comment to make on why they were dropped," Sexton told the press, "but they are all fit."

The dropped players were stunned by Sexton's shake up of the team. "Dave called me in on the Monday morning after the Liverpool game," remembered Ossie. "He said, 'There are going to be some changes for the next game: I'm dropping you, Alan Hudson and Peter Bonetti.' So I went from being captain to being dropped!"

Tommy Baldwin was equally surprised to find himself out of the team. "I was on a great run," he says. "I'd scored something like nine goals in eleven games and Dave Sexton was praising the fuck out of me. 'Look at Tommy,' he'd say, 'that's the effort I want to see from all of you.' Then suddenly he decided to drop me. I couldn't believe it. 'I've dropped Ossie, so I've got to drop you as well,' he said. Huddy and Peter Bonetti were out of the team as well. I was so pissed off I just hopped on a plane to Benidorm, where I had a place I shared with John Boyle just outside Alicante. When I got back I went on loan to Millwall and Manchester United and that was me pretty much finished at Chelsea."

By the time the Sponge returned from his impromptu holiday on the Costa Blanca he found a club in full-scale crisis. Peter Bonetti, obviously, wasn't happy about being replaced by John Phillips but had accepted his demotion in a professional manner. However, Sexton's decision to drop both Osgood and Hudson at the same time had brought the simmering tensions between the manager and his two star players to a head. The row that ensued would have far-reaching consequences for the club and the individuals concerned and, even now, remains one of the most controversial episodes in Chelsea history. As you might expect, the three protagonists have slightly different versions of events.

"Sexton said, 'You two won't be playing on Tuesday against Sheffield United,'" recalls Hudson, "The following day we came out for training and we were knocking balls about before the session on the reserves' side of the ground. Dario Gradi, the reserve team manager, asked us what we were doing and we said, 'Well, we're going to play in the reserves tomorrow so we're training with you.' He got the raving hump with us, and then Dave sent someone across to get us. We were walking over there and Dave left the group of players and came over to us, saying, 'What's it all about?' How Dave and Osgood never had a fight I don't know. It ended up with Ossie saying, 'Fuck this, if you don't want us you can get rid of me, I can't go on like this!' and Dave said, 'Well, I will get rid of you!' I said, 'Well, what's good enough for him is good enough for me.'"

Peter Osgood had a similar recollection of the training ground bust up, although he maintained that Hudson rather than himself asked for a transfer initially. This was an important distinction as, under FA rules, only players who had not asked for a move were entitled to five per cent of the transfer fee when they eventually switched clubs. Dave Sexton, though, has no doubt that both players demanded a move.

"I dropped Bonetti, Osgood, Hudson and Baldwin for a game away to Sheffield United, and we won," he said later. "When I got back the next day, the problems started. Osgood and Hudson took umbrage and asked for a transfer. They were the two heroes, so it weakened my popularity. Nevertheless, I wouldn't handle it any differently today. They couldn't tell me who to pick for the team – that was my prerogative. If they were not happy, they could go. Neither Osgood or Hudson was playing particularly well. The manager has to make the decisions, leave people out, put others in, whatever. You have to do that over years and years. And nine times out of ten it's okay. People will accept it. But on the odd occasions, they won't accept it – and you'll have to get over it."

At the time, the club quickly upped the ante, releasing the following statement to the press within hours of the training ground argument: "Hudson and Osgood both refused to train with the first team squad this morning and have been suspended by the club for one week. Both have expressed a wish to move and Chelsea are making them available for transfer immediately."

For the media the announcement was a sensation and the tabloids, in particular, needed little encouragement to go into overdrive. "Showdown!" shrieked *The Sun's* back page, above the sub-heading "Sexton to sell rebels". The list of clubs supposedly interested in Osgood and Hudson pretty much filled up the rest of the page with Arsenal, Spurs, Manchester United, Leicester, QPR, Southampton and Norwich all getting a name check.

"We are interested in both players because men of that calibre become available very rarely," Southampton boss Lawrie McMenemy told reporters. Norwich manager John Bond echoed those comments, saying, "No manager in his right mind can say he is not interested in two players of their quality. We would like them both but whether they would like to come here remains to be seen."

A few days later the chase for Osgood took a continental twist as *The Sun* reported that Real Madrid were prepared to sell their German midfield star Gunter Netzer to fund a £600,000 bid for the Chelsea centre forward. "We enquired about Osgood six weeks ago and now we hear he is on the transfer list we shall try again," Real President Santiago Bernabeu said. The news of the Spanish giants' interest prompted *The Sun's* Alex Montgomery to write: "Real see Osgood as a carbon copy of the legendary Alfredo di Stefano and their answer to Johann Cruyff's pulling power at Barcelona."

But 'El Os' was not to be. Nothing came of Real's enquiry and on January 10th, during a six-hour board meeting called to discuss the crisis, Chelsea accepted a £175,000 offer from Derby for Osgood with Rams striker Roger Davies moving in the opposite direction in part-exchange. Ossie, however, told Derby boss Dave Mackay he needed more time to consider the move and ultimately decided against it because he didn't fancy moving up north.

The speculation surrounding Osgood's likely destination continued on a daily basis. According to some reports both Arsenal and Spurs were now targeting the England striker, although Chelsea were said to be reluctant to sell their prize asset to either of their main London rivals. "The worry for Chelsea is that Osgood could do a Pied Piper and drag hundreds of his young fans with him to the new club," reported *The Sun*.

While the double transfer saga dragged on, Chelsea had to get on with playing football matches. An FA Cup third round home tie against west London neighbours QPR, now back in the First Division after a four-year gap, revived memories of the classic quarter-final in 1970 at Loftus Road. This time, though, there would be no Osgood hat-trick or words of praise for Hudson from the watching England manager as, to no one's surprise, neither player was recalled to the Chelsea team.

Under manager Gordon Jago, Rangers were already showing signs of the exciting, adventurous football which would soon see them eclipse Chelsea as both the most successful and most entertaining side in west London, if not the whole of the capital. Their team had a good balance between old pros, such as Terry Venables and former Arsenal Double-winning captain Frank McLintock, and promising younger players, including nippy winger Dave Thomas and future England captain Gerry Francis, a skilful and energetic midfielder. The jewel in Rangers' crown, though, was Stan Bowles, a hugely talented but occasionally wayward striker in the Osgood mould.

Without their own two most skilful performers, Chelsea looked pedestrian by comparison. Rangers had the best of the game at the Bridge and seemed set to go through when Francis stepped up to take a second-half penalty. However Phillips, enjoying one of his best games for Chelsea, dived to his right to save the spot-kick and earn the Blues a replay. Not that it mattered much, as a Stan Bowles goal at Loftus Road settled the tie. Chelsea, with David Webb playing the entire match at centre forward, never remotely looked like equalising in a match Rangers dominated throughout.

"Absurdly, it was as though Wellington had carried Waterloo by the margin of a single musket ball," one newspaper informed its readers. "The rout was that complete, that absolute in Rangers' command of all football's most exciting skills."

For Chelsea supporters this Cup defeat against local neighbours, who until recently had been very much in the shadow of the Blues, was hard to stomach. To many fans, the absence of Hudson and Osgood from the line-up at Loftus Road felt like a needless self-inflicted injury. Why weren't the two stars in the team? Were they going to be sold? Couldn't the rift with Sexton be resolved? These questions were asked over and over again in the pubs around the ground and on the tube ride home. Perhaps sensing that the fans were becoming increasingly disgruntled, the club addressed the crisis head on in the home programme against Derby, four days after the defeat at Loftus Road.

After admitting that recent events had caused "anxiety and great distress" and pointing out that a good relationship between manager and playing staff was "an absolute prerequisite for the ultimate success and happiness of a club", the programme notes spoke of "a clash of personalities [which] has existed at Stamford Bridge between manager and one or two players."

For the benefit of any fans who hadn't been avidly following the news on the back pages, the unnamed writer (probably programme editor Albert Sewell) went on to name the two players. "Peter Osgood and Alan Hudson were insistent that the situation could not be improved, [so] the board felt they had no alternative but to make them available for transfer." Nor, it seemed, was there much chance of the two stars returning to the team. "We would like to thank them for their services to Chelsea," the programme notes continued, "and wish them success in the future." In the key part of the final paragraph, the column asserted that "the long-term future and good of our club must come above all other considerations. We have backed manager Dave Sexton 100 per cent in this matter . . ."

In fact, the programme article was already out of date. Alan Hudson had been sold to Stoke for £240,000, a new British transfer record, earlier in the week and was due to make his debut for the Potters against Liverpool that afternoon. "Tony Waddington [Stoke's manager] believes in freedom of expression in training and playing, while Dave Sexton was a coach who had set ideas about training routines," was Hudson's parting shot. Still, as far as Osgood was concerned, the club's policy appeared unequivocal – there was simply no way back for the Shed idol.

There was some better news for Chelsea fans, though. Two days before the Derby game Dave Sexton brought Charlie Cooke back to the Bridge from Crystal Palace, where he had been stagnating in the reserves. The £17,000 fee represented great business for the Blues as they had sold the Scottish international to the Eagles for five times that amount just 16 months earlier. More importantly, Cooke's return gave the team and the crowd a much-needed lift at a time when the Bridge was enveloped in a thick cloud of gloom and despondency. The player himself seemed to sense that the fans were fed up and, above all, craved the sort of thrilling spectacle they had become accustomed to in the glory years.

"All I ask of Chelsea fans is that they are patient with me and I shall try to turn on the old magic in return," Cookie promised.

Before the Derby match Cooke was given a rapturous reception by all three sides of the ground. And once the game kicked off he demonstrated that he had lost none of his dazzling array of skills during his brief sojourn in south London. However, despite Cooke's wizardry, Chelsea could only manage a 1–1 draw. Bill Garner scored the Blues' goal but, along with strike partner Chris Garland, struggled to make much of an impression against the Rams' England international central defensive pairing of Roy McFarland and Colin Todd. Garner and Garland were tireless workers for the cause but, without Osgood, it was apparent that the Blues' attack lacked the necessary craft, cunning and invention to break down the division's most organised defences. The supporters wanted Osgood back and so too did a section of the media.

"Chelsea without Peter Osgood are like Samson with a crewcut," wrote Peter Batt in *The Sun*. "His is not a capricious talent that can be blown away like froth from a pint of Guinness. Whatever the cost to Sexton's pride, however many dents are inflicted on the club's image, Ossie should be wooed back to Stamford Bridge."

The Blues, though, still seemed determined to sell Osgood. Stoke manager Tony Waddington put in a bid, hoping to reunite Ossie with his old mate Alan Hudson, only to be told that Chelsea were now solely interested in a player-exchange package. Ideally, any deal that could be struck would involve a striker arriving at the Bridge. The Blues were in dire need of another forward, especially now that Tommy Baldwin, after years of seeing his requests for a move rejected, had finally joined Osgood on the transfer list.

A week after the draw with Derby, Chelsea travelled to Stoke for the first ever First Division match to be played on a Sunday. The sell-out 32,000 crowd suggested that Sunday football had a bright future and, from a Stoke viewpoint, the day couldn't have gone better as the home side recorded a 1–0 win. Inevitably, Hudson played a blinder against his old club, winning the Man of the Match award and, more importantly, the late penalty which Geoff Hurst smashed past Phillips.

Two weeks later even a hard-fought 1–0 Chelsea win at home to Manchester City couldn't stem the constant crowd chants for Osgood. Yet, if the fans thought they could influence the manager, they were very much mistaken. "Dave was a man of set views and Ossie was a fiery character, so there was always going to be a clash," says John Dempsey. "There was no chance of the other players intervening or saying anything that could possibly change Dave's mind once he had decided what he was going to do."

The supporters could chant all they liked, but it wouldn't make any difference. In fact, if anything, a reconciliation between manager and player seemed even more unlikely than before, especially after Sexton fined both Osgood and Ian Hutchinson for taking an unauthorised holiday in Spain in February.

The last chance of a rapprochement came when Osgood approached Sexton with a view to signing a new contract. "I was training with the reserves," said Ossie, "but eventually I went to see Dave and said, 'Look, this is ridiculous. I'm due a new contract.' He said, 'Okay, let's resolve it. I'll see the chairman for you.' So about two weeks later I went to see the chairman and said, 'Mr Brian, about my new contract?' He looked blank and said, 'Nobody's mentioned it to me, son.' So that was me finished with Dave, and basically I was gone."

Meanwhile, on the pitch, there was little for the fans to cheer. At the beginning of the season the FA had introduced a new 'three up, three down' rule to all divisions of the Football League, and the effect of the change was to spread alarm throughout the lower half of the First Division. Chelsea were still in deep trouble and although two of the relegation places looked destined to be filled by Norwich and Manchester United, it was anybody's guess who would be joining them. For a long while, Birmingham had appeared certainties for the drop but a recent run of good form had given the Brummies cause for hope, producing worried expressions among fans up and down the country. Aside from Leeds and Liverpool at the top and the two stragglers at the bottom there was very little between the rest of the teams; incredibly, towards the end of February, only seven points separated third-placed Derby from Chelsea and West Ham, joint fourth bottom.

At the beginning of March the Blues' relegation worries intensified when they crashed 3–0 at Upton Park, Hammers midfielder Billy Bonds hitting all three goals. In the days after this latest reverse press reports appeared suggesting that Dave Sexton had left the club after refusing to take Osgood off the transfer list.

Brian Mears moved swiftly to quash the rumours, following a meeting with his manager.

"Dave Sexton is still the manager of the club," he said. "There is no question of his being sacked or resigning. The club from the chairman right down to the players has 100 per cent confidence in Dave Sexton. At today's meeting we discussed the problems that have faced the club over the past few weeks. They were both personal and internal."

Soon afterwards, the long-running Osgood transfer epic, which was threatening to spill over into the summer thanks to the impending transfer deadline date, finally came to an end when Chelsea accepted Southampton's offer of £275,000 for the player. The fee was a record for both clubs and, added to the transfer fee received for Hudson, meant the Bridge coffers had swelled by over half a million since the New Year.

If Dave Sexton had hoped to use some of this money to bolster his squad for the relegation run-in he was to be disappointed. With the East Stand continuing to eat up money like a bank cash dispenser in reverse, no funds would be released for new signings.

"We were told the new East Stand was going to take a year to build, but that was a massive underestimate," Sexton complained later. "It wasn't only a drain on resources – it's like if you've got the builders in at your house and they're doing something in the kitchen for a month. It's inconvenient. We had this for over two years. It was like living on a building site."

Meanwhile, two consecutive home wins in March, against Burnley and Newcastle, eased the Blues' relegation fears a little. The headlines after the Burnley game, though, were all about the size of the crowd – a pitiful 8,171, Chelsea's lowest post-war league attendance at that point. The fans were back at the end of the month for the visit of Tommy Docherty's Manchester United but the Blues lost 3–1, a result which did little for United's survival prospects but put Chelsea back in trouble. Much would depend on the Blues' two Easter fixtures, away to Tottenham and Southampton.

For the vital game at White Hart Lane on Easter Saturday, Sexton surprised Chelsea's travelling support by selecting three young, virtually unknown players: left-back John Sparrow, making just his second first-team appearance; highly-rated midfielder Ray Wilkins, in his first start for the team; and, also making his first start, striker Kenny Swain, who had been spotted by Dario Gradi playing for non-league Wycombe Wanderers. It was a bold gamble by Sexton, but at half-time it appeared to have backfired as the Blues trailed 1–0. The trapdoor to the Second Division was beckoning. In the second half, though, Chelsea hit back with goals from two unlikely sources, defenders Ron Harris and Micky Droy, to take the two points.

A 0–0 draw at The Dell two days later virtually guaranteed Chelsea's survival. All the same, a meagre total of one point from their last four games left the Blues just a single point clear of the unlucky team who claimed the third relegation place above Norwich and Manchester United, Peter Osgood's Southampton. A last day defeat at home to Stoke, the eighth time the Blues had lost in front of their fans that season, was particularly galling. Another poor crowd of just over 17,000 turned up to watch Alan Hudson dominate midfield again and score the only goal of the game.

Revitalised and rejuvenated, Huddy had been an inspiration since arriving in the Potteries and had helped guide his new club from the nether regions to fifth place in the league. Unlike Peter Osgood, who was now contemplating life in the Second Division, leaving Chelsea had worked out well for Hudson. Even now he has no regrets about the move.

"I wanted to go in a way because I wasn't enjoying my football," he says. "I was being messed about. I went to Stoke, they were fifth from bottom and finished up fifth from top. It was all down to me going there. Tony Waddington got the other players to give me the ball all the time; it was the complete opposite of what was happening at Chelsea.

"My relationship with Dave was strained by the end. I think his problem was that he was frustrated. He was a clean living chap: he never drank, he never smoked, he was football mad. He was a strong Catholic and wherever we went on tour or in Europe he would go to church. You can understand why he may not have liked what we were getting up to. After all, our mob were professional drinkers.

"It was just a life he didn't like and I think jealousy came into it. He would have liked to have been us, he wanted to be a player. I don't know what he was like as a player because his career had been finished by a knee injury. I think he looked at me, Ossie and Charlie Cooke and thought, 'If I had their ability there's no way I'd live my life like they do', and I think that was his hang up, I really do.

"He was alright as a coach but I trained with Don Howe at Arsenal and I found Don was far superior and he would have an occasional laugh with you, too. The problem with Dave was he should have been a coach. If he'd just have been a coach he would have been alright because then he wouldn't have had any say about the things the manager does at a club. The same with Don Howe; he took over as manager of Arsenal and he was useless so he went back to coaching where he was brilliant. Had Tommy Docherty stayed and Dave been the coach around that time I'm quite sure we'd have won the championship. I'm quite certain about that, because we'd have been able to say to Dave, 'Look, fuck off, just coach', but you can't say that to the manager."

Despite this critique of Sexton, Huddy believes the ultimate responsibility for the partial dismantling of the early seventies team lies with the directors. "Personally, I blame the board," he says. "The directors near enough demanded Sexton to sell Osgood and myself. I can just hear their reasoning: 'We'll get rid of Hudson because young Ray Wilkins can play like him. And Osgood, who needs a troublemaker?' But Peter Osgood has never been replaced since the day Chelsea sold him."

Whichever way you looked at it, the 1973/74 season had been little short of a disaster for Chelsea. Nearly relegated, out of both Cups in the first round, two star players sold and no replacements bought, an unfinished new stand haemorrhaging money, falling gate receipts, a growing hooligan minority among their fans . . . still, on the plus side, at least Chelsea had more to smile about than Manchester United.

The close season should have provided some relief, but it didn't. First David Webb, disillusioned by recent developments at the club, asked for a transfer and left for QPR for £100,000. Then Eddie McCreadie, whose career had been blighted by injury in the past three years, announced his retirement. Their departures represented two more broken links with the FA Cup-winning era. Finally, a petty dispute erupted over the players' daily expenses for the summer tour to Australia.

Clearly it would take more than the forced removal of a couple of so-called malcontents before peace and harmony reigned at the Bridge.

CHAPTER FIFTEEN
DOWN AND OUT

The best thing that could be said about the 1973/74 season from Chelsea's point of view was that it was over. Many supporters were dismayed by the departures of Alan Hudson and Peter Osgood, and to a lesser extent, that of David Webb, but the arrival of a new campaign encouraged fans to look forward rather than back. Whatever the problems of the previous months and whichever unknown difficulties lay ahead, the August sunshine brought a renewed sense of optimism to the Bridge.

The news that the East Stand, minus the much-vaunted heating system which had proved too costly to install, had finally been completed should have added to the prevailing positive mood. However, the champagne toast to the colossal structure had a distinctly bitter aftertaste. The final bill, around £2 million, was double the original estimate and left the club in severe debt. What's more, huge corners had been cut in the building of the stand, which in years to come would cost Chelsea many more millions to fix. "Everything about that design was appalling," complained Ken Bates in 1999. "If you could think of a mistake in a building contract, the Chelsea board made it. They even had an architect who had never worked on a stadium. Since I took over the club, we've spent about £10 million on it trying to make a silk purse out of a pig's ear."

The architectural critics, though, loved the stand. "As a shelter for a crowd of British football fans, the East Stand is in a class of its own," enthused *Design* magazine in March 1975. The huge structure was even the subject of a short film in the BBC2 series 'Building Sites', presented by the Chelsea-supporting architect Nigel Coates. "The stand is expectant even when it's empty," he noted. "The roof is just flying straight out – it's leaping out like a panther towards the pitch." Er, if you say so, Nige.

The East Stand opened to the paying public on 17th August 1974, with ticket prices ranging from 80p in the lower tier to £2.50 in the middle tier. Fittingly, the new look to the ground was matched by a couple of fresh faces in the Chelsea squad: David Hay, a dynamic midfielder who had just put in some eye-catching performances for Scotland at the 1974 World Cup signed from Celtic for a club record £225,000; and left-winger John Sissons, a veteran of West Ham's 1964 FA Cup-winning side, arrived from Norwich. Both made the starting line-up for the first match of the season, an undemanding looking fixture at home to newly-promoted Carlisle.

On a hot summer afternoon in front of 31,268 fans and the *Match of the Day* cameras Chelsea had the bulk of possession but still went down to a dismal 2–0 defeat against the Cumbrians. To say the result didn't augur well for the rest of the season was a massive understatement: Carlisle had been widely tipped to go straight back down and even their one famous name, Chris Balderstone, was much better known as a cricketer than a footballer.

The poor start continued. Just two wins in the first ten league games suggested another season of struggle was looming. At least Chelsea had Tottenham for company in the relegation zone while Arsenal, just four years after winning the Double, had begun the season in abysmal form and were rock bottom. The pressure was mounting on all three London managers: Sexton, Arsenal's Bertie Mee and Tottenham's recently installed boss Terry Neill.

On October 3rd, five days after a 1–0 home defeat by Wolves, Dave Sexton was sacked as Chelsea manager. Officially, Sexton had "resigned", but few fans doubted that the Chelsea board had done little, or nothing, to persuade him to stay.

"I could see my sacking coming," Sexton said. "I wasn't the most popular bloke – managers never are. It's the players who are the crowd's favourites, quite rightly. Still, it wasn't a very pleasant period for me. The fact I had four children and they could all read the papers wasn't nice."

The board's decision to let Sexton go represented a stunning volte-face. Only a few months previously the board had backed their manager in the bitter stand-off with the club's two biggest stars, now they were showing him the door too.

"The only thing I would criticise the board at Chelsea for is that they backed Dave Sexton over Peter Osgood and Alan Hudson but within a matter of months they sacked Dave," says Ron Harris. "I found that strange. I don't think he deserved to get the sack."

Other players, though, were not especially saddened by Sexton's departure. A common view was that while he had great qualities as a coach, Sexton was a remote and uncommunicative manager.

"His man-management of players let him down," argues Steve Kember. "Dave didn't talk to anybody. He rarely used to talk to you or encourage you. Dave took the training and on matchdays he said his bit. After the game, he shot off. Some say managers should be aloof. I think to get the best out of the players you've got to be with them and have them with you. You need to win their respect."

"Dave would have been fantastic in today's modern football where you just coach and don't worry about players' contracts or get involved in discussions with them," adds Ron Harris. "I think he found it a little bit difficult if it got a bit heated, with a contract dispute or something like that."

Even Sexton himself has admitted that he found some aspects

of management trying. "I can't say I enjoyed looking after the contracts and being in charge of discipline, particularly," he said. "But it's something that needed to be done, so I did it. It's been suggested that I would have been happier having someone else taking care of it, but that would have undermined my authority."

Leaving Stamford Bridge for the last time, Sexton said: "Perhaps someone can come and do better things towards the success that Chelsea deserve." He would, though, be a hard act to follow. Whatever his faults as a man manager, the two major trophies he had won made him Chelsea's most successful boss ever – a title, incidentally, he would hold until the Vialli era 25 years later.

Sexton's transfer policy, too, had been generally good, especially in the early years. Nobody would quibble over the signings of the likes of David Webb, John Dempsey, Ian Hutchinson and Keith Weller, all of whom made huge contributions to Chelsea's cup triumphs. The later signings – Steve Kember, Chris Garland and Bill Garner, for example – were not quite in the same category, and certainly compared unfavourably with the players Sexton let go such as Osgood, Hudson and Weller.

The loss of these players left new boss Ron Suart, formerly Sexton's assistant, with a squad which was short on quality, particularly in attacking positions. Nonetheless, Suart got on with the job with the minimum of fuss, enjoying an obligatory honeymoon period of five games without defeat. Sticking faithfully to the old guard, Suart gave few opportunities to the young players who had featured at the end of the previous season. Even Ray Wilkins, who had already shown signs of the visionary passing that was to become his forte at Chelsea, had to settle at first for a place on the bench at best.

The limitations of this policy were soon shown up, however. In a League Cup replay against bogey side Stoke the Blues were hammered 6–2, the briefly recalled Tommy Baldwin scoring his last ever goal for Chelsea. The following month Chelsea lost 5–0 at Newcastle, all the goals coming in the second half as the pace of Gallowgate hero Malcolm 'Supermac' Macdonald left Micky Droy and John Dempsey floundering.

Wilkins eventually returned to the side in December, when his intelligent distribution of the ball helped Chelsea put together their best run of the season, three wins and a draw in four games. Even the Blues' most ardent fans, though, had to admit the team wasn't playing well, while the press reports were scathing. The 2–0 home win over Luton on December 7th, Chelsea's first victory for two months, was described by one journalist as "a game which would find a place on any short-list of the worst First Division matches", while another complained of "a bumbling apology of a match".

There was no shortage of entertainment, however, when a group of Chelsea players, led by goalkeeper John Phillips, put on a spoof pantomime at the club's Christmas dinner a couple of weeks later. "I was the compere and firstly I introduced the chairman, Brian Mears, as a clown and his brother as an alcoholic," recalled Phillips. "Next I introduced Martin Spencer, the club's financial advisor, holding an abacus. Then I made apologies for Viscount Chelsea who was away at a horse race and Richard Attenborough who was absent filming.

"We proceeded to re-enact a meeting, bringing up all the things that had been said during the course of the season including the night we got beat at Stoke when one of the directors remarked to us that we were grossly overpaid. Players are not known for their intellect, but they do have good memories. We also sacked the manager, Ron Suart, who was sitting in the audience at the time. Everyone who was involved with the club was there, from the cleaning lady upwards.

"At the end of the evening the chairman approached and we expected the inevitable, 'You five are on the transfer list. We don't want you. You're bad influences.' Instead, he praised our perform-ance, saying it showed the spirit of the club. And I thought, 'You stupid prat, can't you see what we're saying? Can't you see it?'

"I had sleepless nights at the time because I was so worried about the state the club was in. I'd go in the next day and see the manager and I'd tell him what was wrong with the club. He'd invariably agree with me and tell me what he was going to do. So you'd wait for changes to come and you'd wait and wait. They never came. The club had cancer, which needed cutting out. There should have been an enormous purge. Chelsea didn't have any money to replace what it had, so invariably they got the youngsters in. In a good side you can bring in two or three young players from time to time. But to bring them in *en bloc* – it was never going to come off."

In fact, Suart remained reluctant to play the younger players until after a fourth round FA Cup defeat at home to fellow strugglers Birmingham. John Sparrow, Ian Britton and striker Steve Finnieston all had extended runs along with Wilkins and, for a short while at least, results improved.

The mini-revival, though, came to an end with a 2–1 defeat at home to champions-to-be Derby and, the following week, Chelsea suffered a humiliating 7–1 reverse at Wolves. With their confidence in tatters, the Blues' form continued to dip worryingly. Once again, relegation was on the agenda. In a late bid to avoid the drop Eddie McCreadie, who had been working as Ron Suart's coach, was promoted to team manager with Suart taking on a new role as general manager.

"I want to give the fans something to believe in," McCreadie announced, "they have suffered enough. My policy will be to bring a great team back to a great club."

With three games to go Chelsea were just outside the drop-zone, a point clear of Tottenham and Luton who both had a game in hand. Carlisle, as expected, were adrift at the bottom and all but relegated. Arsenal, though, had recovered after their dreadful start and were safely ensconced in mid-table. The Blues' next fixture, away to Spurs, would go a long way to determining their fate.

In the build up to one of the most important games in Chelsea's history, Eddie McCreadie made the bold decision of selecting 18-year-old Ray Wilkins as his new skipper. "Wilkins will be the future captain of the club," he told reporters. "He captained the reserves on several occasions when I played with them and he is a very capable young man. He has the quality of leadership and is well respected."

Youthful faces also figured prominently in McCreadie's team selection for the game at White Hart Lane. Out went Hollins, Kember and Houseman from the team which had lost 1–0 at home to Manchester City the previous week and in came Sparrow, Britton and, making his Chelsea debut, striker Teddy Maybank. A future *Blind Date* contestant, the blond-haired Maybank had impressed McCreadie in a friendly match against Fulham earlier in the week, but it seemed a reckless gamble to thrust the untried youngster into what promised to be a vicious north London relegation dog fight.

More than 51,000 fans packed into White Hart Lane for what was, in effect, a cup final. Defeat for either side would mean almost certain relegation, while a draw would only please Luton. On the other hand, a win would all but guarantee survival and send the losers spiralling towards the Second Division. No wonder, then, that the supporters of both teams were fired up. The raucous, passionate atmosphere didn't take long to spill over into outright violence as fans decked out in the fashions of the day – multi-coloured tank tops, flared trousers and tottering platform soles – traded blows on the pitch before the game.

Unsurprisingly, the match itself was a tense, nervous, tetchy affair. Chelsea held out until ten minutes into the second half, when Steve Perryman scored for Spurs from close range. Tottenham's frizzy-haired Scottish international striker Alfie Conn added a second 15 mins from time to leave Chelsea staring into the abyss.

The Blues' only hope was to win their final two matches at home to Sheffield United and Everton – a tall order considering that both teams were in the top six and chasing European qualification. In the event, Chelsea could only manage two 1–1 draws and finished second bottom, above Carlisle but behind Luton on goal average. Tottenham survived by a single point – so, as it turned out, a draw at White Hart Lane would have saved Chelsea and relegated Spurs instead.

"I honestly believe if the senior players had played at Tottenham we'd have got a result and stayed up," says Steve Kember, pointing the finger at McCreadie's team selection for the game at White Hart Lane. Certainly, the decision to pitch the totally inexperienced Maybank into a game of such magnitude was hard to fathom. On the other hand, the senior players had performed disappointingly for much of the season. Was there any reason to suppose they would have played any better at Spurs? In any case, there were many more factors behind Chelsea's relegation than a misguided team selection for one match. As the old saying goes, the league table doesn't lie. And, at the end of the 1974/75 season, the table suggested that Chelsea's squad simply wasn't good enough to stay in the First Division. Like Kember and John Phillips, John Dempsey argues that too many young players were rushed into the first team too quickly.

"The young players who came into the side, with the exception of Ray Wilkins who was clearly a fine player, perhaps weren't quite ready for first team football," says Dempsey, "especially as they were being thrown into a relegation battle. Having said that, players like Ian Britton, Steve Finnieston, Tommy Langley and Ray Lewington all did very well under Eddie McCreadie later. It was asking a lot of them, though, to replace the likes of Osgood, Webb and Hudson."

An alternative view came from former manager Tommy Docherty. "Chelsea have kept their senior players too long," he said, shortly after the Blues' relegation was confirmed. "I feel sorry for Eddie McCreadie who will be tagged as the manager who took them down. He only had three games and Ron Suart should have stayed."

If relegation was a shock, it wasn't a complete surprise. Chelsea had been steadily declining for some years. David Webb dates the turnaround in fortunes as early as September 1971 when Dave Sexton sold Keith Weller. Other players point to the morale-sapping loss of two major cup ties in a week in the spring of 1972 as another important turning point. "It all went a bit sour after that," says Dempsey. Clearly, the acrimonious departures of Peter Osgood and Alan Hudson, allied to the lack of funds made available for adequate replacements, were also key moments in Chelsea's subsequent slump.

Maybe, too, the wild lifestyle of some of the players caught up with them a little towards the end. "It was probably part of our downfall that there were too many good nights out," admits Charlie Cooke. "It all seemed kind of innocent at the time, but in the long term it wasn't all that good for the team. We had a couple of moments when we were disciplined for our stupidity, but it was never anything to do with the actual playing of the game. I think there was a kind of self-destruction in there, too. Probably we were all a bit immature. It was hard for Dave Sexton – we were just a bunch of maniacs."

Faced with the prospect of managing the Blues in only their second post-war season outside the top flight, Eddie McCreadie made all the right noises. "Next season? No sweat. We will win the Second Division," he confidently asserted. Despite the mounting financial problems afflicting the club, chairman Brian Mears remained equally bullish: "Any cuts in our playing staff will not be for economy reasons," he insisted. "It is a question of streamlining the staff. If we are successful, the crowds will support us."

As part of the 'streamlining' process five senior players were placed on the transfer list: Steve Kember, Peter Houseman, Tommy Baldwin, Bill Garner and John Hollins, while Peter Bonetti was amongst those given a 'free'. All except Garner would leave in the summer, although Bonetti, to the delight of the Chelsea crowd, soon returned from exile in the North American Soccer

League, joining five other grizzled survivors of the 1970 squad: Ron Harris, John Dempsey, Charlie Cooke, Ian Hutchinson and Marvin Hinton.

But the glory days were well and truly over. Despite a brief resurgence under Eddie McCreadie, who led his young side to promotion in 1977, the Blues would spend seven of the next nine seasons in the Second Division. The period became known among fans as 'the gloomy years' as financial crises, hooliganism, falling crowds, a crumbling stadium and poor football culminating in a close flirtation with relegation to the Third Division combined to make Stamford Bridge one of the English game's more depressing venues. "The whole place became a rancid meat pie crawling with maggots," is Alan Hudson's succinct summary.

The joyous nights in Manchester and Athens soon seemed to belong to a different, far-off era, even while Peter Bonetti, Ron Harris and Peter Osgood, returning to the Bridge for a brief and unproductive spell in the late seventies, played out the last games of their long Chelsea careers. And the more the team struggled in the years that followed, the more fans and the media would hark back to the great days of Ossie, Huddy, Cookie, Hutch and the Cat.

It wasn't simply that those players had enjoyed genuine success while the next two decades only produced a couple of Second Division titles and two triumphs in the much-mocked Full Members Cup. Just as important as the silverware was the team's compelling mix of qualities at the height of its powers. Flair, inspiration and flamboyance in attack, allied to grit, determination and steely resilience in defence. Add to that a commitment to entertainment, which frequently produced football of a breathtaking standard and a healthy dollop of unpredictability which left the fans never quite knowing what to expect.

Above all, the Blues side of the early seventies had more characters than a Russian novel. Virtually all the players stood out from the crowd for one reason or another. Peter Osgood, for his all-round showmanship, spectacular goals and equally spectacular hairstyle. Ian Hutchinson for his gangling gait, incredible long throws and lion-heated bravery. David Webb for his never-say-die spirit and extraordinary ability to turn his hand (or foot) to any role, from goalkeeper to striker. Ron Harris, arguably the most feared hardman of his time and an inspirational captain. Charlie Cooke and Alan Hudson, two of the most naturally gifted players ever to pull on a Chelsea shirt . . . the list goes on.

Idolised and revered by their thousands of fans, these Chelsea boys truly were the kings of the King's Road. And, even if the Abramovich era turns the Stamford Bridge trophy cabinet into an Aladdin's Cave of silverware, their legend will live on.

CHAPTER SIXTEEN
THEN AND NOW

Shortly before the end of the 2003/04 season Ron Harris was at Stamford Bridge one evening being interviewed for Chelsea TV. As he was about to leave the studio he was asked to wait in an office. Somebody wanted to see him.

"Within a couple of minutes Roman Abramovich came in with an interpreter, one of the Chelsea directors," recalls Ron. "I don't really know why he wanted to see me but I sat there talking to him for about an hour and half."

The meeting between the two men, embodiments of Chelsea past and present, was mentioned in the matchday programme for the dreary 0–0 draw with Middlesbrough. "It was fascinating, I believe, for everyone there," wrote editor Neil Barnett, before adding rather coyly, "this is not the place to discuss what was said." Now, for the first time, the details of what was discussed at that meeting can be revealed – and Barnett is right, what was said was fascinating, especially in light of later developments at the Bridge.

"First of all, he asked me what I thought Chelsea's best current team was," says Ron. "So I told him the eleven players I'd pick. Then, he asked me quite a lot about what it was like in my day. He was interested to hear that we never chopped and changed the side like recent Chelsea managers have with the rotation system. I've never been a great believer in that – if I'm playing alongside somebody I want to get to know their good habits and bad habits, and vice versa. So I didn't agree with Claudio Ranieri's tinkering around because if you keep the same team you build up partnerships and understanding.

"I asked Abramovich who he thought was the best team in the Premiership was and he told me 'Arsenal'. I said to him if you name their side which started off at Chelsea when they drew 1–1 in the Champions League only Keown, Reyes, Parlour and Clichy of their recognised first-team squad didn't play. So they've got about 18 players to pick from; under Ranieri, Chelsea had 30-odd. He did say to me that he thought the squad was too heavy and would be coming down to 24 players. I was very impressed with the fellow. He gave me the impression that Chelsea supporters can only look ahead to good times."

Roman Abramovich is a busy man. His time is precious. It seems unlikely, then, that he chatted to Ron Harris for 90 minutes simply for want of something better to do. The nature of the conversation suggests that the Chelsea owner was picking Harris' brains – and why not? As the club's all-time record appearance maker, Chopper has a wealth of experience and his passion for the club is unquestionable – as he says, "I'd run through a brick wall for Chelsea."

While Claudio Ranieri was Chelsea manager a popular pre-match pastime in the pubs around Stamford Bridge was 'guess the team'. Anyone who got eight or nine starters right was doing well; getting ten or all eleven correct was virtually impossible, thanks to the Italian's frequently baffling 'pick 'n' mix' team selection policy.

Under the Chelsea regime of Jose Mourinho things have been different. More like the Ron Harris era, in fact. *Senhor* Mourinho may be interested to learn that when the Blues won the FA Cup in 1970 they used just 13 players during their eight match campaign and one of those, Marvin Hinton, only featured as a substitute in the Final. Just another six players were used in the season as a whole and of those only Alan Birchenall played more than ten games. Success was based on a settled team and a small, close-knit squad.

Winning the FA Cup for the first time in the club's history was a momentous event for the Blues and their fans in 1970. That unforgettable night at Old Trafford when Ron Harris raised the Cup remains embedded in the club's psyche, as even Roman Abramovich may appreciate after his long chat with Chopper. However, times have changed, and doing well in the domestic cup competitions is no longer a top priority for leading English clubs. Chelsea's main focus, like that of Arsenal and Manchester United, is now on the Champions League and the Premiership.

Of those two competitions, the Premiership became something of a Holy Grail for the Blues. Prior to the arrival of Jose Mourinho, Chelsea had won just one league title in a hundred years of trying. Even that sole triumph was back in 1955, as opposition fans used to like to remind the Bridge faithful every so often. "Black-and-white, you won the league in black-and-white," they would sing. Very droll.

The sixties and seventies teams failed to emulate Ted Drake's title-winning heroes of 1955, although Tommy Docherty's 'Diamonds' came close in 1965. Otherwise, despite consistently finishing in the top six, the Blues of Ossie, Chopper and co never really mounted a genuine championship challenge. Considering the talent that the squad possessed, the lack of a convincing title tilt requires some explaining.

"On our day, when we played the football we were capable of, we could beat anybody," said Peter Osgood, keen to downplay any suggestion that the seventies side's failure to lift the title somehow invalidates its claim to greatness. "Leeds were one of the best club sides in the world at the time and we could match them or anybody else on our day, but we just weren't consistent enough. Sometimes we didn't gee ourselves up for the lesser games and that's why we never won the title. But, in full flow, we were an awesome side's. We were bloody good. We had guys who could kill teams off, sometimes in just a ten-minute spell."

And Ron Harris adds: "With the players we had we were always a better bet to win the Cup than the league. We had players who the bigger the game, the bigger the crowd, the better they would perform. Players like Ossie, Huddy and Charlie Cooke. When it came to grinding results out week in week out they weren't consistent at doing it. Oz, who was 'the King', he played like he felt. If he went up to Manchester United, for example, and felt like doing the business he would do it. On the other hand, sometimes in the dressing room he'd go, 'Huh, I don't think I'll be running around much today' and he wouldn't. He wouldn't run from here to there, but he'd be honest enough to tell you. Then, come the big games in Europe or in the cup, he put in some brilliant performances. I always think he was like a matador in the bullring, the way he responded to the occasion and the crowd."

John Dempsey agrees with Harris that Chelsea's main failing was that, unlike the Leeds or Arsenal sides of the time, the team struggled to notch up those ugly 1–0 wins which often form the bedrock of a championship-winning season.

"I think the reason why we never won the championship is that we weren't the sort of team that could grind out the narrow wins when we weren't playing well," he says. "We could win 5–0 one week and then lose 1–0 or 2–1 the next. I think the problem was that we relied so much on our flair players – Ossie, Alan Hudson and Charlie Cooke – that when their form dipped a bit we couldn't dig out results like some other teams."

Typically, Alan Birchenall has a slightly leftfield take on the topic. "I know it sounds daft but we had too many brilliant players to win the championship," he says. "We had great individuals who could always win us a cup because on our day, when we were really flowing, we were as good as any team, not just in this country but in the world. We could be that good. But you couldn't guarantee it. Great teams win championships, but we had great players rather than a great team. Individually, yes, we had some fantastic players, but it wasn't like when we played crap we got a result, a scrappy 1–0. When we played crap we got beat. We had to play well to win, but when we did play well it was unbelievable at times."

That makes the Chelsea team of the early 1970s sound a little like the under-achieving galacticos who have flattered to deceive at Real Madrid in the last couple of years. Certainly, the Blues were unpredictable, but in many ways that only added to the excitement of following Chelsea at the time. One week the fans would be shaking their heads as the team played a collective stinker; the next they'd be roaring their heads off after a five-star virtuoso display. Yet for skipper Ron Harris, this tendency towards inconsistency should not overshadow the underlying cohesion, balance and unity which underpinned the Blues' success.

"We had a terrific blend," he says. "We had three fantastic players – Ossie, Huddy, Charlie Cooke – and then we had a back four who could hold their own. We needed them as much as they needed us. We had Johnny Hollins who was a fantastic competitor, and a fitness freak who could run from the first minute to the last minute. Peter Houseman did a good job. He got a lot of criticism, but I don't think people realised the work he did for the team. Peter Bonetti was second to none in goal. I think we were one of the sides that never feared going up to Leeds and getting rolled over because of their reputation. We had fellows who could look after themselves."

Assessing the team's strengths, Peter Osgood also pinpointed a complex mix of qualities, a delicate interweaving of skill, steel and stamina running through the Blues' core. "Centre forwards who score goals and win you games will always get more accolades than the defence or the goalkeeper and the midfield," he argued. "But I always think that the back four and the midfield makes a team. If you've got a solid back four and a great keeper, which we did have, and geniuses like Charlie Cooke and Alan Hudson in midfield – and I mean real geniuses, because they were world-class and they would be worth fortunes today – as well as a workhouse like Johnny Hollins, then you've got the makings of a side. Even today, I wouldn't swap any of our midfield for any current midfielder, even Patrick Vieira or Frank Lampard."

Of course, Ossie was bound to be biased towards his old team-mates. Yet that doesn't necessarily mean his judgement was wrong, and he was certainly not alone in ranking the stars of the 1970s above those of a more recent vintage. In 2002 the official *Chelsea Magazine* sparked many a pub debate along the King's Road by asking former Blues from the 1950s onwards to nominate their greatest ever Chelsea players. Peter Osgood himself topped the list, while Alan Hudson won the midfielder's section, Peter Bonetti was voted the club's greatest goalkeeper and Ron Harris ran Marcel Desailly very close for the title of best ever defender. Charlie Cooke, Eddie McCreadie and John Hollins also figured in the top 15, cementing the seventies side dominance of the poll.

This wasn't a case of old mates voting for each other, either. Ron Harris, for example, got the nod from both Roy Bentley, the Blues' legendary title-winning skipper *and* Frank Sinclair, goalscoring hero in the 1998 League Cup Final. Alan Hudson, meanwhile, was nominated by his old youth team coach Frank Blunstone *and* Brazilian-born defender Emerson Thome, who clearly didn't neglect his Chelsea history studies during his brief spell at the club in 2000. The two Peters, Osgood and Bonetti, also received votes from across the generations.

Who knows, in years to come a similar list may well feature more players from the Abramovich era and rather fewer from the glory days of the 1970s. Certainly, by helping Chelsea win successive Premiership titles, the likes of John Terry and Frank Lampard can now be considered as equals of their seventies counterparts. Indeed, in the coming seasons, today's Blues may well surpass the achievements of the Docherty and Sexton teams by a considerable distance. Yet, even if that should happen and Chelsea go on to become one of Europe's most successful clubs, the swashbuckling brilliance of the seventies side will never be forgotten. Their place in the all-time Chelsea pantheon is assured.

TOMMY BALDWIN

Still living on the King's Road around the corner from his local, The Imperial, the Sponge does PR work for the Wildwood golf course in Surrey.

ALAN BIRCHENALL

Leicester City's 'club co-ordinator', the Birch is an ebullient figure behind the mic at the Walkers Stadium on matchdays. In 2000 he brought out his hugely entertaining autobiography, *Bring Back the Birch* (Polar Publishing) and in 2002 he was awarded the MBE for his fund-raising efforts for various charities. "It came out on the local radio," he says, '"Alan Birchenall has got an MBE in the New Year's Honours List . . . , but not for football.' I thought, 'You bastards!'"

PETER BONETTI

After a brief period as a guest house owner on the Isle of Mull, the Cat became a goalkeeping coach, working for Chelsea, England and Fulham among others. He now works as an after-dinner speaker.

JOHN BOYLE

Briefly manager of Dartford, Boylers now works as a security guard at the Office of Science and Technology in central London. Given the choice, he says he'd rather watch cricket than football these days.

CHARLIE COOKE

After finishing his career in the USA, Charlie set up a coaching school for children in 1985 and has remained in the States ever since. He lives in Cincinnati.

JOHN DEMPSEY

John managed Dundalk, Maidenhead and Egham after ending his career in the States, where he was voted 'Defender of the Year' in 1979 (ahead of Franz Beckenbauer). He now works as a special needs career in a resource centre in Edgware.

TOMMY DOCHERTY

Following his departure from the Bridge, the Doc managed Rotherham, QPR, Aston Villa, Hull, Scotland, Manchester United, Derby, Preston and Wolves as well as a number of clubs abroad. His ready wit is now employed on the after-dinner circuit.

RON HARRIS

After a spell as manager of Aldershot, Ron branched out into the leisure business owning a golf course and, more recently, a fishing complex. Like Tommy Docherty, Chopper is now a regular after-dinner speaker.

MARVIN HINTON

Marv finally hung up his boots at the age of 46, while with Eastbourne United. Eight years later a car accident left him with two plates in his right leg. Now retired from his job in the removal business, he still watches Chelsea regularly.

JOHN HOLLINS

Chelsea boss for two and a half years until he was sacked by Ken Bates in March 1987, Holly has also managed Swansea, Rochdale, Stockport and, most recently, Crawley Town.

PETER HOUSEMAN

Tragically, Peter and his wife, Sally, and two friends were killed in a car crash in March 1977 two years after the left-winger had moved from Chelsea to Oxford United. A specially arranged game between Chelsea's 1977 side and the 1970 vintage raised nearly £20,000 for the couples' children.

ALAN HUDSON

Huddy spent two months in intensive care after being hit by a car in 1997 and has spent years recovering from his injuries. "I've got to be delighted with how I am now," he says. A year before the accident he brought out his autobiography, *The Working Man's Ballet* (Robson Books), and in August 2004 he produced a new book about Chelsea in the Abramovich era called *The Tinker and the Talisman*.

IAN HUTCHINSON

Hutch died in September 2002 after a long illness. "He was my best mate," said Peter Osgood. "We called each other 'bruv' and that's what we were like, brothers. I wouldn't have swapped him for anyone in the league." The club marked his death with a minute's silence before the Blues' UEFA Cup home game with Viking FK.

STEVE KEMBER

After ending his career back where he started at Crystal Palace, Steve has managed the Eagles on four occasions, most notably saving them from relegation to the Second Division on the last day of the 2000/01 season.

EDDIE McCREADIE

Chelsea manager from 1975 to 1977, Eddie resigned as Blues boss after the board refused to provide him with a club car and a written contract. He emigrated to the USA and now lives in Memphis.

PETER OSGOOD

Ossie died from a heart attack in March 2006 (see *Postscript*). At the time of his death he was working as an after-dinner speaker and matchday host at Stamford Bridge.

DAVE SEXTON

Dave managed QPR, Manchester United and Coventry after leaving the Bridge and, well into his seventies, was still working in the game at the highest level, checking out England's future opponents for Sven Goran Eriksson. In 2005 he was awarded an OBE for services to football.

BOBBY TAMBLING

Chelsea's all-time leading scorer, Bobby now lives in Ireland. In 2004 he made an emotional return to the Bridge for a series of events held in his honour.

DAVID WEBB

Manager of Chelsea for three months in 1993, Webby has been boss of Southend on no fewer than four occasions. He has also managed Torquay, Bournemouth and Brentford.

KEITH WELLER

Another player to finish his career in America, Keith lived for many years in Seattle. In 2002 he was diagnosed as suffering from leomysarcoma, a rare form of cancer. An appeal fund set up by his former Leicester team-mate Alan Birchenall allowed Keith to seek alternative medical treatment for his condition at a clinic in Mexico, but sadly he died in November 2004.

POSTSCRIPT
LONG LIVE THE KING

On Wednesday March 1st 2006 Peter Osgood suffered a heart attack while attending a family funeral at Slough crematorium. He died later the same day after being taken to Wexham Park hospital for treatment.

Many Chelsea fans first heard of the news of Ossie's death when they picked up a copy of that afternoon's *Evening Standard*, which devoted the whole of its front page and three inside pages to the 'King of Stamford Bridge'. Some supporters immediately rushed to the Bridge to place flowers, shirts, scarves and posters outside the ground, and over the next few days the memorial site grew in size as more and more fans came to the stadium to pay their respects.

Tributes to Ossie were led by his friends and team-mates in Chelsea's 1970 FA Cup-winning side. "Apart from being a very, very good friend of mine for the best part of 30-odd years, I think he was the most gifted player I ever played with in my time at Chelsea Football Club," said Ron Harris. "He had a fantastic first touch, was a big, strong lad and put the fear up centre halves. He was a terrific lad and had some fantastic skill. He was a pleasure to play with. People will always say the best player at Chelsea has been Gianfranco Zola but I would say Peter was the greatest."

Chopper's sentiments were echoed by Tommy Baldwin, for many years a strike partner of Ossie's. "He had a great football brain and could score goals from anywhere," said the Sponge. "If you could say there was one player from the older generation that could have played today and still be a legend, it was Peter."

Other colleagues expressed dismay that, for all his undoubted ability, Osgood only acquired a mere handful of international caps. "He was different class, among the very best in Chelsea's history," said Tommy Docherty, the man who gave Ossie his Chelsea debut as a 17-year-old in December 1964. "It was an insult to his ability that he only won four England caps. He had all the ability in the world. A Hungarian referee came to see us once and said Ossie was the best player he'd seen since the great Nandor Hidegkuti, which was an amazing tribute."

Alan Hudson, who set up the Blues centre forward for many of his 150 goals for the club, made a similar point. "I have no doubt that Ossie was the greatest centre forward in the history of the club," he said. "He was by far the best in the country in 1970 and should have played for England then. For such a big man he was like a ballet dancer in comparison with many players, and yet he'd still give stick to centre halves."

Apart from memories of his skills on the pitch, there were also tributes to the man himself. "He would always give time to people," recalled Ken Shellito, a former Chelsea team-mate who, as Blues boss, brought Ossie back to the Bridge for a brief spell in the 1978/79 season. "After a game he'd sign autographs for kids, he'd play a great game and then spend time with fans in the public bar. He knew they paid his wages."

Bobby Tambling, along with Kerry Dixon one of only two players to score more goals for Chelsea than Ossie, also remembered the striker's strong bond with the supporters.

"He never lost where he came from," said Tambling. "When we were away in Europe, there'd be a good few travelling from the Shed end, and Ossie would make sure if there were any players' tickets left over that they got to those lads. He had a feeling for the fans."

There were also tributes for Ossie from members of the current Chelsea squad. "I have only been at Chelsea a short time but, of course, I know Peter Osgood was a legend at Stamford Bridge," said Jose Mourinho. "He was one of the greats at Chelsea and will be missed." Blues skipper John Terry spoke for many latterday players when he said, "Peter Osgood was an absolute legend. He was a fantastic player, but also a great man as well, and still very involved with the current team and club." Intriguingly, Chelsea chairman Bruce Buck suggested Osgood was precisely the type of star attraction club owner Roman Abramovich would have loved to sign for the Blues. "He was the sort of footballer that Roman would have immediately spotted as someone he would like to see play at Chelsea," said Buck.

Three days after Ossie's death Chelsea fans held aloft posters of the Shed icon during a minute's silence before the Blues' match at West Bromwich Albion. As a sharp blast of the referee's whistle signalled the 60 seconds was up the away end launched into a rousing chorus of 'Born is the King of Stamford Bridge'. While the fans belted out their emotional farewell many, no doubt, were revisiting their own favourite Ossie memories: his vital and never-to-be-forgotten cup final goals; the spectacular 'Goal of the Season' volley against Arsenal and numerous other memorable strikes during his decade-long career at the Bridge; even, perhaps, more personal recollections of a man who, while he was keenly aware of his own place in Chelsea history, was always an approachable figure to the fans who still idolised him.

At the Blues' next home game, against Tottenham, many of Osgood's old team-mates were introduced to the crowd before the striker's life and career were celebrated with a minute's appreciation. In the matchday programme, which featured a classic shot of a smiling Ossie on a black-fringed cover, fans were informed that they could pay tribute to their hero in a book of condolence opened at the stadium. Many thousands subsequently signed the book, either in person or on-line.

On October 1st 2006, exactly six months after his death, the club held a memorial service for Ossie at Stamford Bridge. Around 2,500 fans attended the ceremony, which included speeches by Ron Harris, Peter Bonetti and Tommy Docherty. At the end of the hour-long memorial Ossie's ashes were laid to rest beneath the Shed end penalty spot and a commemorative plaque was unveiled in front of the same stand. All in all, it was a fitting send off to one of Chelsea's finest and most popular players.

Meanwhile, the 'Osgood' song continues to feature at virtually every Blues game. Delivered with gusto both home and away, the song represents both a personal tribute to Ossie and, perhaps, a pervading sense among Chelsea fans that his flamboyant individual style is a quality that should always be present in the team's football.

In short, the 'King' may be dead, but his legend lives on.

Clive Batty, 2007

APPENDIX
'IT WAS ONE HAPPY CLUB'

In the autumn of 2004 Ron Harris, Alan Hudson and Peter Osgood appeared on a number of radio programmes to promote the original hardback edition of *Kings of the King's Road*. The following is the full transcript of the Radio 5 Live show, *Sport on Five*, hosted by Jonathan Pearce, which went out live on the evening of 16th November 2004, and was dedicated to the book . . .

[The programme opens with a burst of 'Blue is the Colour' intercut with commentary from classic Chelsea games of the period]

Jonathan Pearce: Good evening to you all, chaps. I'm going to come to you first, Ron – can I call you 'Chopper' or do you like to be called 'Ron' these days?

Ron Harris: Well, I've been called a few names over the years, it doesn't make any difference to me.

JP: Well, in one of your first games you were called names by the Chelsea fans as well, because Sir Stanley Matthews was in the opposition line-up and you gave him a reminder you were there in the first five minutes . . .

RH: Yeah, I think Stan was 49 at the time and I was 17 and it was his last ever game in London. Myself and Eddie McCreadie gave him a bit of a hard time and the Chelsea supporters had a bit of a pop at the two of us. There were a few choice words passing between me and Stan as well.

JP: But everyone at Chelsea came to love you and these were great times, weren't they? The book talks about the Chelsea successes and late failures as well of the early seventies but also, Huddy, the wonderful times with The Rolling Stones, The Who, The Beatles and The Animals and the King's Road having this massive effect on Chelsea Football Club . . .

Alan Hudson: Amazing, absolutely amazing. It was the swinging sixties and I was born there, and I saw everything that went on. People like Ossie would send me out on the King's Road to look for afternoon drinking clubs, so I was like the scout for the team. I would do all the running for them on the field and all the running around for them off the field. I was 18 when I got in the team and it was just electric, really, it was so exciting. Amazing.

JP: And you, Peter, were a bit of an outsider because you were from Windsor, weren't you?

Peter Osgood: Yeah, I don't know why I got all these headlines for being out drinking because I was always down in Windsor, a country boy. So I don't know where it all comes from, to be honest.

JP: [*sceptically*] Yes, exactly. Great times, though, because this was a young Chelsea team from the youth ranks, wasn't it? You were there first, Ron?

RH: Yes, I'm a little bit older than Os and Huddy. I started off as a 15-year-old lad and one of the great things Chelsea had at the time was that there were a lot of homegrown players. If you look through the side we had in the seventies you had people like Peter Bonetti, myself, Johnny Hollins, Huddy, Ossie, Peter Houseman, they all came through the youth ranks and were tremendous players. I was very privileged to captain a great bunch of lads, both on and off the field.

JP: And off the field I'm going to use a quote from you, Alan, in the foreword to the book. "Off the pitch we were like a bunch of desperadoes riding into Dodge City looking for excitement. Pubs, afternoon drinking clubs and nightclubs were all part of our regular itinerary. We'd tie up our horses and the whole saloon would turn their heads." Bit like the Wild West then, was it?

AH: Well, it was, yeah. It reminds me so much when I watch those old films, I just think of us all the time. They'd fling the doors open and in we'd walk and just turn heads all the time. And we had such fun, it was unbelievable.

JP: When people think of Chelsea in the seventies they think of the FA Cup final and Dave Sexton's team. But it all actually started with Tommy Docherty, they forget Tommy Doc's part in all this . . .

PO: Yeah, Tom was coach there and he inherited, as Ronnie says, a great bunch of lads. You had Venables, Bonetti, Shellito, the Harris brothers, McCalliog, Hollins, you could go through them all. When I got in the first team I think George Graham was the only outsider. As Ron says all the rest were homegrown and when you've got that feeling for the club, when you've grown up at the club, you keep that feeling even when you leave. You're still Chelsea through and through because you've grown up there, and I'm sure that's the same for Ron and Alan.

JP: The chance to succeed for the Tommy Docherty team was the 1967 FA Cup final, but you didn't play very well . . .

PO: That's because I was injured and didn't play in the game!

JP: Er, yes, you burst into the team as a teenager and then you broke your leg, didn't you?

PO: No, Emlyn Hughes broke my leg. He broke it when I was 18 and I missed the Cup Final in '67.

RH: It was a very poor game, actually. We never played well on the day but I think prior to that Tommy Docherty had transformed Chelsea Football Club. In the years before we had some great players like Ken Shellito, Barry Bridges, Bobby Tambling and Bert Murray. These were all lads that had come through the youth ranks and I think they were as good a side as the one we had in the seventies. But then Tom got a little bit impatient and split the side up. Then we had another crop of youngsters that came through and took us to the Cup Final again and the European Cup Winners Cup.

JP: Terry Venables was very much the boss of the midfield. I think perhaps the egos clashed between him and Tommy, but did you look up to Terry when you were coming through the youth ranks as a kid, Alan? Was he influential on you as a player?

AH: Yeah, he was. I was more of a Fulham supporter and Johnny Haynes was my man. But I remember Terry Venables scoring a hat-trick against Roma in the Inter-Cities Cup. I was standing behind the goal in the north stand and it was the most amazing game. Venners was unbelievable. He wasn't even that old when he left us, it was just that him and Docherty had that terrible falling out. I don't think they've even spoken to each other since. I had to follow him into the team which was quite something. But I learnt quite a lot from him and when I played in the FA Cup at QPR – when Os got a hat-trick on our cup run – it was great to play against him, to pit your wits against him.

JP: He didn't think you were going to do very well in that game, did he?

AH: No, he didn't. He did the foreword for my first book and he said that he tested me out early on and it didn't really work. I could run a lot faster than him.

RH: Didn't he kick you up the khazi and you didn't have to look round because you heard it was Terry? [*laughs*]

PO: Is that the reason you came to Chelsea because Fulham turned you down?

AH: They did turn me down, they said 'he's too small'. My father said to them, 'Well, he's only 12, he will grow'. But I did want to play for Fulham.

JP: The book goes on to talk about the 'Blackpool Incident', which probably broke the Tommy Docherty team up, when some of the players were out late at night. But none of you three were involved, were you? You were all very good boys throughout your careers, he says with his nose growing by the second. It also goes on to tell how you beat the German national side, but I think the most impressive aspect of the first part of the book is this camaraderie. Alan just touched on it, he stood on the terraces and watched Chelsea. And all the way through, be it in The Markham Arms, The Lord Palmerston or The Ifield Tavern – and if you don't know Chelsea, these were all great pubs frequented by the Chelsea players and fans – you were there, making the fans feel very much part of it. You don't get that these days . . .

PO: Some of the fans used to say, 'How did you get in the Ifield after the game before we did?' These were the 'in' places to go. The fans used to recognise us, they were great to us and we had a great rapport with them. We were all just one of the lads, it was really fantastic at the time.

AH: I think another exciting thing for the fans was that, unlike today, we used to go up and back to away games on the train and coming back they'd all be on the same train as us. We'd be sitting down having a drink or playing a game of cards in the corner and the fans would keep coming through. Basically, they were part of the team.

JP: The Bridge was the place to be, wasn't it? Actors like Rodney Bewes, Tom Courtenay, Alan Price and Steve McQueen were guests, but of all these legends nothing came close to the visit of Raquel Welch. The man who introduced her to the team was the film stars' photographer Terry O'Neill. Welcome to the show, Terry.

Terry O'Neill [*on phone*]: Hi, good evening. Good evening lads.

JP: You introduced Raquel Welch to Chelsea. What happened?

TO: She used to wonder where I disappeared to every other Saturday. So I took her to the match after arranging it with Dave

Sexton. We had to walk all around the ground and suddenly everyone recognised her and they were all cheering. She went to her seat and totally fell in love with Peter Osgood. So that's what happened with that. I had to buy her the number nine shirt, the shorts, the socks, the lot and then I took some pictures of her as Ossie.

JP: You were very much a part of the 'Swinging Sixties' scene, but how much were the team a part of that? You hear the history of the sixties and it's all about the film stars, the Stones and the Beatles but you don't hear too many mentions of Chelsea Football Club . . .

TO: Well, there should be because anybody who was anybody used to go there. There was a whole gang of us who went, Vidal Sassoon, Terry Stamp, loads of people, Doug Hayward the tailor. And I must say, lads, you gave us the greatest time in football except for the Chelsea now. I must thank you all very much.

JP: What do you think of Chelsea now, Terry?

TO: Absolutely fantastic!

JP: But do they have the characters that these boys have?

TO: If let loose, yes, but I think the boss is too tough.

JP: Do you hanker back to those days when people like yourself but also the fans could get really close to the players?

TO: Oh, yeah, it was fantastic, you really were moved by it. It was a sort of more dangerous football then, and when Ossie got cruising and Huddy got going and Chopper was pulling them all down at the back it was fabulous.

JP: You're talking about them on the field. How bad were they off the field, Terry?

TO: I didn't see too much of them, did I, boys? [*laughs*] We used to go out to lunch, but not too often.

JP: Peter being the gentleman he is probably won't give us any more details of his friendship with Raquel, which is a shame. But you can, Terry, so spill the beans . . .

TO: She just took a fancy to Ossie, he was having one of those fabulous days when it all went right. I can't remember who you were playing . . .

PO: It was Leicester, and I had a diabolical game.

TO: Well, she didn't think so!

PO: Shows that she was a good judge, doesn't it, bless her!

TO: I don't think she was too interested in the football . . .

PO: No, and neither was I – that's why I had a bad game! [*laughs*]

JP: Didn't she blow you a kiss as she was leaving?

PO: Yes, a nice little kiss and she waved to me . . .

TO: Yes, you've just got that magic, Os!

PO: I know mate, I just wish I had it now, I can tell you.

TO: She's 60-odd now, you know?

PO: Is she really? I'd still take my chance with her, mate.

AH: Terry? We've got to reinvent 'The Clan'!

JP: [*excitedly*] What's this? What's this?

AH: It was the most wonderful photo Terry took of five or six of us in a little Italian restaurant. Terry Venables, Alan Ball, Marshy [Rodney Marsh] was there, although we won't have him in the next one . . . Terry Mancini and Geoff Hurst.

TO: That's right. Yeah, we've got to recreate that, with all your stories about what happened to you all since. It would be fabulous.

AH: With different faces . . .

JP: Yes, you might have to touch the faces up a little bit in the new photo, Terry!

TO: I don't think so. I saw Ossie down at the Bridge recently and you look good, Peter.

PO: Yes, I've done well, mate, I've been off the booze for three months now. I went to see George [Best] and it made me feel really bad, so I've been off it. I feel a lot better, but George has been off it for 60 days too I'm pleased to say. I saw him the other day, Bestie, and he's still kicking on. But it would be nice to see you again, mate, we must get together.

TO: Yes, mate, I look forward to that.

JP: Terry O'Neill, thanks very much for joining us tonight. Peter, you mentioned the name of George Best there and he was also on the London King's Road scene. Were you lads competitive with him, not just on the football field but on the women-pulling front and the drinking front?

AH: I remember when, being a local, I introduced Ossie to The Duke of Wellington in Sloane Square. That was the day when Dave Sexton told us to get out of the club, Ossie and I went there. That was the first pub George went in, and from there he moved around Sloane Square. These were his moves, and he used to go in The Duke of Wellington a lot. But he always used to be on his own in the corner. I'd be on one side of the bar and he'd be on the other side of the bar and he never really got involved. But he wanted to come to Chelsea so badly it was unbelievable, he wanted to play with us. Obviously, though, Sexton couldn't handle us so what chance would he have with George as well?

JP: Were all the players involved in this swinging scene? When people think about Ron Harris they think about him being very sensible off the field of play, hard and rugged on it. Were all of you part of this scene?

RH: No, I don't think so. You had some lads who were quite happy to shoot off home after training. But we had about 16 players in our first team squad, and if we went abroad or somewhere you could always guarantee that about 14 of them would want to go out. We had three exceptional players in Ossie, Huddy and Charlie Cooke and they were the ones who would get the headlines for going out on the King's Road and for what they did on the field.

JP: But it was a mix of players, wasn't it? You had someone like John Hollins who put in so much work . . .

RH: As I say, we had three exceptional players and we had a back four that kicked anything or anybody that moved. They needed us and we needed them. We had a tremendous blend.

And, behind the scenes, from Brian Mears the chairman to Millie who used to wash all the kit we had one happy club.

PO: George [Anstiss], the groundsman as well. We loved them all, that's the sort of club it was at the time. That's why we were so close together, and the feeling in the dressing room was just electric.

JP: And when you were training outside, and you were doing these five-a-sides on the gravel and concrete of the forecourt of the stadium did Ron really go in slide tackling on that surface?

PO: He used to put himself about very rarely, but when he did he hurt somebody. [*chuckles*] No, not really, no.

AH: Some of those five-a-sides were tougher than Saturday games.

RH: It was very, very competitive.

PO: I remember I broke Johnny Boyle's nose in one game.

JP: On a similar subject, we have a text here from a fan who wants to know why the 1970 FA Cup final was so violent when there were so many quality players on both sides? You missed out, Alan, and watched from the sidelines. Was it violent for you?

AH: Apart from my two marriages and my accident that was one of the worst experiences of my life, not being able to play in both those two games. I still haven't come to terms with it. I couldn't even go on the open top bus with the boys, nothing, I was heartbroken.

JP: But some of the tackles in the game were like collisions . . .

PO: The thing with Leeds was that they were bullies. They tried to intimidate other players, they tried to intimidate the ref. That was down to [Don] Revie, they were a horrible team. As Ron's just said, they couldn't beat our back four at kicking – they wouldn't bow down to anybody – and in midfield we had Johnny Hollins, who wasn't a hard boy, but he was tough and strong and he wouldn't back down either. Then, up front we had big Hutch, Tommy Baldwin and myself and we could all look after ourselves, so we battled with them, they didn't like it and retaliated.

JP: Was it any more brutal than other matches between during that period? There was another match a couple of years earlier when John Boyle, I think, was kicked very badly in the face . . .

PO: That was the [1967] semi-final when Gary Sprake came rushing out of his goal . . .

JP: Maybe the final just seemed worse because it was on telly?

PO: No, it was the most brutal game I've ever played in and the most violent I've ever seen in football. I watched it again on video down in Wales after I gave an after-dinner speech and, I tell you, the oohs and aahs from the people in the crowd were incredible. They just couldn't believe what they were seeing, they'd never seen anything like it before.

JP: It was a cup final, though. Be honest, you were lucky to take it to a replay, weren't you, Ron?

RH: Well, on the balance of play in the first game we were a little bit fortunate. But in the end, over the two games, we came from behind three times and there weren't too many sides who did that against Leeds. They were a good side, we were a good side, and there was great respect between us. We wouldn't give an inch and neither would they, and I think that's why there's always been great rivalry between the two clubs – although, of course, now they're in a different division.

JP: David Elleray did a video study of the game a few years ago and I think he said that 21 of you would have been sent off!

PO: When I watched the video of the game I took it all in, and some of the tackles were just incredible. He [Ron] did two tackles on the back of Eddie Gray's knee which were just unbelievable. Eddie McCreadie kicked Billy Bremner in the head with a scissor kick in the [Chelsea] penalty box and never got a foul given against him. Jack Charlton had a go at me and knocked me over, Hutch blatantly pushed Billy Bremner over . . . it was just incredible the things that were going on.

JP: Great quote from Ron in the book, referring to Jack Charlton's 'black book' of people he was going to catch up with: 'I didn't need a black book – I've always had a good memory.' [*Laughter*]

And we mentioned Eddie Gray there. He had a fantastic first game at Wembley against poor old David Webb . . .

PO: You're right, but nothing ever came from it. No goals came from it. And in the second game Dave Sexton swapped Ronnie and Webby over, and Ronnie knew what to do. In the first five minutes – wham!

AH: It was a bad decision by Dave Sexton to play Webby at right-back against Eddie Gray in the first game, especially with the big, open spaces of Wembley. Webby was a centre-half not a full-back.

PO: Al's right there. Eddie Gray was the only dangerman who could do something different. Clarkey [Allan Clarke] and Jonesy [Mick Jones] couldn't do the things that Eddie Gray could do, nor could Bremner and Giles. Eddie Gray was the one guy in their side who could turn it on and beat people. And the only guy to mark him was him [Ron] because he used to mark Bestie, Greavsie and the best of them – and Eddie Gray was a great player, no doubt about it.

JP: And the story ended with Webby getting the winning goal . . .

RH: Well, I think he deserved it, Webby, because he had a fierce time at Wembley. But what a lot of people don't remember is that, just before the final whistle in the first game, Webby cleared a Johnny Giles shot off the line with a scissor kick which would have won them the cup if it had gone in. But Webby was a battler, we swapped over positions, he picked himself up and the scored the winning goal – although I think Tommy Baldwin still claims that he got the final touch.

AH: But the strange thing about the team selection was that when we played Stoke in the [1972] League Cup final Dave Sexton played David Webb at right-back. And if you remember their winning goal, Terry Conroy went by him so easily and just put the cross in and it cost us the game. Ron and Webby should have been the other round again.

JP: Let's look now at the epic European Cup Winners Cup triumph. There was a wonderful game against Bruges in the quarter-final, then the final itself against Real Madrid in Athens. The first game ended in a draw and you, Peter, were unfit for the replay two days later and, typical of Chelsea at the time, you went to the swimming pool and had a few drinks . . .

PO: Well, first of all, I missed the first game with Bruges. We lost 2-0 away and I came back after a six-week suspension. We got through and I missed the semi-final against Man City with knee ligament trouble, and by the time of the final I still wasn't right. I told Dave Sexton that I wasn't quite right, but he said the doctor could get me through the game with an injection. So I had the cortisone injection, which is what we did in those days, and I got through to about 85 minutes. We were 1-0 up, I'd scored which was great and the lads were battling away, but then they scored in the last minute. We got through extra-time and we had the next day off before we played the replay on the Friday. On our days off what we normally did was meet up and have a few drinks – me, Tommy Baldwin, Hutch and Al when we got a bit older, but not in those days. So me, Charlie Cooke and Tommy Baldwin went down the local Hilton Hotel and had a drink by the swimming pool. I just dangled my leg in it because I didn't think I would be playing the next day anyway.

JP: And you won the next day. Having missed the FA Cup final, that must have been doubly sweet for you, Alan Hudson?

AH: It was, yeah. I got a knock in the thigh in the first game, a dead leg, so I was struggling a little bit. I remember the day before I told Dave I was fine. I just thought, 'You're not going to leave me out of the replay'. So I played with that, but there was no way I was going to miss the game after missing the Leeds matches. I think Charlie and I played well together that night. What helped was that they had a guy called Pirri who played with a cast on his hand. Probably Ronnie did it when he shook hands with him! That helped us a bit but we deserved to win it over the two matches. But can you imagine the players today playing 48 hours later?

JP: There were other players in the squad who we haven't mentioned much – the likes of Peter Houseman, John Boyle, Marvin Hinton, John Dempsey and Keith Weller, who recently lost his long battle with cancer. He moved to Leicester with another Stamford Bridge great, Alan Birchenall, who joins us now. Good evening, Alan.

Alan Birchenall [*on phone*]: Good evening Jonathan.

JP: Well, a sad week for you, because I know that you had helped to raise money for Keith's treatment a while back . . .

AB: Very sad. As the lads there, the 'three amigos', know I still frequent hostelries and I was in my village pub on Friday night and when I got back home about eleven o'clock I got a call from another old team-mate of mine, Steve Earle, who told me the bad news. Then Keith's brother Phil rang me about five minutes later. It wasn't unexpected but it was still a shock.

JP: I'll come back to you in a moment, Alan. But, Peter, how important was Keith Weller to that team? The book suggests that when he was sold it started the downfall of the club . . .

PO: Hi Alan.

AB: Hi Os.

PO: Yes, Keith came and he was a bit of a flash boy but he was a good player. The thing with Keith, though, was that he wanted to play up front with me, he wanted to play down the middle. But Dave wanted to play him wide on the right. He broke Bert Murray's record for a winger when he got something like 17 goals in a season for us. He was quick, he wasn't frightened of defenders, he was an excellent player for us. With Peter Houseman on one wing and Keith on the other it was fantastic for me and big Hutch or Tommy Baldwin in the centre.

JP: And, Alan, to happier stories . . . you keep cropping up in the book in various pubs and hostelries and there are some lovely stories as well. There's a great one about Ossie when he was lagging behind in a cross-country over Epsom Downs. Just tell us that story . . .

AB: Oh, Dave Sexton used to take us over there, didn't he? And he got so fed up with us middlers because people like Catty [Peter Bonetti] and Holly would stream off and they'd be home half an hour before us, sat on the bus. Then we'd all have to wait for Marvin Hinton, Ossie and big Hutch. Anyway, Dave threatened to bring us all back in the afternoon if Ossie didn't pull his finger out. At the time I was living in Ascot and Ossie was in Windsor and I said to him, 'Os, for God's sake, we can do without having to come back.' And he said, 'Birch, I'm going to put a real effort into the next cross-country.' So we ran round Epsom Downs again and the same people flew off, Catty and Holly. I looked over my shoulder and there was Os going at his normal speed, just above a walk. We were coming round Tattenham Corner and I heard this sound – trrrump, trrrump, trrrump – and Ossie's flying past us all on a race horse. He'd got his mate from some stables down in Berkshire to saddle him up in the gorse. Whether it was a plan he'd hatched over eight pints of beer I don't know, but those were the days . . .

JP: They were great days, weren't they, Alan?

AB: Yes, happy days.

JP: Lovely, thanks for joining us, Alan.

AB: Yeah, well thanks for giving me a few memories about Keith Weller, a great player.

JP: We have some texts from listeners I want to read out. But first, where did this team break up, Ron? What happened to it? I know that Dave Sexton had his differences with these two . . .

RH: Well, when Os and Huddy left the scene it just seemed to disintegrate really. They were the first two lads to move away from Chelsea and the results weren't going particularly well. Then it was just a mass exodus of players leaving.

JP: Does he still stand out as a coach, though?

PO: He was a brilliant coach. Obviously, he made mistakes and he made one with Webby playing right-back but the things he did with us were tremendous. I mean, he took the whole team to see a rugby game and we thought, 'What are we doing?' because we trained for three or four days afterwards with a rugby ball and we never saw a football. What we had to do was get to the byline and we had to pass the ball back not forwards, so what you had to do was get support – as soon as a player got the ball you had to go and support him. It was unbelievable how well it worked. Those are the sort of things Dave did, you know, the near post and far post, with me and Hutch making runs, getting the crosses in early. It was terrific, he really was a great coach, yeah.

JP: And, the ten pound ball and the five pound ball . . .

PO: Tommy Baldwin used to love that because he was only a little lad although he was good in the air. The big centre half would come alongside him and Tommy would say 'fiver' and he'd spin off, off he'd go and they'd knock it over the top for him. And he got loads of goals from it, Tom.

JP: And he got a fiver a time, did he?

PO: Yeah.

AH: It made us laugh because after he scored the first time Dave Sexton said, 'Here's your fiver, but I think you ought to give Johnny Hollins £2.50 because it was his pass' and Tommy said, 'No chance!'

JP: £2.50? They're on 90 grand a week now . . . Susan [Bookbinder] has got some texts for you . . .

Susan Bookbinder: Yes, loads of Chelsea fans texting in asking what you think of the current squad. One here from a fan who says, after watching Chelsea for 25 years, he's still not sure about this year's team – what are your thoughts?

JP: Start with Alan . . .

AH: Um, after watching Porto last year and the mess Ranieri made of it in Monte Carlo I think this manager [Jose Mourinho] is top notch. I fancied Chelsea to win the Premiership right from the beginning of the season. I doubted it a little bit when Arsenal went five points clear because I put it in my latest book as well. I thought, 'What have I said? I'll look a mug', but this fella is a fantastic manager. I believe Chelsea will go real close, if not win it.

JP: And your thoughts on Frank Lampard?

AH: I used to watch Frank a lot at West Ham, I used to go over there nearly every home game to see Harry [Redknapp]. Frank is the most improved player I've seen over a couple of seasons, just phenomenal. His all-round game has improved, he's just become a huge player for them, him and John Terry. The two local lads have been out of this world.

JP: And, Ossie, what about the strike force and, indeed, this season's hopes?

PO: Well, we have a good side. But when I went away to Lazio and we won 4–0 and then we beat Newcastle 5–0 in consecutive weeks, that was the best I've ever seen a Chelsea team play since we played. It was awesome. I thought it was the best squad of players that Chelsea's ever had, including us, and then Ranieri messed around a little bit and we've got this guy in, Mourinho, and he's awesome. He's got this side together in such a short space of time because so many players have come in, and he's transformed them into a right good side straightaway. And they're getting better, don't worry about that.

JP: Have they got a 30-goal player in there? Drogba, can he do it? Kezman, can he do it? Gudjohnson?

PO: I think Drogba might be able to do it. I don't think Kezman can, because he looks out of sorts at the moment and can't get a goal to save his life. He's a proven goalscorer because his record in Holland was second to none. But we don't need him at the moment, because Lampard is scoring, Robben is scoring, Tiago is scoring – so we don't need the forwards!

JP: Ossie, you are 'The King of Stamford Bridge' but Arjen Robben could take your crown. He's some talent, isn't he?

PO: Well, after 30 years he's welcome to it! It's getting a bit heavy on me now.

But he's a fantastic talent, let's be fair. He's like George Best, like a Huddy or Charlie Cooke. They could change games, and he can change games for you. And you talk about Frank Lampard, well, he's almost as good as Huddy now. That's how good he is. He will become a legend, because he's a great athlete, he's got a great engine and he just loves to play football.

JP: And Ron, what are your thoughts on John Terry?

RH: John's been a tremendous player over the last couple of seasons for Chelsea. He's not been playing regularly in the England side, but I think any other manager other than Sven Goran Eriksson would have kept him in the side.

SB: We have another text from a fan who wants to know which current player you would have liked to play alongside?

RH: Well, obviously, I'd love to be playing with John Terry. I think he's very similar to myself: he's come through the youth side, he's Chelsea through and through, and yes I'd love to play alongside him.

AH: As a midfield player or inside forward I could see myself playing with Frank Lampard. And if you could imagine Charlie Cooke being on the right and Robben on the left, me and young Frank, I think that would be a tremendous engine room. We'd have to get Charlie sober because a lot of people only saw him when he'd been out too much, but sober he was some player.

PO: Well, I've watched them over the years and worked there on the hospitality side and I'd have loved to have played with Luca Vialli and Zola. Of the guys now, I'd have liked to have played with Jimmy Floyd and Eidur Gudjohnsen, so those four. I'm not going to say Kezman or Drogba because, for the moment, I don't think they've fulfilled their potential. There's more to come from those two, I'm sure.

SB: Another fan says Peter O was the player who converted me from supporting Man United as a lad. Can Robben do the same for my son, he asks?

PO: Well, if his son has got any sense he certainly can. He's an awesome talent, he's a young lad of 20 and he is an exciting player. He scores goals as well, and he's as good as Ryan Giggs now, the way he's playing.

SB: I have a text here which asks if Ossie and Hud, given their time again, would like to have a better relationship with Dave Sexton?

AH: It was a strange. We were talking earlier about him as a coach, and if he'd just been our coach everything would have been fine. But he should never have been our manager. You can't fall out with players in the manager's office and then go out on the training pitch with them and have a laugh and a joke. That's where he got it wrong.

PO: The thing with Dave is that he looked at fellows like Ron, John Hollins, Peter Houseman and Peter Bonetti, who weren't the great socialisers, and he never gave them a bollocking in their lives. But us lads, the flair players, me, Huddy and Charlie, when we had a mediocre game he'd have a go at us. He expected us to turn it on week in and week out, and even if we had a good, grafting game he didn't see it from our point of view. Every time somebody got a rollicking in the dressing room it was one of us.

AH: I don't think it was when we were mediocre. I think it was more when something went wrong he would hit on our social-ising and say, 'it's you lot!'.

PO: He was an average centre forward himself who thought we were abusing our talents.

JP: Great coach, but one who didn't make it as a manager perhaps. Yet he's one of the most successful Chelsea managers of all time . . .

AH: How many ex-players have become great manager/coaches?

PO: Deep down he is a smashing guy, a lovely fellow but it's a shame we had to work with somebody like that because if you didn't work with him he would be a good mate who would never let you down.

JP: [*following a news break*] We're talking about the great Chelsea team of the Sixties and Seventies. The place to be seen on the King's Road at the time was the Aretusa nightclub and restaurant and we're joined now by the owner, Alvaro Maccioni. Good evening, Alvaro.

Alvaro Maccioni [*on phone*]: Good evening.

JP: We've got Alan Hudson, Peter Osgood and Ron Harris with us. I guess, Alvaro, that you'll be able to tell us that Dave Sexton came into your nightclub looking for them once or twice, is that right?

AM: Yes, indeed, but we had a system in place that if the boss came in we'd never seen them!

JP: So you had a system of spies and back doors, did you?

AM: Well, we had a discotheque downstairs which had a back door so we could hide them if necessary, yes.

JP: What sort of days were those, Alvaro? Because you had rock stars, pop stars and film stars in there as well . . .

AM: We had people from showbusiness, the film business, footballers, models coming to the club. That was the kind of clientele we had coming to the club.

AH: It's nice to hear your voice, Alvaro. What a club we ran! What are you up to now?

AM: I have a restaurant, *La Familigia*, in Chelsea, not very far away.

AH: Well, I'll see you very soon then. It was the best club in London, wasn't it?

AM: Yes, unbelievable.

JP: Do the current Chelsea players go to *La Familigia*, Alvaro?

AM: Yes, very often in fact. Nearly all of them. For Cudicini, this place is like his canteen.

JP: And how does their behaviour compare with the players of the sixties and seventies?

AM: Well, the Sixties were the Sixties. Today is different, everything is under more control.

PO: So, they're boring now, is that what you're saying?

AM: [*laughs*] I didn't say that, you said that!

PO: Alvaro, listen, next time I come in and my missus comes in asking for me, can you hide me again please?

AM: [*laughs*] I will!

JP: Thanks, Alvaro. Times have changed, but would you like to be playing today, even though there aren't the same characters around?

PO: Well, talking about what we used to get up to, these players are in the papers all the time for being drunk and raping people. We never got round to that sort of thing, we never upset anybody. We used to enjoy ourselves but it wasn't as though we were down the King's Road every day. After home games I used to go straight home, and nine times out of ten I'd meet up with Ron in Epsom. We'd go to Ewell village and have a few pints in The Green Man. Ronnie would go for a Chinese and I'd go home for dinner with the missus. After away games I used to go home on Sunday mornings after going out on the King's Road. I didn't drink-drive so I arranged somewhere to stay over. And we trained hard too. Everyone thinks we had a fun time, but I bet players today don't do the cross-country runs like we used to do.

SB: We've had so many texts from Chelsea fans; we can't read them all out, but here's a flavour. 'Chopper Harris used to work for my dad at the University of Surrey. I was only 12 but he still kicked me up in the air in five-a-sides,' says Tom. 'I can confirm that Ossie is off the booze. I saw him in the Counting House pub in the City and he was drinking fizzy water,' says Mike.

JP: Thanks, Susan. It's now part of modern Chelsea folklore that Roman Abramovich had a very long chat with Chopper Harris when he took over at the club. No one really knows what happened in that chat but Clive Batty's book *Kings of the King's Road* does tell you and I'm not going to spoil it by telling you about it. Get the book. Thanks to my guests Ron Harris, Alan Hudson, Peter Osgood who were, and are, 'Kings of the King's Road' . . .

THE STATS
1961-1975

LEAGUE DIVISION 1

		P	W	D	L	F	A	W	D	L	F	A	Pts
1.	Ipswich Town	42	17	2	2	58	28	7	6	8	35	39	56
2.	Burnley	42	14	4	3	57	26	7	7	7	44	41	53
3.	Tottenham Hotspur	42	14	4	3	59	34	7	6	8	29	35	52
4.	Everton	42	17	2	2	64	21	3	9	9	24	33	51
5.	Sheffield United	42	13	5	3	37	23	6	4	11	24	46	47
6.	Sheffield Wednesday	42	14	4	3	47	23	6	2	13	25	35	46
7.	Aston Villa	42	13	5	3	45	20	5	3	13	20	36	44
8.	West Ham United	42	11	6	4	49	37	6	4	11	27	45	44
9.	West Bromwich Albion	42	10	7	4	50	23	5	6	10	33	44	43
10.	Arsenal	42	9	6	6	39	31	7	5	9	32	41	43
11.	Bolton Wanderers	42	11	7	3	35	22	5	3	13	27	44	42
12.	Manchester City	42	11	3	7	46	38	6	4	11	32	43	41
13.	Blackpool	42	10	4	7	41	30	5	7	9	29	45	41
14.	Leicester City	42	12	2	7	38	27	5	4	12	34	44	40
15.	Manchester United	42	10	3	8	44	31	5	6	10	28	44	39
16.	Blackburn Rovers	42	10	6	5	33	22	4	5	12	17	36	39
17.	Birmingham City	42	9	6	6	37	35	5	4	12	28	46	38
18.	Wolverhampton Wanderers	42	8	7	6	38	34	5	3	13	35	52	36
19.	Nottingham Forest	42	12	4	5	39	23	1	6	14	24	56	36
20.	Fulham	42	8	3	10	38	34	5	4	12	28	40	33
21.	Cardiff City	42	6	9	6	30	33	3	5	13	20	48	32
22.	**CHELSEA**	**42**	**7**	**7**	**7**	**34**	**29**	**2**	**3**	**16**	**29**	**65**	**28**

Top league scorer: Bobby Tambling, 20 goals
Average home attendance: 27,013

FA CUP
(3) Liverpool (A)   L3–4

LEAGUE CUP
Did not enter

LEAGUE DIVISION 2

		P	W	D	L	F	A	W	D	L	F	A	Pts
1.	Stoke City	42	15	3	3	49	20	5	10	6	24	30	53
2.	**CHELSEA**	42	15	3	3	54	16	9	1	11	27	26	52
3.	Sunderland	42	14	5	2	46	13	6	7	8	38	42	52
4.	Middlesbrough	42	12	4	5	48	35	8	5	8	38	50	49
5.	Leeds United	42	15	2	4	55	19	4	8	9	24	34	48
6.	Huddersfield Town	42	11	6	4	34	21	6	8	7	29	29	48
7.	Newcastle United	42	11	8	2	48	23	7	3	11	31	36	47
8.	Bury	42	11	6	4	28	20	7	5	9	23	27	47
9.	Scunthorpe United	42	12	7	2	35	18	4	5	12	22	41	44
10.	Cardiff City	42	12	5	4	50	29	6	2	13	33	44	43
11.	Southampton	42	15	3	3	52	23	2	5	14	20	44	42
12.	Plymouth Argyle	42	13	4	4	48	24	2	8	11	28	49	42
13.	Norwich City	42	11	6	4	53	33	6	2	13	27	46	42
14.	Rotherham United	42	11	3	7	34	30	6	3	12	33	44	40
15.	Swansea Town	42	13	5	3	33	17	2	4	15	18	55	39
16.	Preston North End	42	11	6	4	43	30	2	5	14	16	44	37
17.	Portsmouth	42	9	5	7	33	27	4	6	11	30	52	37
18.	Derby County	42	10	5	6	40	29	2	7	12	21	43	36
19.	Grimsby Town	42	8	6	7	34	26	3	7	11	21	40	35
20.	Charlton Athletic	42	8	4	9	33	28	5	1	15	29	56	31
21.	Walsall	42	7	7	7	33	37	4	2	15	20	52	31
22.	Luton Town	42	10	4	7	45	40	1	3	17	16	44	29

Top league scorer: Bobby Tambling, 35 goals
Average home attendance: 29,356

FA CUP

(3) Tranmere (A)	D2–2
(Rep) Tranmere (H)	W3–1
(4) Charlton (A)	W3–0
(5) Manchester United (A)	L1–2

LEAGUE CUP

Did not enter

LEAGUE DIVISION 1

		P	W	D	L	F	A	W	D	L	F	A	Pts
1.	Liverpool	42	16	0	5	60	18	10	5	6	32	27	57
2.	Manchester United	42	15	3	3	54	19	8	4	9	36	43	53
3.	Everton	42	14	4	3	53	26	7	6	8	31	38	52
4.	Tottenham Hotspur	42	13	3	5	54	31	9	4	8	43	50	51
5.	**CHELSEA**	**42**	**12**	**3**	**6**	**36**	**24**	**8**	**7**	**6**	**36**	**32**	**50**
6.	Sheffield Wednesday	42	15	3	3	50	24	4	8	9	34	43	49
7.	Blackburn Rovers	42	10	4	7	44	28	8	6	7	45	37	46
8.	Arsenal	42	10	7	4	56	37	7	4	10	34	45	45
9.	Burnley	42	14	3	4	46	23	3	7	11	25	41	44
10.	West Bromwich Albion	42	9	6	6	43	35	7	5	9	27	26	43
11.	Leicester City	42	9	4	8	33	27	7	7	7	28	31	43
12.	Sheffield United	42	10	6	5	35	22	6	5	10	26	42	43
13.	Nottingham Forest	42	9	5	7	34	24	7	4	10	30	44	41
14.	West Ham United	42	8	7	6	45	38	6	5	10	24	36	40
15.	Fulham	42	11	8	2	45	23	2	5	14	13	42	39
16.	Wolverhampton Wanderers	42	6	9	6	36	34	6	6	9	34	46	39
17.	Stoke City	42	9	6	6	49	33	5	4	12	28	45	38
18.	Blackpool	42	8	6	7	26	29	5	3	13	26	44	35
19.	Aston Villa	42	8	6	7	35	29	3	6	12	27	42	34
20.	Birmingham City	42	7	7	7	33	32	4	0	17	21	60	29
21.	Bolton Wanderers	42	6	5	10	30	35	4	3	14	18	45	28
22.	Ipswich Town	42	9	3	9	38	45	0	4	17	18	76	25

Top league scorer: Bobby Tambling, 27 goals
Average home attendance: 31,347

FA CUP

(3) Tottenham (A)	D1–1
(Rep) Tottenham (H)	W2–0
(4) Huddersfield (H)	L1–2

LEAGUE CUP

(2) Swindon (A)	L0–3

LEAGUE DIVISION 1

		P	W	D	L	F	A	W	D	L	F	A	Pts
1.	Manchester United	42	16	4	1	52	13	10	5	6	37	26	61
2.	Leeds United	42	16	3	2	53	23	10	6	5	30	29	61
3.	**CHELSEA**	**42**	**15**	**2**	**4**	**48**	**19**	**9**	**6**	**6**	**41**	**35**	**56**
4.	Everton	42	9	10	2	37	22	8	5	8	32	38	49
5.	Nottingham Forest	42	10	7	4	45	33	7	6	8	26	34	47
6.	Tottenham Hotspur	42	18	3	0	65	20	1	4	16	22	51	45
7.	Liverpool	42	12	5	4	42	33	5	5	11	25	40	44
8.	Sheffield Wednesday	42	13	5	3	37	15	3	6	12	20	40	43
9.	West Ham United	42	14	2	5	48	25	5	2	14	34	46	42
10.	Blackburn Rovers	42	12	2	7	46	33	4	8	9	37	46	42
11.	Stoke City	42	11	4	6	40	27	5	6	10	27	39	42
12.	Burnley	42	9	9	3	39	26	7	1	13	31	44	42
13.	Arsenal	42	11	5	5	42	31	6	2	13	27	44	41
14.	West Bromwich Albion	42	10	5	6	45	25	3	8	10	25	40	39
15.	Sunderland	42	12	6	3	45	26	2	3	16	19	48	37
16.	Aston Villa	42	14	1	6	36	24	2	4	15	21	58	37
17.	Blackpool	42	9	7	5	41	28	3	4	14	26	50	35
18.	Leicester City	42	9	6	6	43	36	2	7	12	26	49	35
19.	Sheffield United	42	7	5	9	30	29	5	6	10	20	35	35
20.	Fulham	42	10	5	6	44	32	1	7	13	16	46	34
21.	Wolverhampton Wanderers	42	8	2	11	33	36	5	2	14	26	53	30
22.	Birmingham City	42	6	8	7	36	40	2	3	16	28	56	27

Top league scorer: Barry Bridges, 20 goals
Average home attendance: 37,054

FA CUP

(3) Northampton (H)	W4–1
(4) West Ham (A)	W1–0
(5) Tottenham (H)	W1–0
(6) Peterborough (H)	W5–1
(S/F) Liverpool (Villa Park)	L0–2

LEAGUE CUP

(2) Birmingham City (A)	W3–0
(3) Notts Co. (H)	W4–0
(4) Swansea (H)	W3–2
(5) Workington (A)	D2–2
(Rep) Workington (H)	W2–0
(S/F-1) Aston Villa (A)	W3–2
(S/F-2) Aston Villa (H)	D1–1
(Final-1) Leicester City (H)	W3–2
(Final-2) Leicester City (A)	D0–0

LEAGUE CUP FINAL TEAM

1st leg: Bonetti, Hinton, Harris R, Hollins, Young, Boyle, Murray, Graham, McCreadie, Venables, Tambling Scorers:
Tambling, Venables (pen), McCreadie

2nd leg: Bonetti, Hinton, McCreadie, Harris R, Mortimore, Upton, Murray, Boyle, Bridges, Venables, Tambling

LEAGUE DIVISION 1

		P	W	D	L·	F	A	W	D	L	F	A	Pts
1.	Liverpool	42	17	2	2	52	15	9	7	5	27	19	61
2.	Leeds United	42	14	4	3	49	15	9	5	7	30	23	55
3.	Burnley	42	15	3	3	45	20	9	4	8	34	27	55
4.	Manchester United	42	12	8	1	50	20	6	7	8	34	39	51
5.	**CHELSEA**	**42**	**11**	**4**	**6**	**30**	**21**	**11**	**3**	**7**	**35**	**32**	**51**
6.	West Bromwich Albion	42	11	6	4	58	34	8	6	7	33	35	50
7.	Leicester City	42	12	4	5	40	28	9	3	9	40	37	49
8.	Tottenham Hotspur	42	11	6	4	55	37	5	6	10	20	29	44
9.	Sheffield United	42	11	6	4	37	25	5	5	11	19	34	43
10.	Stoke City	42	12	6	3	42	22	3	6	12	23	42	42
11.	Everton	42	12	6	3	39	19	3	5	13	17	43	41
12.	West Ham United	42	12	5	4	46	33	3	4	14	24	50	39
13.	Arsenal	42	8	8	5	36	31	4	5	12	26	44	37
14.	Blackpool	42	9	5	7	36	29	5	4	12	19	36	37
15.	Newcastle United	42	10	5	6	26	20	4	4	13	24	43	37
16.	Nottingham Forest	42	11	3	7	32	26	3	5	13	25	46	36
17.	Sheffield Wednesday	42	11	6	4	35	18	3	2	16	21	48	36
18.	Aston Villa	42	10	3	8	39	34	5	3	13	30	46	36
19.	Sunderland	42	13	2	6	36	28	1	6	14	15	44	36
20.	Fulham	42	9	4	8	34	37	5	3	13	33	48	35
21.	Northampton Town	42	8	6	7	31	32	2	7	12	24	60	33
22.	Blackburn Rovers	42	6	1	14	30	36	2	3	16	27	52	20

Top league scorer: George Graham, 17 goals
Average home attendance: 31,344

FA CUP

(3) Liverpool (A)	W2–1
(4) Leeds (H)	W1–0
(5) Shrewsbury (H)	W3–2
(6) Hull City (H)	D2–2
(Rep) Hull City (A)	W3–1
(S/F) Sheffield Weds. (Villa Park)	L0–2

LEAGUE CUP

Did not enter

FAIRS CUP

(1) AS Roma (Italy) (H)	W 4–1
AS Roma (A)	D0–0
(2) Wiener SC (Aust) (A)	L0–1
Wiener SC (Aust) (H)	W2–0
(3) AC Milan (Italy) (A)	L1–2
AC Milan (H)	W2–1
(Play-off) AC Milan (A)	D1–1 (Won on toss of coin)
(4) Munich 1860 (A)	D2–2
Munich 1860 (H)	W1–0
(S/F) Barcelona (A)	L0–2
Barcelona (H)	W2–0
(Play-off) Barcelona (A)	L0–5

LEAGUE DIVISION 1

		P	W	D	L	F	A	W	D	L	F	A	Pts
1.	Manchester United	42	17	4	0	51	13	7	8	6	33	32	60
2.	Nottingham Forest	42	16	4	1	41	13	7	6	8	23	28	56
3.	Tottenham Hotspur	42	15	3	3	44	21	9	5	7	27	27	56
4.	Leeds United	42	15	4	2	41	17	7	7	7	21	25	55
5.	Liverpool	42	12	7	2	36	17	7	6	8	28	30	51
6.	Everton	42	11	4	6	39	22	8	6	7	26	24	48
7.	Arsenal	42	11	6	4	32	20	5	8	8	26	27	46
8.	Leicester City	42	12	4	5	47	28	6	4	11	31	43	44
9.	**CHELSEA**	**42**	**7**	**9**	**5**	**33**	**29**	**8**	**5**	**8**	**34**	**33**	**44**
10.	Sheffield United	42	11	5	5	34	22	5	5	11	18	37	42
11.	Sheffield Wednesday	42	9	7	5	39	19	5	6	10	17	28	41
12.	Stoke City	42	11	5	5	40	21	6	2	13	23	37	41
13.	West Bromwich Albion	42	11	1	9	40	28	5	6	10	37	45	39
14.	Burnley	42	11	4	6	43	28	4	5	12	23	48	39
15.	Manchester City	42	8	9	4	27	25	4	6	11	16	27	39
16.	West Ham United	42	8	6	7	40	31	6	2	13	40	53	36
17.	Sunderland	42	12	3	6	39	26	2	5	14	19	46	36
18.	Fulham	42	8	7	6	49	34	3	5	13	22	49	34
19.	Southampton	42	10	3	8	49	41	4	3	14	25	51	34
20.	Newcastle United	42	9	5	7	24	27	3	4	14	15	54	33
21.	Aston Villa	42	7	5	9	30	33	4	2	15	24	52	29
22.	Blackpool	42	1	5	15	18	36	5	4	12	23	40	21

Top league scorer: Bobby Tambling, 21 goals
Average home attendance: 35,525
Player of the Year: Peter Bonetti (Inaugural season)

FA CUP

(3) Huddersfield (A)	W2–1
(4) Brighton (A)	D1–1
(Rep) Brighton (H)	W4–0
(5) Sheffield Utd (H)	W2–0
(6) Sheffield Weds. (H)	W1–0
(S/F) Leeds (Villa Park)	W1–0
(Final) Tottenham (Wembley)	L1–2

FA Cup Final team: Bonetti, Harris A, McCreadie, Hollins, Hinton, Harris R, Cooke, Baldwin, Hateley, Tambling, Boyle
Scorer: Tambling

LEAGUE CUP

(2) Charlton (H)	W5–2
(3) Blackpool (A)	D1–1
(Rep) Blackpool (H)	L1–3

LEAGUE DIVISION 1

		P	W	D	L	F	A	W	D	L	F	A	Pts
1.	Manchester City	42	17	2	2	52	16	9	4	8	34	27	58
2.	Manchester United	42	15	2	4	49	21	9	6	6	40	34	56
3.	Liverpool	42	17	2	2	51	17	5	9	7	20	23	55
4.	Leeds United	42	17	3	1	49	14	5	6	10	22	27	53
5.	Everton	42	18	1	2	43	13	5	5	11	24	27	52
6.	**CHELSEA**	**42**	**11**	**7**	**3**	**34**	**25**	**7**	**5**	**9**	**28**	**43**	**48**
7.	Tottenham Hotspur	42	11	7	3	44	20	8	2	11	26	39	47
8.	West Bromwich Albion	42	12	4	5	45	25	5	8	8	30	37	46
9.	Arsenal	42	12	6	3	37	23	5	4	12	23	33	44
10.	Newcastle United	42	12	7	2	38	20	1	8	12	16	47	41
11.	Nottingham Forest	42	11	6	4	34	22	3	5	13	18	42	39
12.	West Ham United	42	8	5	8	43	30	6	5	10	30	39	38
13.	Leicester City	42	7	7	7	37	34	6	5	10	27	35	38
14.	Burnley	42	12	7	2	38	16	2	3	16	26	55	38
15.	Sunderland	42	8	7	6	28	28	5	4	12	23	33	37
16.	Southampton	42	9	8	4	37	31	4	3	14	29	52	37
17.	Wolverhampton Wanderers	42	10	4	7	45	36	4	4	13	21	39	36
18.	Stoke City	42	10	3	8	30	29	4	4	13	20	44	35
19.	Sheffield Wednesday	42	6	10	5	32	24	5	2	14	19	39	34
20.	Coventry City	42	8	5	8	32	32	1	10	10	19	39	33
21.	Sheffield United	42	7	4	10	25	31	4	6	11	24	39	32
22.	Fulham	42	6	4	11	27	41	4	3	14	29	57	27

Top league scorer: Peter Osgood, 16 goals
Average home attendance: 35,746
Player of the Year: Charlie Cooke

FA CUP

(3) Ipswich (H)	W3–0
(4) Norwich (H)	W1–0
(5) Sheffield Weds (A)	D2–2
(Rep) Sheffield Weds (H)	W2–0
(6) Birmingham (A)	L0–1

LEAGUE CUP

(2) Middlesbrough (A)	L1–2

LEAGUE DIVISION 1

		P	W	D	L	F	A	W	D	L	F	A	Pts
1.	Leeds United	42	18	3	0	41	9	9	10	2	25	17	67
2.	Liverpool	42	16	4	1	36	10	9	7	5	27	14	61
3.	Everton	42	14	5	2	43	10	7	10	4	34	26	57
4.	Arsenal	42	12	6	3	31	12	10	6	5	25	15	56
5.	**CHELSEA**	**42**	**11**	**7**	**3**	**40**	**24**	**9**	**3**	**9**	**33**	**29**	**50**
6.	Tottenham Hotspur	42	10	8	3	39	22	4	9	8	22	29	45
7.	Southampton	42	13	5	3	41	21	3	8	10	16	27	45
8.	West Ham United	42	10	8	3	47	22	3	10	8	19	28	44
9.	Newcastle United	42	12	7	2	40	20	3	7	11	21	35	44
10.	West Bromwich Albion	42	11	7	3	43	26	5	4	12	21	41	43
11.	Manchester United	42	13	5	3	38	18	2	7	12	19	35	42
12.	Ipswich Town	42	10	4	7	32	26	5	7	9	27	34	41
13.	Manchester City	42	13	6	2	49	20	2	4	15	15	35	40
14.	Burnley	42	11	6	4	36	25	4	3	14	19	57	39
15.	Sheffield Wednesday	42	7	9	5	27	26	3	7	11	14	28	36
16.	Wolverhampton Wanderers	42	7	10	4	26	22	3	5	13	15	36	35
17.	Sunderland	42	10	6	5	28	18	1	6	14	15	49	34
18.	Nottingham Forest	42	6	6	9	17	22	4	7	10	28	35	33
19.	Stoke City	42	9	7	5	24	24	0	8	13	16	39	33
20.	Coventry City	42	8	6	7	32	22	2	5	14	14	42	31
21.	Leicester City	42	8	8	5	27	24	1	4	16	12	44	30
22.	QPR	42	4	7	10	20	33	0	3	18	19	62	18

Top league scorer: Bobby Tambling, 17 goals
Average home attendance: 37,595
Player of the Year: David Webb

FA CUP

(3) Carlisle (H)	W2–0
(4) Preston (A)	D0–0
(Rep) Preston (H)	2–0 (Abandoned – floodlight failure)
(Rep) Preston (H)	W2–1
(5) Stoke (H)	W3–2
(6) WBA (H)	L1–2

LEAGUE CUP

(2) Birmingham City (A)	W1–0
(3) Derby Co. (H)	D0–0
(Rep) Derby Co. (A)	L1–3

FAIRS CUP

(1) Morton (Scot) (H)	W5–0
Morton (A)	W4–3
(2) DWS Amsterdam (Holl) (A)	D0–0
DWS Amsterdam (H)	D0–0 (Lost on toss of coin)

LEAGUE DIVISION 1

		P	W	D	L	F	A	W	D	L	F	A	Pts
1.	Everton	42	17	3	1	46	19	12	5	4	26	15	66
2.	Leeds United	42	15	4	2	50	19	6	11	4	34	30	57
3.	**CHELSEA**	42	13	7	1	36	18	8	6	7	34	32	55
4.	Derby County	42	15	3	3	45	14	7	6	8	19	23	53
5.	Liverpool	42	10	7	4	34	20	10	4	7	31	22	51
6.	Coventry City	42	9	6	6	35	28	10	5	6	23	20	49
7.	Newcastle United	42	14	2	5	42	16	3	11	7	15	19	47
8.	Manchester United	42	8	9	4	37	27	6	8	7	29	34	45
9.	Stoke City	42	10	7	4	31	23	5	8	8	25	29	45
10.	Manchester City	42	8	6	7	25	22	8	5	8	30	26	43
11.	Tottenham Hotspur	42	11	2	8	27	21	6	7	8	27	34	43
12.	Arsenal	42	7	10	4	29	23	5	8	8	22	26	42
13.	Wolverhampton Wanderers	42	8	8	5	30	23	4	8	9	25	34	40
14.	Burnley	42	7	7	7	33	29	5	8	8	23	32	39
15.	Nottingham Forest	42	8	9	4	28	28	2	9	10	22	43	38
16.	West Bromwich Albion	42	10	6	5	39	25	4	3	14	19	41	37
17.	West Ham United	42	8	8	5	28	21	4	4	13	23	39	36
18.	Ipswich Town	42	9	5	7	23	20	1	6	14	17	43	31
19.	Southampton	42	3	12	6	24	27	3	5	13	22	40	29
20.	Crystal Palace	42	5	5	10	20	36	1	9	11	14	32	27
21.	Sunderland	42	4	11	6	17	24	2	3	16	13	44	26
22.	Sheffield Wednesday	42	6	5	10	23	27	2	4	15	17	44	25

Top league scorer: Peter Osgood, 23 goals
Average home attendance: 40,341
Player of the Year: John Hollins

FA CUP

(3) Birmingham (H)	W3–0
(4) Burnley (H)	D2–2
(Rep) Burnley (A)	W3–1 (aet)
(5) Crystal Palace (A)	W4–1
(6) QPR (A)	W4–2
(S/F) Watford (White Hart Lane)	W5–1
(Final) Leeds (Wembley)	D2–2 (aet)
(Rep) Leeds (Old Trafford)	W2–1 (aet)

FA Cup Final Team (both games)
Bonetti, Webb, McCreadie, Hollins, Dempsey, Harris R, Baldwin, Cooke, Osgood, Hutchinson, Houseman Sub: Hinton
Scorers (Wembley): Houseman, Hutchinson
Scorers (Old Trafford): Osgood, Webb

LEAGUE CUP

(2) Coventry City (A)	W1–0
(3) Leeds (A)	D1–1
(Rep) Leeds (H)	W2–0
(4) Carlisle (A)	L0–1

LEAGUE DIVISION 1

		P	W	D	L	F	A	W	D	L	F	A	Pts
1.	Arsenal	42	18	3	0	41	6	11	4	6	30	23	65
2.	Leeds United	42	16	2	3	40	12	11	8	2	32	18	64
3.	Tottenham Hotspur	42	11	5	5	33	19	8	9	4	21	14	52
4.	Wolverhampton Wanderers	42	13	3	5	33	22	9	5	7	31	32	52
5.	Liverpool	42	11	10	0	30	10	6	7	8	12	14	51
6.	**CHELSEA**	**42**	**12**	**6**	**3**	**34**	**21**	**6**	**9**	**6**	**18**	**21**	**51**
7.	Southampton	42	12	5	4	35	15	5	7	9	21	29	46
8.	Manchester United	42	9	6	6	29	24	7	5	9	36	42	43
9.	Derby County	42	9	5	7	32	26	7	5	9	24	28	42
10.	Coventry City	42	12	4	5	24	12	4	6	11	13	26	42
11.	Manchester City	42	7	9	5	30	22	5	8	8	17	20	41
12.	Newcastle United	42	9	9	3	27	16	5	4	12	17	30	41
13.	Stoke City	42	10	7	4	28	11	2	6	13	16	37	37
14.	Everton	42	10	7	4	32	16	2	6	13	22	44	37
15.	Huddersfield Town	42	7	8	6	19	16	4	6	11	21	33	36
16.	Nottingham Forest	42	9	4	8	29	26	5	4	12	13	35	36
17.	West Bromwich Albion	42	9	8	4	34	25	1	7	13	24	50	35
18.	Crystal Palace	42	9	5	7	24	24	3	6	12	15	33	35
19.	Ipswich Town	42	9	4	8	28	22	3	6	12	14	26	34
20.	West Ham United	42	6	8	7	28	30	4	6	11	19	30	34
21.	Burnley	42	4	8	9	20	31	3	5	13	9	32	27
22.	Blackpool	42	3	9	9	22	31	1	6	14	12	35	23

Top league scorer: Keith Weller, 13 goals
Average home attendance: 39,546
Player of the Year: John Hollins

FA CUP

(3) Crystal Palace (A)	D2–2
(Rep) Crystal Palace (H)	W2–0
(4) Manchester City (H)	L0–3

LEAGUE CUP

(2) Sheffield Weds. (A)	D1–1
(Rep) Sheffield Weds. (H)	W2–1
(3) Middlesbrough (H)	W3–2
(4) Manchester Utd (A)	L1–2

EUROPEAN CUP WINNERS CUP

(1) Aris Salonika (Greece) (A)	D1–1
Aris Salonika (H)	W5–1
(2) CSKA Sofia (Bulg) (A)	W1–0
CSKA Sofia (H)	W1–0
(3) Bruges (Belg) (A)	L0–2
Bruges (H)	W4–0 (aet)
(S/F) Manchester City (H)	W1–0
Manchester City (A)	W1–0
(Final) Real Madrid (Athens)	D1–1 (aet)
(Rep) Real Madrid (Athens)	W2–1

European Cup Winners Cup Final Team
Bonetti, Boyle, Harris R, Hollins, Dempsey, Webb, Weller, Hudson, Osgood, Cooke, Houseman
Subs: Mulligan, Baldwin
Scorer: Osgood

Replay: As above, except Baldwin for Hollins. Sub: Smethurst
Scorers: Dempsey, Osgood

LEAGUE DIVISION 1

		P	W	D	L	F	A	W	D	L	F	A	Pts
1.	Derby County	42	16	4	1	43	10	8	6	7	26	28	58
2.	Leeds United	42	17	4	0	54	10	7	5	9	19	21	57
3.	Liverpool	42	17	3	1	48	16	7	6	8	16	14	57
4.	Manchester City	42	16	3	2	48	15	7	8	6	29	30	57
5.	Arsenal	42	15	2	4	36	13	7	6	8	22	27	52
6.	Tottenham Hotspur	42	16	3	2	45	13	3	10	8	18	29	51
7.	**CHELSEA**	**42**	**12**	**7**	**2**	**41**	**20**	**6**	**5**	**10**	**17**	**29**	**48**
8.	Manchester United	42	13	2	6	39	26	6	8	7	30	35	48
9.	Wolverhampton Wanderers	42	10	7	4	35	23	8	4	9	30	34	47
10.	Sheffield United	42	10	8	3	39	26	7	4	10	22	34	46
11.	Newcastle United	42	10	6	5	30	18	5	5	11	19	34	41
12.	Leicester City	42	9	6	6	18	11	4	7	10	23	35	39
13.	Ipswich Town	42	7	8	6	19	19	4	8	9	20	34	38
14.	West Ham United	42	10	6	5	31	19	2	6	13	16	32	36
15.	Everton	42	8	9	4	28	17	1	9	11	9	31	36
16.	West Bromwich Albion	42	6	7	8	22	23	6	4	11	20	31	35
17.	Stoke City	42	6	10	5	26	25	4	5	12	13	31	35
18.	Coventry City	42	7	10	4	27	23	2	5	14	17	44	33
19.	Southampton	42	8	5	8	31	28	4	2	15	21	52	31
20.	Crystal Palace	42	4	8	9	26	31	4	5	12	13	34	29
21.	Nottingham Forest	42	6	4	11	25	29	2	5	14	22	52	25
22.	Huddersfield Town	42	4	7	10	12	22	2	6	13	15	37	25

Top league scorer: Peter Osgood, 18 goals
Average home attendance: 38,787
Player of the Year: David Webb

FA CUP

(3) Blackpool (A)	W1–0
(4) Bolton (H)	W3–0
(5) Orient (A)	L2–3

LEAGUE CUP

(2) Plymouth (H)	W2–0
(3) Nottingham Forest (A)	D1–1
(Rep) Nottingham Forest (H)	W2–1
(4) Bolton (H)	D1–1
(Rep) Bolton (A)	W6–0
(5) Norwich (A)	W1–0
(S/F-1) Tottenham (H)	W3–2
(S/F-2) Tottenham (A)	D2–2
(Final) Stoke (Wembley)	L1–2

League Cup Final Team
Bonetti, Mulligan, Harris R, Hollins, Dempsey, Webb, Cooke, Garland, Osgood, Hudson, Houseman
Sub: Baldwin
Scorer: Osgood

EUROPEAN CUP WINNERS CUP

(1) Jeunesse Haut. (Lux) (A)	W8–0
Jeunesse Haut. (Lux) (H)	W13–0
(2) Atvidaberg (Swed) (A)	0–0
Atvidaberg (H)	1–1 (Lost on away goals)

LEAGUE DIVISION 1

		P	W	D	L	F	A	W	D	L	F	A	Pts
1.	Liverpool	42	17	3	1	45	19	8	7	6	27	23	60
2.	Arsenal	42	14	5	2	31	14	9	6	6	26	29	57
3.	Leeds United	42	15	4	2	45	13	6	7	8	26	32	53
4.	Ipswich Town	42	10	7	4	34	20	7	7	7	21	25	48
5.	Wolverhampton Wanderers	42	13	3	5	43	23	5	8	8	23	31	47
6.	West Ham United	42	12	5	4	45	25	5	7	9	22	28	46
7.	Derby County	42	15	3	3	43	18	4	5	12	13	36	46
8.	Tottenham Hotspur	42	10	5	6	33	23	6	8	7	25	25	45
9.	Newcastle United	42	12	6	3	35	19	4	7	10	25	32	45
10.	Birmingham City	42	11	7	3	39	22	4	5	12	14	32	42
11.	Manchester City	42	12	4	5	36	20	3	7	11	21	40	41
12.	**CHELSEA**	**42**	**9**	**6**	**6**	**30**	**22**	**4**	**8**	**9**	**19**	**29**	**40**
13.	Southampton	42	8	11	2	26	17	3	7	11	21	35	40
14.	Sheffield United	42	11	4	6	28	18	4	6	11	23	41	40
15.	Stoke City	42	11	8	2	38	17	3	2	16	23	39	38
16.	Leicester City	42	7	9	5	23	18	3	8	10	17	28	37
17.	Everton	42	9	5	7	27	21	4	6	11	14	28	37
18.	Manchester United	42	9	7	5	24	19	3	6	12	20	41	35
19.	Coventry City	42	9	5	7	27	24	4	4	13	13	31	37
20.	Norwich City	42	7	9	5	22	19	4	1	16	14	44	32
21.	Crystal Palace	42	7	7	7	25	21	2	5	14	16	37	30
22.	West Bromwich Albion	42	8	7	6	25	24	1	3	17	13	38	28

Top league scorer: Chris Garland and Peter Osgood, 11 goals
Average home attendance: 29,739
Player of the Year: Peter Osgood

FA CUP

(3) Brighton (A)	W2–0
(4) Ipswich (H)	W2–0
(5) Sheffield Weds. (A)	W2–1
(6) Arsenal (H)	D2–2
(Rep) Arsenal (A)	L1–2

LEAGUE CUP

(2) Southend (A)	W1–0
(3) Derby Co. (A)	D0–0
(Rep) Derby Co. (H)	W3–2
(4) Bury (A)	W1–0
(5) Notts Co. (H)	W3–1
(S/F-1) Norwich (H)	L0–2
(S/F-2) Norwich (A)	2–3 (Abandoned – fog)
(S/F-2) Norwich (A)	L0–1

LEAGUE DIVISION 1

		P	W	D	L	F	A	W	D	L	F	A	Pts
1.	Leeds United	42	12	8	1	38	18	12	6	3	28	13	62
2.	Liverpool	42	18	2	1	34	11	4	11	6	18	20	57
3.	Derby County	42	13	7	1	40	16	4	7	10	12	26	48
4.	Ipswich Town	42	10	7	4	38	21	8	4	9	29	37	47
5.	Stoke City	42	13	6	2	39	15	2	10	9	15	27	46
6.	Burnley	42	10	9	2	29	16	6	5	10	27	37	46
7.	Everton	42	12	7	2	29	14	4	5	12	21	34	44
8.	QPR	42	8	10	3	30	17	5	7	9	26	35	43
9.	Leicester City	42	10	7	4	35	17	3	9	9	16	24	42
10.	Arsenal	42	9	7	5	23	16	5	7	9	26	35	42
11.	Tottenham Hotspur	42	9	4	8	26	27	5	10	6	19	23	42
12.	Wolverhampton Wanderers	42	11	6	4	30	18	2	9	10	19	31	41
13.	Sheffield United	42	7	7	7	25	22	7	5	9	19	27	40
14.	Manchester City	42	10	7	4	25	17	4	5	12	14	29	40
15.	Newcastle United	42	9	6	6	28	21	4	6	11	21	27	38
16.	Coventry City	42	10	5	6	25	18	4	5	12	18	36	38
17.	**CHELSEA**	**42**	**9**	**4**	**8**	**36**	**29**	**3**	**9**	**9**	**20**	**31**	**37**
18.	West Ham United	42	7	7	7	36	32	4	8	9	19	28	37
19.	Birmingham City	42	10	7	4	30	21	2	6	13	22	43	37
20.	Southampton	42	8	10	3	30	20	3	4	14	17	48	36
21.	Manchester United	42	7	7	7	23	20	3	5	13	15	28	32
22.	Norwich City	42	6	9	6	25	27	1	6	14	12	35	29

Top league scorer: Tommy Baldwin, 9 goals
Average home attendance: 25,983
Player of the Year: Gary Locke

FA CUP

(3) QPR (H)	D0–0
(Rep) QPR (A)	L0–1

LEAGUE CUP

(2) Stoke (A)	L0–1

LEAGUE DIVISION 1

		P	W	D	L	F	A	W	D	L	F	A	Pts
1.	Derby County	42	14	4	3	41	18	7	7	7	26	31	53
2.	Liverpool	42	14	5	2	44	17	6	6	9	16	22	51
3.	Ipswich Town	42	17	2	2	47	14	6	3	12	19	30	51
4.	Everton	42	10	9	2	33	19	6	9	6	23	23	50
5.	Stoke City	42	12	7	2	40	18	5	8	8	24	30	49
6.	Sheffield United	42	12	7	2	35	20	6	6	9	23	31	49
7.	Middlesbrough	42	11	7	3	33	14	7	5	9	21	26	48
8.	Manchester City	42	16	3	2	40	15	2	7	12	14	39	46
9.	Leeds United	42	10	8	3	34	20	6	5	10	23	29	45
10.	Burnley	42	11	6	4	40	29	6	5	10	28	38	45
11.	QPR	42	10	4	7	25	17	6	6	9	29	37	42
12.	Wolverhampton Wanderers	42	12	5	4	43	21	2	6	13	14	33	39
13.	West Ham United	42	10	6	5	38	22	3	7	11	20	37	39
14.	Coventry City	42	8	9	4	31	27	4	6	11	20	35	39
15.	Newcastle United	42	12	4	5	39	23	3	5	13	20	49	39
16.	Arsenal	42	10	6	5	31	16	3	5	13	16	33	37
17.	Birmingham City	42	10	4	7	34	28	4	5	12	19	33	37
18.	Leicester City	42	8	7	6	25	17	4	5	12	21	43	36
19.	Tottenham Hotspur	42	8	4	9	29	27	5	4	12	23	36	34
20.	Luton Town	42	8	6	7	27	26	3	5	13	20	39	33
21.	**CHELSEA**	**42**	**4**	**9**	**8**	**22**	**31**	**5**	**6**	**10**	**20**	**41**	**33**
22.	Carlisle United	42	8	2	11	22	21	4	3	14	21	38	29

Top league scorer: Ian Hutchinson, 7 goals
Average home attendance: 27,396
Player of the Year: Charlie Cooke

FA CUP
(3) Sheffield Weds. (H)	W3-2
(4) Birmingham City (H)	L0-1

LEAGUE CUP
(2) Newport Co. (H)	W4-2
(3) Stoke City (H)	D2-2
(Rep) Stoke City (A)	D1-1
(Rep) Stoke City (A)	L2-6

Also available from
Vision Sports Publishing . . .

Special edition: Signed by Ron 'Chopper' Harris
(Genuine signature, comes with certificate of authenticity)
Just £9.99
Only available online at www.visionsp.co.uk

THE
CHELSEA
MISCELLANY

BY CLIVE BATTY
FOREWORD BY RON 'CHOPPER' HARRIS

New edition: fully revised and updated
On sale: September 3rd 2007
£9.99
Available for £6.49 online at
www.visionsp.co.uk

C000060104

VICTOR GIBSON

RIGMOVES

La Madrila Press

With best wishes,

Victor Gibson.

Dec 2011

La Madrila Press

A Division of:

Ships and Oil Ltd,
Bon Accord House,
Greyhope Rd,
Aberdeen, UK
AB11 9RD

www.shipsandoil.com

Published in 2011

Copyright Victor Gibson

All rights reserved. This book is sold subject to the condition that it is not reproduced in any material form, including photo-copying, or storing in any medium by electronic means, without the written permission of the copyright holder.

ISBN NO: 978-0-9557002-3-1

Design Layout and production by Ships and Oil Ltd.

Printed and bound in the UK by MPG Books Group, Bodmin and Kings Lynn.

INTRODUCTION

I had the idea for this book when I was master of a small American anchor-handler chartered by Saudi Aramco in the Arabian Gulf. We worked out of the purpose built port of Tanajib, which was little more than a hole in the desert. We were totally isolated from world outside except for censored newspapers and censored TV. No-one was allowed ashore from the ship except for me. I was allowed to walk to the barge office for instructions. I had plenty of time to think.

Over the years I have picked away at the story and finally after the publication of Supply Ship Operations, buckled down and completed it. I have also been able to engage the services of an editor, Claire Askew, who took time off from her various creative writing activities in Edinburgh to carry out the task. I am very grateful to her many suggestions, and for her words of encouragement.

Having no expectation that any agent or publishing house would show interest in this work within my lifetime, like my two non-fiction volumes, it is published by my own imprint.

Also from La Madrila Press

Non fiction

The History of the Supply Ship
Supply Ship Operations

This book is dedicated to shipmasters all over the world who struggle on anonymously, often dealing with impossible owners, arrogant officials and unrealistic regulations, not to mention the threat of being robbed at gunpoint or held captive in some pirate stronghold. If something goes wrong, they may be criminalised, vilified and fined or gaoled. On the face of it my guys have a better time out in the asteroid belt.

CHAPTER 1

A Rigmover's Handbook (Notes)

All rig moves must be carried out with the utmost
consideration for the safety of the rig, its crew and the other
craft involved.

Do not on any account recover the jacking screws
before the tugs are in place. Rigs have been lost from asteroids
where there has not been a gravitational field strong enough to
hold the unit onto the surface.

Always ensure that communications with all tugs are
established before the start of the move. The Commnet is the
system of choice since it is common to all ships operating in
controlled space. In extremis other systems may be used but only
if they are common to all tugs. The approved language is earth
English. Any tug captains who are not fluent in this language
must either be replaced, or a translator put aboard. Other
possible languages are earth Spanish and earth Arabic.
Speakers of either of these languages are to be provided with
translators, or else alternative tugs employed.

The Acme Drilling Corporation has a contract with
the Cygnus group, who manage the operation of all tugs in the
sector of the asteroid belt for which Acme has the mining
concession. Acme have audited that company but as our
representative for the operation, it is up to you to assess the
capability of the directly employed contract tugs, and to report
any deficiencies. The management will expect a report to be
forwarded to base control on completion of the move. This
should detail the performance of each of the ships involved.

Do not, on any account, hazard any Acme property
during the move, and remain on board until the unit is safely

secured at the new location. We would remind you that "safely secured" means that the jacking screws are fully extended into the surface of the asteroid and that you have tested them by operating the propulsion of the upwardly aligned tugs to apply an appropriate level of torque.

Only once you are certain that the rig is secure will you be allowed to release the tugs, even if they are urgently needed for other work, or if the rig manager suggests to you that they should be released due to budgetary considerations. The cost of a few hours tug time counts for nothing when compared to the loss of the rig itself.

The lead time for new rigs is measured in earth years. We would remind you that none of the personnel assigned to the rig have the skill or knowledge to overrule your decisions. If in doubt at any time do not hesitate to contact the duty base operations manager, who will rule on any disagreement between yourself and the rig team.

"OK guys," said Big Jim, the rig-mover, over the Commnet. "Let's do it. You ready, Cygnus Two?"

"Ready," I replied, placing my hands on the controls as Jim called out the names of the other three tugs. I heard their responses and waited for the next instruction.

Cygnus Two and Archimedes were positioned nose down on either side of the rig. At ninety degrees to us Cygnus Four and Oceanus were latched nose up. The rig, a ponderous haphazard structure of tubes, rotors, engines and struts, topped by its accommodation and control module, had just completed mining one of the smaller asteroids in the Eos group, and was still held onto the surface by its jacking screw.

There was limited gravitational attraction between the rig and the asteroid, so during the recovery of the legs it was necessary for us to hold it in place.

Cyg Two and Archie, give me five percent," said Jim.

We acknowledged the instruction and I pushed the throttles forward slowly, listening to the rising pitch of the motors until I judged that I had applied sufficient power.

"Watch it Archie, you're moving the whole bloody rock!" Big Jim was shouting into the microphone.

Damon was notoriously heavy handed, and the Archimedes well known for its sensitivity to the controls. The combination could be lethal. Too much power and the asteroid would start to spin.

I felt the rock shudder beneath us. Damon had caught it in time and balanced the thrust. "Control Room, give me a reading on the legs," said Jim. "Ten metres and coming up," was the reply.

We waited in tension, feeling the vibration as the legs screwed up into the body of the rig. Easan, my engineer, was strapped in next to me reading the engine instrumentation on his console and checking the tension on the latches. I looked in his direction and he gave me a thumbs up. He was a man of few words while we were working.

Cygnus Four, and Oceanus were inactive, waiting for their first orders. None of us knew the Oceanus. She had been chartered from the pool, coming in when the rig was already preparing for the move and latching straight into position. She was old and her hull showed the scars of a hundred operations. The easy way in which she had dropped into position and latched on, and the crisp replies of her captain to Jim's questions indicated to us that he was a veteran of numerous shifts.

"Screws are home," said the Jacktech.

"OK," replied Jim and issued the four tugs with instructions, which would result in a slight down-thrust onto the surface. I nudged the throttles forward, watching the digital readouts intently until I judged that I had the correct settings. The readout on the port engine flashed intermittently, reminding me that we had no spares and the replacement which had been

3

on order for months had not yet arrived.

"Cyg Two and Archie, zero thrust." In response to the instruction I pulled back the throttles into the neutral setting. Easan looked at me but said nothing. All engineers had difficulty with the rapid changes in engine power which were necessary during the rig-moves. The thrust of the two other tugs took over, rapidly pushing the rig away from the surface, and I saw the rock receding below me until the whole mass of it was visible - though I knew that now it was just a shell.

In the fifty years of its operations the Acme Mining Corporation had developed its drilling techniques so as to leave only as much of the asteroid as was necessary to maintain the stability of the rig itself. They lost Rig AMC 23 during an unsuccessful attempt to pioneer an elliptical cutting technique. It was supposed to leave the rig standing on a secure segment of the original rock, but during the final phase of the operation the tiny planet had disintegrated, sending the rig spinning out of orbit. It is due back from its journey round the sun in a hundred and fifty years.

This move was a short one. Cygnus Four had been designated as lead tug and Big Jim gave Nadia Abdull, its pilot, the co-ordinates of the new location. I heard her instructing the captain of Oceanus, who responded with some surprise in his voice. Female tug captains were a rarity, although some freighters were operated by female crews.

Nadia continued to give the captain of Oceanus updates on increases in power. I felt a bit jealous. Although we had worked together on the Acme charter for almost a year my interaction with her had been limited to brief exchanges of information and instruction. I usually tried to manipulate our assignments so that either she or I would be the lead tug, and the other latched onto the opposite quadrant. This gave me the maximum opportunity for conversation.

Looking out of our viewport I could see the asteroid

receding until it became no more than a dot, and then nothing as it merged with the carpet of stars filling the darkness. It was impossible to tell how fast we were travelling. For some reason the velocity indicators on Cyg Two only worked if we were moving forward. This gave us some problems during approaches, requiring Easan to read the bounce indicators on his console. The rigs were not fitted with any form of instrumentation at all, since they spent most of their time anchored to the surface of an asteroid. But Big Jim's position indicator would respond to the survey beacon placed on the surface of Eos 231, our next location.

"Nadia cut the thrust. Oceanus cut the thrust," said Jim over the Commnet. The two pilots responded and I was pressed back a little into my seat as acceleration ceased. I felt just a little sorry for the captain of the Oceanus, a lone stranger within a group who obviously knew each other well and had worked together many times.

Back at the Acme base I had met Jim once, and occasionally visited the Archimedes to exchange movies, but of course I had never actually met Nadia Abdull or her engineer, Rollo Vespasian. Like all mining bases, Acme had established a separate facility for its female workers and contractors. This fulfilled the levels of segregation required by the mopo, the Morality Police, while still allowing women to work in the system. The Acme base on Eugenia in the Eos asteroid belt provided plenty of room for such segregation.

"Damon, Sully, give me ten percent," said Jim. I responded. He was slowing the rig down as we approached the next asteroid; the new location. "Cyg Four, Oceanus, rotate 90 red to green."

Each of the latch points on the rig was designated with a colour. I was on black, Damon was on white, Nadia on red and Oceanus on green. The Oceanus and the Cyg Four were now firing their thrusters to turn the rig through 90 degrees. The

5

whole tow would end up moving through space sideways, the base of the rig oriented to the surface of the asteroid over the position of the marker beacon.

From our position, facing what had become down, we could see the surface of Eos 231 come into view through the port. Jim's timing had been spot on, as it always was, and we appeared to be stationary above the asteroid. There followed a barrage of instructions to all the tugs until we were easing towards the surface, all of us powering the main engines, but with a balance pushing the rig towards the rock.

The asteroid was about seven kilometres across, almost spherical in shape and pitted with small craters due to impact with space debris. It was typical of the asteroids selected by the Acme survey. It was big enough to support the weight of the rig and there was space enough for us to land it, and for it to be screwed into position. Like most of the selected bodies it was probably made up of nickel-iron and iron, mixed with magnesium silicates. Of course we were just tug drivers, and no-one ever bothered to tell us anything about the rest of the job. We just took the rigs to the place where they were going to work and then went away. Sometimes we had to wait until the last of the freighters had loaded up to take the product back to the foundry, and on those occasions we would drift in orbit while the great slug that was the freighter rested on the surface next to the rig. The freighters also re-supplied the guys on the rigs with food and water.

This site was clear of any encumbrances. There were no rocks, gullies or moguls, and it was apparently completely level, indicating to us that in all probability the job would be straightforward.

On Jim's orders I made tiny adjustments to the controls to slow the descent, until we were stationary a few metres above the beacon. It was gradually obliterated in the dust-cloud created by the thrust from Cyg Four and Oceanus, then gently the rig touched down.

"OK, pin it," said Jim. He was cool and precise. As usual he had done a perfect job. The rig vibrated as the legs rotated and began to screw down into the surface. The survey craft had already carried out a profile of the top twenty metres at the landing position, to determine that there was no high density material which would stop the legs taking hold.

Jim adjusted the forces until Cyg Two and Archimedes were holding the rig onto the surface. Time passed and the dust gradually began to settle, and I found myself having to look at the levels to make sure that we were remaining upright. Of course something should have been happening but nothing was, and there was dead silence. There was not even any vibration from the screws. "What's the trouble?" asked Jim. We all knew who he was talking to.

"There's a bit of a glitch with one of the screws," replied the Jacktech. We sighed. Doubtless so did the guys in the other tugs. Only too frequently we were left pressing a rig to the surface of an asteroid for hours at a time, while they tried to repair defective machinery. There was no way we could leave the rig if it was not secured to the surface. In the most extreme situation we would have to power up and take it back out into orbit while they carried out the repairs. Even though the tugs were provided with legs, and pins on the landing pads to secure them to the surface of an asteroid, or if necessary, a planet, when they were connected to a rig the legs would not reach the surface.

We waited, and I made miniscule adjustments to the main power and the thrusters to keep everything in balance. Damon was probably doing the same. On the rig they would be working away at their machinery.

We could only hope that they had some competent engineers capable of assessing the problem, and of carrying out the repair. Regardless of the competence of their team it would

7

be unlikely that we would hear anything from them until the repair was completed. We could be stuck there for two minutes, two hours or two days.

"This is the AMC 24," said Easan.

Obviously this meant something to him. "So?" I answered.

"It's the sister rig to AMC 23. They say that it wasn't the break up of the asteroid at all which resulted in the rig going out there on its slingshot. One of the jacking screws broke off."

I did not buy this particular rumour. If one of the jacking screws had broken off, there would have been time for the crew to ask for assistance, and one or some of us would have got there.

"Even if it's not true," continued Easan "There must be something in the whole business of the jacking screws giving problems."

"You could be right," I answered. We were just filling in time.

I studied the read-outs again to make sure that all was well. Even in the minimal gravity provided by a five kilometre asteroid, hanging face down in the seat harnesses was not comfortable. My hands rested on the console to take a little of my weight and to steady me up. Now that the dust was completely settled we could see the feet of the rig, or at least the foot closest to us. It was a metal pad about three metres across, connected to the rig itself by a pair of titanium struts. When the screws were fully extended, the pads would slide outwards at the end of their struts until the hull of the rig was pressed against the surface.

We could see that there was still about a metre of space between the bottom of the rig and the asteroid. I looked at my watch it was 1532. We kept earth time. Everybody kept earth time, with 24 hours, each of 60 minutes, even though both Jupiter and Mars rotated at different speeds and that therefore

8

their real days were of different length. Day and night meant nothing to us. We were in the asteroid belt about half way between the two planets.

Our base was a station built on the asteroid Eugenia, which had been mined by Acme back in the early days. It was considered big enough to resist the tendency of asteroids to become comets if one crashed into another, but in order to minimise the possibility of death due to such a collision, most of the facilities were below ground. It kept earth time as well.

I looked at my watch again. It was 1540. I thought I might try not to look at the watch again for ten minutes, so I scanned the interior of the pilot house. We were surrounded by padding, provided to minimise any injuries we might suffer due to unintended movements when not secured in our seats. Recessed into the console in front of me were all the dials and switches required to control the tug. At my right hand was the joystick, which when it was working, would provide a single stick control for the speed and direction of our little spacecraft.

This control was also duplicated at Easan's seat next to me. In the bulkhead on my right – the pilot's seat is the right hand seat in tugs - were the individual controls for the engines and the thrusters. It was often necessary to resort to using these, so all tug drivers were able to operate their vessels using these little sticks.

Between the seats, in what was currently the deckhead, was a hatch which led from the pilot house into our accommodation, and beyond that into the technical area and the engine compartment. The technical area contained all the stuff that was supposed to keep us alive in the vacuum of space, including the oxygen scrubbers and the food and water synthesisers, as well as the heating and cooling equipment. We needed both, depending on whether we were in sunlight or shadow.

I pondered whether I might ask what the problem

was, or at least how long it might take to fix. Doubtless the team on the rig had congregated in the control room, and were talking about it. Big Jim would have received a report on the from the Rig Boss, and they would either be preparing for action or else settling back with some refreshment and waiting for the engine men to sort everything out. No-one had though to let us know what was going on.

"Twenty-four, this is Cyg Two." I had made the decision almost without thinking about it.

"Yes Cyg Two?" Jim answered.

"We were wondering how long this problem might take to fix."

"They're still trying to find out what the problem is. Then when they know that, they've still got to work out whether they can fix it, and then how long it will take. Just keep the rig balanced. When I know I'll let you know. OK!" Jim had been irritated by the question, but what the hell.

I eyed my instruments for the thousandth time and settled as best I could, facing the surface of the asteroid. I vaguely wondered about applying for a rig-mover's job with Acme. At least then I would know what was going on. The money was good, but the opportunities did not come up very often, and there were drawbacks. It meant living in the base on Eugenia, which in itself was probably not too much of a problem, apart from having to share a living space with another rig-mover, but there would be the Acme management to contend with, and to a degree the management of the tug operating companies as well. I could hardly imagine the levels of tolerance required. On top of that there would be the constant visits to different rigs, for indeterminate periods of time. We were not under the illusion that the people on the rigs were better off that we were. At least we had our own space. It might be small, but it was all ours.

Suddenly, there was a noise. It was the Jacktech

communicating with his control room. "Hi Jim," he said. "That seems to have fixed it. If you're ready we'll carry on with the jacking."

"OK everybody," said Jim into the Commnet. "Did you all get that? Cyg Two and Archie keep a check on the levels and make sure this thing stays upright when we start to screw in again. The last thing we want to do is to have to change location."

It was not actually the last thing we wanted to do. That would be having to take the rig back out into space, but it was the second to last thing. Changing location meant moving a few metres one way or the other, and would be required if the jacking screws started to tip the rig at an angle.

I needed no second bidding, and concentrated on the levels. I could hear the screw motors grinding away, and could feel the vibrations as they began to bite into the surface. This part of the job always seemed to take for ever, but we knew that the screws would be penetrating the crust of the asteroid until they were fully extended, or until they came up against a particular solid bit of rock. In the latter case the rig crew would do an evaluation to determine whether the screws had penetrated sufficiently, if penetration had been insufficient it might be necessary for us to move the rig.

Eventually one of these two things happened. After some minutes the vibrations stopped, and there was silence. I kept my eye on the levels, but Easan altered his position so that he had a good view of the rig foot that was in sight from our viewport.

"Yes!" exclaimed Easan "It's going down. It's getting closer to the surface. Fifty centimetres to go, forty, thirty, twenty. Yes, it's down." And there it was. AMC 24 was now hunkered down on the surface of the asteroid. The four jacking screws were extended about ten metres into the strata, and the rig itself had been pulled down until it was in contact with the surface at every point on its perimeter.

Within a few hours it would start to dig out the metals from the interior of the little planet, and once a freighter arrived it would be loaded with the results, for onward transfer to the foundry.

We relaxed, but kept the engines running, waiting for the moment when Jim deemed the rig to be secure. Nothing happened fast in the world of the mining rig, and after about an hour during which I knew Jim and the rig crew had been carrying out the post move checks we finally heard him on the Commnet.

"OK guys," he said. "Good job. We'll let you go now. Oceanus, you go back to base for off-hire. Archie, we'll unlatch you, but you wait alongside until I'm ready to go back to Eugenia. Cyg Two and Cyg Four, you're due to move AMC 10 in twenty-four hours, so go straight there from here. Oceanus, we'll take you first."

We listened to the exchange of information between the rig and the tugs as one by one they went through the process of unlatching and going on their way to their next assignment. As Oceanus was unlatched the thrust from its main jets once more raised the dust on the asteroid's surface and our visibility was reduced to zero. But on asteroids the dust settled almost immediately. There was no atmosphere.

Next came the departure of Cyg Four. Nadia Abdull exchanged instructions briefly with the rig crew. As a nose up tug she had to balance the thrust while the rig unlatched it. Too much thrust and it was possible to bend the mechanism during disengagement, leaving the tug attached. Then some-one would have to put on a space suit and go out there with a gas axe to release it. No such worries with Cyg Four. Nadia was possibly the most skilful driver in the sector, although few of us were prepared to admit it. I heard the rumble of Cyg Four's motors and sensed the change in the area as it lifted off and went on its way towards the AMC 10.

We had an easier job. When it came to our turn Easan extended the nose-ring until he read pressure from the surface, and when the latch tension reduced to zero, instructed the rig to let us go. There was a clang and we wobbled slightly. I squeezed the thrusters to steady us, then rotated them downwards to lift us from the surface of the asteroid. "Thanks Jim." I spoke into the Commnet "See you later."

"Go to it Sully," he responded.

I backed up Cyg Two until we were a few hundred metres above the surface. The rig looked like a beetle clinging to a watermelon. Then I rotated the thrusters until the nose was pointing outwards. In the pleasure of being free I pushed the sticks forward, incurring another look of dismay from Easan, as the engines lit up and pressed us into our seats. I smiled at him and set the course for AMC 10.

CHAPTER 2

The Cygnus Group Safety Manual (An Extract)

Unless instructed otherwise Cygnus tugs will proceed from one location to another at an economical and safe speed, and it is essential that close attention is paid to navigation within the asteroid belts. Not all asteroids are plotted on the electronic charts, and unrecorded changes of location, even of quite large bodies, can take place. Therefore a constant watch must be maintained on the radar system. In heavily populated areas, the autopilot and its related computer processors must be disengaged since experience has shown that human pilots are superior in this area. (This is due to their ability to anticipate rather than react.)

If a Cygnus tug is required to stand by in preparation for a rig move it should acquire the survey beacon at the rig, and initiate a geostationary orbit at a distance. This will ensure that if the lock is lost the tug will not be attracted to the surface of the asteroid by the gravitational pull. Obviously this judgement will depend on the size of the asteroid. However, if a very small body is the objective, it may be necessary for the tug to take up an orbit based on the position of the unit in space rather than on the position relative to the survey beacon. Very small asteroids have a low gravitational field and therefore the geostationary gravitationally neutral orbit will be too close to the surface.

Engine settings should be adjusted to minimise fuel use in accordance with our Technical Manual, and in all cases special instructions from the client will take precedence over the instructions stated here.

On no account should a Cygnus tug land on the surface of an asteroid that has not been surveyed by a client survey

14

vessel, or for which data is not available. Incautious landings have resulted in damage and sometimes losses of tugs. Some asteroids are honeycombed with caverns and tunnels caused by the cooling of magma at the time when the rocks were part of the planet from which they all came.

Tug captains are reminded that in the event of a need, for any reason, to deviate from these instructions there will be a Cygnus manager available at the Eugenia base, who can be contacted day or night. Do not hesitate to call this manager if there are any problems. He has authority to assist you in any way he can, and also to initiate discussions with the client if necessary for the safety of the tug or its personnel.

It should be remembered that the communications systems are to be used only for official business, and not for social purposes. Cygnus supports the monitoring operations carried out by the Morality Police, which ensures that this instruction is followed.

I struggled back into the control room after six hours of fitful slumber. Easan was in the engineer's seat but I could tell he had been sitting at the pilot's console. My dials were decorated with small blue markers and a piece of tape covered the normally bright light of the airlock safety. I removed them and settled in. Easan had a habit of customising everything he came across. It did not suit me but I tolerated it. He was a good engineer. Suddenly we lurched ahead and then settled again. A thruster had fired briefly.

"We're geostationary over the location," he said in response to my questioning look. "The shift's been put back by twenty-four hours. I've put a lock on the rig's beacon."

I made a gesture of despair. To maintain our position in relation to the asteroid the thrusters would fire in response to any drift away from the spot at the end of the lock. Cyg Two's thrusters were old, and the fuel metering did not allow for the sensitivity required to maintain a smooth orbit. We would spend twenty-four hours being thrown from side to side, and occasionally up or down.

"Where's Cyg Four?" I asked.

Easan pointed through the viewport. I could just see a spot of light ahead moving against the stars.

"Come on," I said. "Let's go down."

"What do you mean, come on, let's go down? You know the Cygnus rules on unauthorised landings. And it says specifically in the standing orders that no vessel is allowed to land on the surface of any asteroid licensed to the Acme Mining Corporation without the specific permission of the base mobile unit supervisor." Easan was a great reader of official documentation.

Ignoring him, I called Nadia on the Commnet. "Let's go to P Four," I said. We switched channels. The company had its own channels to allow ship-to-ship communication. They could be monitored by security, but even if we were overheard, it was unlikely that we would be understood. Security was more interested in obtaining evidence of immoral activities than anything else.

"I'm going down," I said. "I can't stand being thrown about up here for heaven knows how long."

"We're with you," she replied. "We're already beginning to feel sick." Cyg Four was no better in geostatic orbit than Cyg Two.

"OK," I said. "I'll go first."

I switched off the lock as Easan fired up the engines, and squeezed the thrusters to give us a nose-down attitude towards the surface of the asteroid. I could see the rig in the middle of a flat plain on the rock, looking more like a pile of scrap metal than a mobile industrial complex. I nudged the throttles forward. For a while nothing seemed to be happening, and then suddenly the surface was rushing towards us, the rig getting bigger and bigger. My fingers itched on the thruster controls, but I left it until the very last moment before tumbling Cyg Two over so that the tail was facing the surface and the thrust was now slowing us down.

Easan slid his fingers over his console and I heard the landing struts extend and click into place. I steadied up and cut the engines, swivelling the thrusters upwards to push us down onto the surface. Out of habit I glanced at the speed readout. As usual it had thrown its hand in on being asked to measure speed backwards. It flashed - 888, 888.

I felt the landing pads hit the surface and the springs in the struts bend as they took the weight. The altimeter read zero. "We've arrived," said Easan. "I'll fire securing pins."

There was a ripple of explosions as the recoilless pins in the four landing pads were fired into the surface. I eased off the thrusters. We were secure.

I allowed myself to fall out of the seat, a sort of slow motion activity in the low gravity, and grabbed the handle by the viewport so that I could watch Nadia coming in.

Cyg Four was powering down towards the surface. I saw the flare of the thrusters as she tumbled over, smoothly taking up the landing attitude. The flames from the main nozzles reduced and the tug slowed until it appeared to be hovering just above the surface. It looked like a corrugated can of soup with a domed top. The dome was studded with viewports, black against the bright metal. It was rumoured that the tugs had been painted when they had been shipped out, but years of abrasion in the asteroid belt had removed any vestige of coating.

Cyg Four's nose ring was retracted to a position just behind the dome of the control room, so that it looked like a collar. Four pods positioned round the tug housed the struts for the nose-ring, and the landing struts and pads. Down one side of the body the latch rail extended like a spine, and from between two of the nose ring pods a circular protuberance showed the position of the airlock connection point. In a similar position close to the rear was the machinery space lock.

As I watched, the landing struts extended from the tail pods. I could almost hear them click into place, then the tug dropped slowly onto the surface until the struts were bent with the continuing power of the thrusters. There was no doubt about it, Nadia Abdull was good.

There were four puffs of dust from the pads as the securing pins fired, but before Nadia could cut the downthrust I saw the tug begin to fall. Two of the pads disappeared through a widening hole in the surface, and Cyg Four subsided onto the crust of the asteroid, bouncing slightly and then becoming still. Two of the landing struts stuck up into the air. The tug looked like a beetle on its side.

I gulped. "Oh shit," said Easan, who was looking out of the viewport beside me. "What are we going to do now?"

I pushed my way back into the pilot's seat and triggered the Commnet. "Cyg Four - this is Cyg Two. Do you read?" There was silence. "Cyg Four, Cyg Two, come on Nadia, where are you?" I wondered if they had been injured in the crash. Somehow it did not seem likely. There was no visible damage to the tug. "Cyg Four, this is Cyg Two - speak to me." I flicked through the channels but got no response.

"Cyg Two this is AMC 10. What's the problem?" The rig was calling us. Miners knew nothing. "We're busy," I responded. "I'll get back to you."

The shape of the asteroid gave the rig a close horizon, so they could not immediately see what was going on, and as far as I could tell there would be little they could do to assist.

"Try the intercom," suggested Easan. The intercom

was a system of small portable transceivers, which allowed us to talk to each other from different parts of the ship. I picked it up and plugged in the headset. "Cyg Four, this is Cyg Two. Do you read me on this?" My voice echoed through the console speaker, followed by Nadia Abdull's rich contralto.

"Cyg Two, this is Cyg Four. Hiya Sully. That was another great idea." I looked at Easan and we both sighed with relief.

"I read you, Nadia," I replied. "Are you guys OK? I can't get you on the Commnet."

"Yeah, we're fine. The ship's not too good though. Rollo's doing a damage assessment now, but it doesn't look as if we've got a chance of lifting off from here without help. The new control unit they fitted came adrift and went straight into the mainframe. Up to now we know it's knocked out the Commnet and one of the thruster controls, but we don't know what else. There's no way I can lift out of this by myself, so it looks like a salvage job unless you can think of something."

I looked at Easan. He shook his head slowly. "Well," I said. "The main thing is that you're OK. We've just got to bite on the bullet and go public." We both knew that the likely outcome would be the withdrawal of our Acme approval, and the termination of our contracts with Cygnus, which might not have been such a bad thing, except that jobs were getting a little hard to find.

"I'll start off by calling Trantor and he can tell Acme and Cygnus. If we're lucky they might even come back with some ideas."

Trantor was the Cygnus Base Engineer. He was bad tempered, incompetent and insecure. Sometimes I was able to forgive him. Anyone who spent twelve months at a stretch under the ground in the Acme base was entitled to be out of his tree.

I punched the code into the teelink and Trantor's face

swam into the screen. "Hi Sulliman," he oozed, his red jowls quivering in the attempt to be pleasant. "Sorry we haven't been able to get the new read-outs to you yet, but I'm assured they're on their way."

"Listen Trantor," I said. "Give me your full attention. Cygnus Four has had a crash and we need help. It could be serious. She's on her side on the surface of Eos 235 and some of her systems are down. We have the only contact because we are just within range of each other's intercoms, so any communications have to go through us. At present we're playing it low key. There doesn't seem to be the need to send out a distress but we're probably going to need salvage. You are our first contact. There's a good chance that Acme may have an idea what's going on if the company man on AMC 10 was monitoring our Commnet."

Trantor's mouth dropped open. "When... what... where did this happen? Hassan's not going to like this." Hassan was the Acme Mobile Unit Manager. "We'll have to get another tug for the rig move. I want a full report on the incident immediately. Tell Mizz Abdull to make a full report immediately." Now his face was bobbing from side to side on the screen. I knew that out of frame he was waving his arms. Trantor was an insect scurrying about to avoid being trodden on.

"Sully, are you there?" Nadia's voice, a little frightened, came out of the console speaker.

"Stand by, I've got something coming in from Cyg Four," I said, and before Trantor could say anything I pressed the mute key. His face was still full frame on the screen, but I knew that he could neither see nor hear us.

"What is it, Nadia?"

"We have another problem. The PCBs in the air scrubber control are completely shattered, so we're not getting the air cleaned any more. Rollo's looked into the compressed air

20

stock and we have enough for about ten hours if she can't jury rig something."

This is all Cygnus' fault, I thought. But it was not so. Accidents are always a combination of misfortunes. If the shift had not been delayed we would not have thought about landing. If we had not landed then Cyg Four would not have toppled. If Cyg Four had not toppled the combustion control unit would not have fallen out of it's fittings. If Cygnus had done the job properly in the first place...

"Sully, did you get that?"

"Yes Nadia," I replied "Don't worry, I'm on to Trantor now. We'll get you out of there one way or another." I hoped that my voice gave her more confidence than I felt.

I keyed in the teelink again. "Trantor, the situation is more serious than we thought. Our first priority is to get the crew out. The air scrubbers have failed and they estimate that they only have ten hours left in the bottles. I think we should upgrade to a distress."

Trantor was still waving his arms out of frame. "No, you can't do that. It's going to reflect very badly on us. Tell me what happened and I'll get onto Hassan, and Macgregor."

I described the events which had resulted in the situation, only increasing our orbital discomfort to one of impossibility, and indicating that to do running repairs to the thrusters we had to get down onto the surface. Cyg Four, I said, had come down with us in case we had any problems. I indicated that it had been the failure of the Cygnus repair squad to fix the forward thrusters properly that had given us the problem, and emphasised that despite the embarrassing position Cyg Four now found herself in, had the control unit been screwed down properly, they would probably have been able to extricate themselves.

The colour was gradually draining from Trantor's

face. He could see that it was going to be very difficult for him to stay in the clear, so his policy would be to spread the blame wherever he could. Mainly on me, I suspected. Well, there was a certain justice in that. It was really my fault. What had not crossed his mind was the possibility that things could get even worse.

"I'm going to get them off," I said. "Then after that we can organise the salvage."

"You can't do that," he replied, "they're women."

"I know they're women," I replied. "But if I don't do something they could be dead women."

I had never been sure whether Trantor was really religious, or whether he was doing nothing more than conforming in the hope that it would advance him in the company. We were all acquainted with the Acme regulation which forbade all contact between male and female employees, except in what were termed "collective" situations. It was well known that Acme had gained the mining concession on the basis of rigid morality policies and the enthusiasm with which they enforced them on their workers. Basically, the more devout you were the better you got on.

I judged that Trantor had stopped waving his arms. The sheer enormity of the information which he was going to have to impart both to Hassan Kyzyski and Macgregor, the President of Cygnus, was more than he could deal with.

"You'll have to leave it with me," he said. "And in the meantime, get a written report in." He cut the line and I was faced with a blank screen, and a problem of what to tell Nadia.

Nadia's voice came over the intercom. "Sully, I heard that. I think we're going to have to rely on them to work something out." She sounded cool and composed.

"Well they'd better," I replied. "I'm coming to get you anyway. Whatever they can do to me won't be as bad as what could happen to you, if they don't get their fingers out."

"Sully, I'm touched. I didn't know you cared."

She was joking, but there was no possible response. In my dreams I had made love to Nadia Abdull. I had run my fingers through her silky dark hair. I had looked into her serious blue eyes. I had felt her long slim fingers running down my spine, but that was in my dreams. I had never seen her.

I did know a little about her. During a quiet moment back in the Cygnus base office, while Trantor had been about some of his pointless business, I had dialled up her profile. There had been enough for me to create an image. Height - 1.7 metres, Weight - 51 kilos, Hair - black, Eyes - blue. Skin colour - light, Age - thirty-three years. She was obviously of middle-eastern origins with a dash of Caucasian. A dream woman. I had also, out of curiosity, dialled up her engineer, Rollo Vespasian. Her profile showed her to be tall and very dark, maybe black, heredity African, possibly Ethiopian.

I set Easan onto working out a way in which we could extract them from their tin can, while I began typing the report into the computer. I dotted the narrative with figures on thruster response and a projection of the possible consequences during the rig move, but in the end could not escape from the fact that under no circumstances should we have landed on the asteroid. To say that we had done it many times in the past would be no excuse. Most regulations were written to cover people's backs, and whoever had written this one had decided to save themselves from the responsibility of having to deal with such situations.

When it was finished I dialled the access code to the Cygnus base computer and sent it through.I was surprised when, as soon as my transmission was complete, a single page slid out of the printer. It was on Cygnus paper, and read:

PENDING A FORMAL INVESTIGATION YOU WILL BE SUSPENDED FROM DUTY ON THE RETURN OF YOUR CRAFT TO BASE. DO NOT TAKE ANY FURTHER ACTION WITHOUT AUTHORISATION FROM THIS OFFICE. THE SAME APPLIES TO CAPTAIN N.ABDULL OF CYGNUS 4 PLEASE RELAY THIS MESSAGE VERBALLY AND CONFIRM TO THIS OFFICE IN WRITNG WHEN THIS HAS BEEN DONE. SIGNED, G.TRANTOR BASE SUPERVISOR.

Typical of Trantor. I wondered what the G stood for.

Almost immediately two further sheets slid out of the printer and dropped into the catch basket. I picked them up. The first was headed Acme Mining Corporation and read:

TO THE CAPTAIN CYGNUS 2.

IT HAS BEEN REPORTED TO US THAT AN ACCIDENT HAS OCCURED TO CYGNUS 4 ON THE SURFACE OF EOS 235 DUE TO UNAUTHORISED LANDING AND THAT CYGNUS 2 ALSO LANDED ON THE SURFACE IN DIRECT CONTRAVENTION OF REGULATION A234/091B. AS A CONSEQUENCE WE HAVE INSTRUCTED CYGNUS INC TO REPLACE YOU AS CAPTAIN OF CYGNUS 2 AND FOR MIZZ N.ABDULL TO BE SIMILARLY REPLACED ON CYGNUS 4. UNDER THE TERMS OF YOUR CHARTER YOU ARE INSTRUCTED TO ATTEND A SAFETY INVESTIGATION ON YOUR RETURN TO ACME BASE. WE UNDERSTAND THAT COMMUNICATION IS ONLY POSSIBLE TO CYGNUS 4 THROUGH YOU, SO WE WOULD INSTRUCT YOU TO INFORM MIZZ ABDULL OF THIS REQUIREMENT, AND CONTACT US IN WRITING TO CONFIRM YOUR COMPLIANCE. H.KYZYSKI. ACME BASE MANAGER.

The next page was headed with the badge of the Morality Police.

24

TO SULLIMAN SMITH, CYGNUS 2. WE ARE INFORMED BY G.TRANTOR OF THE CYGNUS BASE OFFICE THAT YOU HAVE INDICATED AN INTENTION TO BOARD CYGNUS 4, [COMMANDER N.ABDULL, ENGINEER R.VESPASIAN]. WE WOULD REMIND YOU THAT UNDER THE CODE THERE ARE NO CIRCUMSTANCES ALLOWING YOU INTO DIRECT AND UNSUPERVISED CONTACT WITH FEMALES WHO ARE NOT OF YOUR IMMEDIATE FAMILY. WE WOULD THEREFORE COUNCIL YOU EARNESTLY AS TO THE DIRE CONSEQUENCES OF SUCH AN ACT. YOUR SUPERIORS HAVE A FULL UNDERSTANDING OF YOUR SITUATION AND THE MANAGERS OF THE ACME CORPORATION ARE ACTING TO RECOVER THE CREW OF CYNUS 4 IN A MANNER AUTHORISED BY OURSELVES. CARL SEDIKI. POLICE COMMANDER.

"Bollocks" I said as I crumpled the sheets into a ball and threw them into a corner. I hammered a response onto the computer and keyed it through to Trantor with an instruction to pass on the message to whoever he thought might like to hear it. He was obviously rushing round everyone he could think of trying to cover his arse.

I punched in the code for Trantor's office and he was there, attempting to look composed.

"So," I said. "Now we've all covered ourselves, what the hell are you guys doing about getting these girls out? You'd better have something good. Come on, give."

Trantor looked aggrieved. "There's no need to take that tone," he replied. "I'm only obeying the rules. We've decided to upgrade the incident to a grade three emergency and as such have broadcast request for immediate assistance from a salvage ship on the basis of a recovery contract. We've located a suitable ship manned by a female crew at the other side of the sector. We expect them to be on your location in twenty-two hours. We're also chartering two tugs to replace you. They'll be on location at the same time. Then at least the rig shift can go ahead."

"I think you're missing something," I shouted "Their air is going to give out in" - I looked at my watch – "seven hours and fifty minutes. And there'll be an increase in carbon dioxide build-up. No air scrubbers means no air-conditioning, and this asteroid is rotating at ninety degrees to its orbit round the sun. We are at the pole in the sunlight. It's going to get damn hot in there."

"As far as the air is concerned," he replied, "we have made some calculations in the office and we think that there will be an adequate air supply for the period in question. Mizz Abdull and Mizz Vespasian will be in no danger. In the event of a shortfall it will be necessary for them to don their survival suits, which will give them three extra hours of air.

I realised that the teelink was being monitored; probably by Acme and certainly by the Morality Police. Trantor could be very prim if the situation called for it.

I broke the link and turned to Easan, who had been punching his keyboard between interludes of rushing about taking measurements and looking at Cyg Four through the binoculars. "What's the score with the air supply?" I asked.

"If they had the full set of bottles they would be right, but Cyg Four had five of her bottles removed when they failed survey last year. It's still legal to have five bottles. The SOLIS regs only require a capacity of ten hours without scrubbers on registered tugs. I think they figure that we'd be bound to be rescued by then." SOLIS was the acronym for the Safety of Life in Space regulations.

"OK," I said, "It looks like it'll take longer than the time we have left to convince them they've made a mistake. I think we should go ahead and take them off and to hell with the consequences."

Easan was looking thoughtful. "There might be a way to keep them going until the salvage ship arrives, without actually breaking any rules, then at least we might keep ourselves out of the religious pokey and only lose our jobs."

I looked questioningly at him. He continued. "If we land nose down next to them we can connect our airlock to their machinery space hatch. We predatory males would then be unable to get to the defenceless women because the internal hatch to the machinery space can only be opened from their personnel space."

"That's fine," I said, just feeling a little disappointed that in saving Nadia Abdull I was not actually going to meet her face to face. "But how are they going to get the air?"

"It's just a matter of reversing the pressure relief valves in the pilot house." Easan replied. "Rollo can do that in ten minutes. What's more, we've got a bit of a lever with Cygnus and particularly Trantor. Although the SOLIS Regs only require ten hours of air, the Acme charter specifies a capability of 20 hours. Cygnus has been cutting corners as usual and relying on us to keep quiet. All we have to do is ask Nadia for the reference numbers of the survey report and the work order, which must have been authorised by Trantor. We give him a call and tell him to look them up, and then make our proposal. After that he's got to start running around for us, because that's the only way he'll be able save himself."

For the first time I was really pleased that Easan spent so much time reading the small print. But we still had to get agreement for his plan, and time was running out.

CHAPTER 3

New Rules for Rig Supervisors An Extract

In addition to his/her responsibilities for all activities aboard the Acme mining unit to which he or she is assigned, the Acme Rig Supervisor is responsible for all events on the Acme controlled asteroid, where the rig is located. No space vessels are allowed to land or take off from the surface without his/her express permission. All space craft contracted to the Acme Corporation have been issued with the Company Operations Manual, which contains specific instructions as to how contact with the rig will be initiated and what protocols will be followed, to ensure that the unit remains safe at all times.

As a result of these instructions the only vessels authorised to land on the asteroid to which your rig is assigned, are the Acme contracted freighters, survey vessels and support craft being used for freight, supply purposes and for rig relocation.

In the event of an emergency anywhere on the surface of the asteroid the Rig Supervisor is to take charge of any rescue operations. To this end the rig is provided with a surface crawler capable of maintaining a habitable environment for two men for a period of twenty-four hours. This vehicle must be kept ready for immediate deployment at all times.

In the event of an emergency on the rig itself the crawler can be upmanned to four men giving it habitable environment of twelve hours. An additional emergency pod for ten men is provided, which can support life for twelve hours. The pod can be towed by the crawler if necessary, and both the crawler and the pod are capable of pinning themselves to the surface should the emergency warrant such action.

28

It is important to remember that there are no circumstances where unrelated men and women can be allowed to be present in the same space, at pain of extreme sanction. Hence, on rigs that are operated by female crews, every effort will be made to ensure that freighters also crewed by females will be used to uplift cargo. In the event that this is not possible, strict segregation is required. Similarly, when a rig has male personnel, every effort will be made to employ freighters piloted and supported by male crews.

After getting the survey and work order numbers for the downgrade of the emergency air system from Nadia I called Trantor, and told him to look them up and call us back. In five minutes he was back on the teelink, white in the face and ingratiating. Of course he made no mention of the contents. We were both aware of the possibility of monitoring. His jowls wobbled as he spoke.

"Well, Sulliman." He was adopting his serious professional tone. "I see what you mean. What can I do to help?" We had him. Now it was just a matter of getting him to persuade Acme, the Morality Police and Cygnus to fall into line. His job depended on it.

I outlined Easan's plan, allowing Trantor time to scribble notes. I could see the relief in his face, but I knew that at no time had it occurred to him that our proposal would save the lives of two Cygnus personnel. Two human beings. All he was thinking was that now there was a chance that he would save his job.

"OK Sully," he said, "I've got it all. I'll do what I can." It would not be beyond Trantor to put the plan forward as his own idea, as long as no blame would attach to him if it went wrong. It did not matter. The important thing was to get air to Cyg Four.

With two hours to go before the girls would have to put on their survival suits, the teelink beeped and lit up. The head and shoulders of a swarthy, hook-nosed man, wearing the dark blue uniform and shoulder insignia of a commander in the Morality Police, filled the screen. He transfixed me with his hooded dark eyes. He had said nothing, yet I began to get the idea of what dire consequences might mean.

"Captain Smith," he said. "I am Commander Carl Sediki of the Morality Police. We have to talk, and then Captain Abdull and I have to talk, and if our talks go well then you may be able to help in the unfortunate accident that has befallen your colleagues. Mr Trantor has been to see me. His view is that the margin of safety between the arrival of the salvage ship and the loss of air in Cygnus Four is very small, and I agree with him. In view of this possible threat to the safety, and indeed the lives of the personnel in Cygnus Four he has suggested that Cygnus Two connects with the machinery lock on Cygnus Four and pressurises it using your air. He has also stated that entry into the personnel area cannot be gained from the machinery space and so you will be effectively segregated from Captain Abdull and Engineer Vespasian."

Yes sir," I replied. "That is true. We would naturally avoid doing anything in contravention of morality code. It is our wish to be of whatever assistance we can. We can see no problem with this method of assistance." I found myself falling into the formal speech patterns always used by the Morality Police.

"Good," he said. "Now I wish to speak with Captain Abdull. I am told that you are in touch with her by intercom, so please open the line to her. In this way I will be able to speak to her, even though I will be unable to see her."

I had no means of warning Nadia without muting the teelink, so I hoped that she had been listening in. I called her on

30

the intercom.

"Captain Abdull, I have Commander Sediki to speak with you."

Nadia responded immediately. "Go ahead Commander Sediki." Sediki's dark eyes made holes in the screen of the teelink. I found myself thankful that Nadia could not see him. He was a frightening man.

"Captain Abdull. You are no doubt acquainted with the plan put forward by the Cygnus management to provide you with a margin of safety pending the arrival of the salvage vessel. The Cygnus Two will make an airlock joint with your machinery hatch and will pressurise your vessel. In this way you will be provided with a fresh air supply and suitable cooling for whatever time is necessary before you are rescued. The men of the Cygnus Two will remain in their craft and you will remain in the personnel area of yours. You will under no circumstances un-dog the door between your pilot house and the machinery space. We are sure that your natural modesty as women would not allow you to do this, but we must instruct you in your duty."

Nadia answered, "Commander Sediki, although we are on familiar terms with the men of Cygnus Two, this has been, and always will be restricted to Commnet communication. Our religion forbids any closer contact, and neither Engineer Vespasian or myself would dream of doing anything at variance with our beliefs. We will spend the time between now and our rescue in meditation and prayer."

Her sincerity was obvious and I was sure that Sediki would readily accept her word, that we would indeed be able to ensure their safety despite the bungling on the part of Cygnus. I realised why I was becoming depressed. I was about to be St George, but I was only going to kill the dragon. There was going to be no pay-off. I was not going to loosen the bonds of the maiden and have her fall into my arms. I was going to have to sheath my sword and stand back while someone else released and walked away with her. Worse, when Nadia Abdull climbed through the lock into the salvage ship, the access hatch of the Cyg Four still closed between us, she would take my dreams with her. Even in fantasy I could not make love to a lady with such strong moral convictions. How could she possibly respond? I cursed the course of events that had precipitated the accident. In the asteroid belt life is hard and bleak, but to be unable to dream. That was the worst cut of all.

Sediki signed off, and I was left staring glumly at a blank screen. "Come on," said Easan "We'd better get on. By the time we get hooked up their survival will be measured in minutes." I wondered if Easan was in love with anybody. He had never said, but then I had not said I was in love with Nadia, or at least in love with my image of her. I shook myself and climbed into the pilot's seat. Easan was already at the engineer's console flicking switches, and Cyg Two was rumbling and whirring in response.

"This is what we have to do," he said. "We have to land nose down next to the machinery space airlock. Once we're balanced on the nose-ring we can adjust the height until our personnel lock is exactly level with the Cyg Four machinery lock. It's going to be a bit tight - with the ship lying on it's side their lock is very close to the dirt, but I don't think it's really a problem."

Suddenly the Commnet burst into life. "Cyg Two, this is AMC 10. The base has been in touch, telling us that you have a problem. What's going on?"

"Oh shit," said Easan. "That's all we need".

I cleared my throat and keyed the mike. "Hi AMC 10. Yes, there's been a bit of a problem here. Cyg Four has toppled and has also suffered a mechanical failure. We have been authorised to carry out a rescue by the Acme management."

"What can we do to help?" asked the voice.

It was difficult at this point not to respond negatively to such a well-meaning question. What on earth could the rig, which was no more capable of doing anything than a beetle on its back, do to help us with what was going to be a particularly difficult problem? They were barely capable of helping themselves.

I gave it a moment's thought and then replied. "Hi AMC 10. Thanks very much for the offer. I think we have it in hand. We are being forced at the moment to use our short range comms to talk with Cyg Four, so you can't hear us. But we'll let you know if we need anything."

"You're going to have to do better than that," was the response. "This is the Rig Boss speaking. As you well know I am responsible for everything that happens on this asteroid, particularly anything that can impinge on the safety of anyone here. I want to know what happened, what the resulting problem is, and what you are going to do about it. And... as you know we do have a surface vehicle, which we can send out. It could be useful."

"Do you have any female crew members? Because if you don't your surface vehicle will have to stay where it is. You probably don't know, but Cyg Four has a female crew, and we have permission to carry out a plan which will maintain their segregation". I went on to explain what the plan was, as briefly as possible, trying to keep the frustration out of my voice. The minutes ticked by and we got closer and closer to the time when things would get serious for Nadia and Rollo.

"Fair enough," said the Rig Boss. "Let me know when you take off, when you land and when you have accomplished your task, which, as I understand it is to supply Cygnus Four with air from Cygnus Two. And I believe this is to be done by means of connecting your airlock to their machinery space?"

"That's all correct," I replied "And we're going to take off now."

Easan recovered the securing pins by lifting the pads one at a time and then pressing them back into their holders. He checked the readings on the engine, and when he was happy with everything, nodded in my direction.

I operated the collective control, easing the tug into the air, and balancing it on the tail thrust. Once we were a few metres above the surface we could see the rig. Both we and it were on a flat plain randomly dotted with nodules of metal of one sort or another, with a visible curvature, which gave us a horizon of about one kilometre.

The rig, two kilometres away, still looked like a beetle, but a silver one, with a number of antennae and other bits and pieces sticking out of it. On top of its more or less rectangular body we could see the viewports of its control room. We were on the sunny side of the asteroid, so our tiny world was extremely bright. It would only take a little too much thrust, on the part of any of the vessels used to put the rig in position, for it to start tumbling slowly in any direction, giving those on its surface flashes of sunlight followed by equal periods of darkness.

But now, on the bright side, the rig gleamed and its viewports twinkled with reflected sunlight. Like everything else out here with a metal surface it had been polished by the impacts of very small solid objects. Had there been an atmosphere anywhere, those objects would have burnt out as shooting stars. Had there been an atmosphere the plain would have been dusty, but dust takes some air for its suspension, or some force to displace it. Our jets were the only force in the area.

I turned my head so as to bring Cyg Four into view and without changing the attitude of our tug I moved the collective so that it edged sideways while still effectively balancing on the downthrust. The stranded vessel got closer until it disappeared from view. Easan undid his safety straps and edged over until his head was pressed up against the glass of the viewport.

He made a clockwise circular rotation with his index finger, with his hand pointing towards his feet. I took this to mean a requirement to rotate the tug red to green around its vertical axis. I made the necessary adjustment to the thrust and saw the rig disappear from view to my left. Easan held up his hand and I countered the thrust until the rotation was stopped. I took a bit of a chance, eased off my safety straps and leaned over until I could look down on the hull of Cyg Four. Easan looked questioningly at me. He obviously felt I did not trust his signals.

I saw the round protrusion of the machinery hatch sticking out of the side close to the nozzles. We were more or less in the right position. I got back into my seat and gestured to Easan to do the same. When he was secured I tumbled the ship so that we were now head down alongside. Easan extended the nose ring and I lowered the tug slowly onto the surface. Although we had not spoken of it, there was the possibility of another hole opening up, maybe dropping us all into the interior of the asteroid. I hoped that the additional bearing surface of the nose-ring would spread the load, but in any case I kept the thrusters going and gradually eased the weight onto the surface.

As I balanced the tug on the ring Easan gradually retracted it, lowering the nose, and soon we were staring at the surface of the asteroid through the viewports.

"That's it," said Easan. "I'm going to extend the lock now and once we've got it locked on I'll crank it. It should be solid enough to support us."

There was a hiss of air as the lock extended and then a solid click as it mated with the connection on Cyg Four. Easan dropped out of his seat and climbed out of sight through the hatch between us in the direction of the airlock. I remained strapped in, eyeing the read-outs and keeping the ship vertical on the ring, trying not to think about what might happen if there was actually a hole under both ships. Most of the unfortunate events we could imagine had happened to someone. In the early days, when there were no regulations to prevent tug drivers from doing whatever they liked, on more than one occasion a tug had fallen through the surface of an asteroid, mainly due to lack of survey information.

There were two possibilities resulting from such an accident. The first was that the hull would be breached, in which case it was goodbye to everyone inside, and the second was that the hull would remain intact but it would never ever move again. This meant that the crew would have to don their suits and somehow climb out onto the surface and await rescue. Even the less problematical of the two results was extremely unattractive. For us, if both tugs fell through the surface we would be extremely lucky if we all survived, despite the presence of the rig in the distance.

So I kept my fingers crossed until I heard Easan cranking the lock, which effectively turned it from a flexible into a solid tube. Usually we cranked the lock at base so that the joint provided a means of access to the ship and secured it at the same time. Easan re-appeared through the hatch, leaned over the back of my seat and gave me a thumbs up. I held my breath as I reduced the thrust, gradually knocking back the little levers in the bulkhead and listening to the corresponding reduction in engine noise.

The two ships were now effectively one, making a

distorted L on the surface. There was a minimal possibility that we would collectively detach and drift off from the surface, but with two of Cyg Four's legs jammed into the rock it seemed pretty unlikely.

I called the rig and told their controller that we were now secured alongside Cyg Four, and that we were about to embark on the next phase of the process. He responded with no more enthusiasm than if I had just provided him with a weather report.

We both went back to the airlock. Easan opened the inlet valve and pressurised the joint, then we lifted the dogs and pulled back the hatch. We now had a connection to the outside of Cyg Four. The hatches to the machinery spaces were set up to be opened from the outside only, since there was no reason for access except for maintenance squads at a base port. Just for safety we donned our survival suits and Easan operated the pressure equalising valve. We heard our air system working to fill the space with breathable air. Once we had a green light to show that the air outside our personnel hatch was OK, we worked on the dogs of our own hatch and finally eased it open. Because of the limited size of tugs the passage created by the air lock was extremely small, so we ended up crawling towards the engine hatch of Cyg Four and, in my case constantly banging the back of my helmet against things sticking down from the roof of our tunnel.

Easan pulled out his motorised spanner, which he always seemed to have concealed somewhere about his person, and applied it to the bolts of the Cyg Four machinery space. I counted them as he eased each off and pushed the hinge back. There were twenty. I itched to give him a hand, but there was only room for one person and one spanner, but finally he had the twenty bolts out of the way. He put his right hand on the handle and pulled the hatch back towards him. Once more I heard our machinery working to replenish the air supply in this space.

"So how's that, Rollo?" asked Easan, using the headset installed in his suit. "Have you got the green light there?"

"Yeah man," she responded in her rich contralto, which, because she was an engineer, we did not hear enough of. "I'm going to connect our pilot house to the machinery space, and as far as I can tell that's going to do the job."

We waited for a while, until finally we heard her voice again, telling us that they were now breathing sweet fresh air, courtesy of Cygnus Two.

There was nothing else to do except wait for the salvage vessel, after which we would be on our way back to the base. We had been successful in carrying out what was actually a lifesaving operation, but I found myself to be unaccountably depressed..

"Who's going to tell the rig what's going on?" asked Easan.

"I will," I responded. Anything to relieve the tension I felt, at being in a position to see, and possibly to touch, Nadia Abdull, but knowing that it would never be possible. And so I turned and crawled back through the airlock, though our living space and back to my pilot's seat. I disconsolately thumbed the mike. "AMC 10, this is Cyg Two".

"Yes Cyg Two, go ahead," said the disinterested voice of their control room operator.

"Can I speak with the Rig Boss?" I asked. "Stand by one," was the reply.

I waited while they went away and got the Rig Boss. As usual it took ages. What did these guys do, I wondered. Even though he was the boss over there, he was only in charge of about ten people, and once the mining had been started there was little to do except have the operation monitored, and wait until the warehouse was filled up, and then wait until the freighter had arrived, and then wait until it left, and then wait until the warehouse was full again. Perhaps all this waiting was what made him keep everyone else waiting.

Eventually I heard his voice on the Commnet, and responded, bringing him up to date on how things were on our part of the asteroid. Our machinery was working away and keeping us all breathing and seemed likely to do so for as long as was necessary.

"By the way," said the Rig Boss, "I've heard from the salvage vessel. It's crewed by some females so there's no problem there. I don't think it's too far away from us, so you should stand by to hear from it in the not too far distant future."

The sooner the better, I thought. The sooner we get away from this and back to base the better. Then we'll just have to face the music. But actually what could they do? How could we end up doing anything worse than what we were engaged in now? But they would probably send Easan and I to one end of the solar system and Nadia and Rollo to the other end.

I found that I was beating my right fist on the console, and had to stop because it was hurting. There was a sound behind me.

"So, are they OK over there, Easan?" I asked. "Will they survive until the salvage ship arrives?"

There was no answer, but as I turned to greet my engineer I saw a dark young woman lower herself through the hatch. She grabbed hold of the console, pushed herself back into the engineer's seat and strapped herself in, as I sat there tongue-tied. Of course I recognised her from the photo I had turned up in her file in Trantor's office. I gulped.

"Hello Sully," she said.

It was very warm and she was stripped down to her body suit. Her slim brown arms were covered with a thin sheen

39

of perspiration. A bead of moisture detached itself from her neck, sliding slowly into the vee of her suit until it came to the visible curve of her left breast, then it changed direction and accelerated out of sight behind the scoop neck of her body suit. Her blue eyes looked at me steadily. She smiled and pointed to my portable intercom, which stuck out of my top pocket. I switched it off.

"Where's Easan?" I asked.

"Is that the best you can manage?" she replied. "We've spent what seems like a lifetime talking to each other, being nice to each other, sometimes being quite nasty to each other. And now finally we are together, and all you can come up with is to ask where your engineer is. Well I just hope he's making better use of his time than you are."

"I'm sorry," I replied, "I heard you talking to Carl Sediki. I heard what you said, and I thought you meant it."

She laughed. "Well that makes you a really naïve young chap, and to cut a long story short I like that in a man. And I have to say that we do not have all the time in the world, so perhaps we should be moving our relationship to the next level."

"Well, yes," I replied cautiously.

"So, are you going to sit there all day?" she said. "We've only got a few hours before we're due to be rescued."

CHAPTER 4

Safety of Life in Space (SOLIS) Documentation

All vessels are required to respond to Mayday calls, however they are received. Each space craft is to be fitted with at least one EPIRB (Emergency Position Indicating Radial Beacon). Larger vessels are to be provided with two, and escape pods and crawlers are also to be similarly equipped. EPIRBs transmit to all geostationary positioning satellites, and their signal is re-transmitted to all receiving stations. They are therefore capable of being heard throughout the sector.

When any vessel hears either a Mayday signal, or an EPIRB transmission, they must report the reception of the signal immediately to the nearest control station. Main stations are located at the Eugenia Base and at the Io foundry. Secondary stations are to be found at the Ganymede Correction Facility and on board all mining rigs.

When contact is made, the main station or secondary station should pass on the contact to the central emergency control, which is on Io. When all contacts have been received, central control will determine the level of assistance required. In the most extreme cases and where this is possible, a salvage vessel will be deployed. These vessels are capable of rescuing personnel from any wreck as long as they have been able to maintain the integrity of a single space, or have donned their emergency suits.

All space vessels are required to be able to maintain a habitable living environment for twelve hours. Freighters are required to carry detachable rescue pods that must support the whole crew for a similar time. Rigs must carry a crawler and a rescue pod. Tugs must be provided with a strengthened pilot house and living area which is capable of withstanding an impact at a velocity of 20 metres per second, either with another vessel or the *surface of an asteroid or planet.*

All emergency suits must conform to the required SOLIS standards and should be overhauled annually by an accredited service provider.

Before any vessel responds to a Mayday call, permission must be obtained from the Morality Police, their charterers and their owners. It should be noted that permission for male crews to rescue female crews, or vice-versa, will be unlikely to be given, but to deal with situations which impinge on morality factors the authorities have provided salvage vessels that are suitably crewed, so that these can be dealt with.

Cautiously I took her hand. It was small and well formed, with carefully manicured and well polished fingernails.

"Look," she said. "We'd really like to be doing something different. Not totally different, but at least it would be good if we could have a meal together in a nice place. Get to know each other better than we do now, and finally if everything seemed to be going well, possibly after meeting a number of times, and having kissed and cuddled a bit, go into one of our sleeping compartments, help each other out of our clothes and then bingo, the big event.

But we have to look at where we are now. We've been working together for ages. How long is it?"

"Fifteen months," I replied, remembering in some detail the first time I had heard Nadia's voice.

"That's right. So we're off to a pretty good start. We know each other's work well. I know that you're as straight as a die. And you tell it to others like it is. And you don't tolerate fools gladly. You are also pretty good at what you do, which makes you quite admirable, but not quite as good as me which is even better. And you've managed to be entertaining, even given the limitations of only being able to talk on the radio in a formal manner, within the hearing of the Morality Police."

"Is that having a good sense of humour?" I asked. She laughed, flashing her even white teeth. "There you are. Even now you're making me laugh. But look. You can see what I'm getting at. I'm not ready to have sex with just anyone, just because the opportunity has occurred. You'd be surprised how often the opportunity actually occurs, but it may be once in a lifetime that there is an opportunity to have sex with someone you like, and with someone you find attractive. And frankly that's where I am. I wish I could be more subtle but there's no time for that, because we have no idea how far away the salvage ship is. I've told Rollo to detain your man Easan. Whether they decide to get close and personal is up to them. I'm only interested in us. And to be honest now I've said all that I'm not quite sure what to do next."

I took her other hand. "We could try a kiss and see how it goes from there?" I replied. Which was pretty good, since my mind was in turmoil at the thought of having all my prayers answered.

So we tried the kiss. It is difficult now to describe the feeling. I was intoxicated with the touch of her lips on mine, and I realised that I had stopped breathing. We separated and I gasped for air.

Before we could go on to the next step, for which we both seemed to be ready, despite the briefness of our initial contact, we were interrupted by a voice on the Commnet.

"Cyg Two, this is the AMC 10 crawler. Do you read?"

Nadia looked at me questioningly. I held up my hand to ask for silence and reached for the mike. "Yes AMC 10 crawler, what can I do for you?"

"We are approaching your location and request permission to board. We have been asked by the Rig Supervisor to monitor your activities."

Nadia and I looked at each other. The arrival of this gooseberry, in the form of a surface vehicle from the rig, ensured that there was little point in doing anything other than getting on

43

with the job. All the rigs carried a couple of crawlers, which could collectively carry the whole crew. All ten of them. While they were being used as emergency craft they were a bit crowded, but a couple of guys in one could last for some time. They moved on tracks, which would give them the maximum opportunity for transit no matter what the terrain, and they carried supplies, which would keep two people going for a month.

Nadia pulled me towards her and we held on tight, pressing against each other as if to make an imprint we would be able to feel in the lonely nights to come. We kissed and I experienced again the electricity generated between us despite the gentleness of the contact. "Don't say anything. Let's just go and face the music," she said. "Don't worry, we'll get together again."

I was only slightly heartened by her optimism. There was a good chance that just to punish us they would send us to the opposite ends of the solar system, even though none of the management or the authorities involved would have the least idea how serious this punishment would be. "I've got to go," she said.

And with that she stepped back and pulled herself up through the hatch towards the connection between the two ships. Within a couple of minutes Easan was lowering himself beside me, breathing hard.

"Don't worry. We're due to meet again, apparently," I said.

"Cyg Two this is the AMC 10 crawler. Did you read my last message?"

In our position head down with our viewports pointing towards the sand we had a horizon of about five metres. I got down on my knees and tried to see how far away the crawler was. I could see the lower part of the hull of Cyg Four, but not its viewports, so did not know where Nadia and Rollo now were. I presumed that they were sitting there looking chaste, and that they would be able to see the approaching crawler.

I keyed the mike. "Hi AMC crawler. I don't know what

you hope to achieve, but there is no way you can board our vessel. Our airlock is extended and is connected with the machinery lock of Cyg Four. Even if you could board them through their personnel lock, it would not be allowed. Would you like me to relay a message to the captain of Cyg Four?"

There was silence while the rig guys tried to think what to do next.

"Perhaps we could see that the crews of the two tugs are where they should be?"

The voice was by now cautious; it did not reflect any sort of certainty. They had obviously been sent out to do something that was far beyond their normal remit.

"I can't speak for Cyg Four," I responded "But I can't see you from our viewports so I presume that you can't see us. You seem to be implying that the crew of Cyg Four may not be conforming to the morality regulations. I'm not sure that Captain Abdull will take kindly to the implication that that she might be doing something illegal. Just a minute I'll give her a call on our intercom."

I kept my thumb on the Commnet mike and called Nadia on the intercom. When she responded, we had a formal exchange, which in the end told the guys in the crawler that the girls had never left their pilot house and in fact if the crawler chose to get close enough they would give it a wave.

"I wish I could see this," said Easan.

It would have been nice to see the crawler stationary at the front end of Cyg Four, while the girls and the chaps in it exchanged waves, but it would have been even nicer if we could have exchanged waves ourselves. The whole process was fairly pointless, and actually, if we had had the nerve, we could probably have consummated our relationship, while talking to the crawler on the Commnet at the same time. They had come out on a wild goose chase, and could not really monitor us if we chose not to be monitored.

"AMC crawler this is Cyg Two," I called. "When the salvage vessel arrives we will be disconnecting from Cyg Four and then our airlock will be available. Would you like to board us then? In any case perhaps you would like to stand by in case we need assistance with the next part of the rescue."

Easan rubbed his hands. "That should get them," he said. And we both visualised the crawler having to remain in our immediate vicinity for several hours while we waited. It might be uncomfortable for us, head down in the dust, but it would probably be more uncomfortable in the crawler, on the limits of its AC and without any form of entertainment whatsoever other than looking out at two stationary tugs, one on its side, and one connected to it head down.

"OK," replied the crawler, without enthusiasm, and then there was silence as we all waited to see what would happen next. The crisis seemed to be over. Indeed we had all forgotten about the extreme distress we had been feeling only an hour or two ago, but had not really taken on board the level of distress we were all going to feel once we got back to base.

However, what the crawler had achieved, unbeknown to those in it, was our return to our respective vessels, so now all we could do was wait. Easan and I lolled back against the viewports, the only comfortable position in the ship when it was nose down, and stared out into space.

"It's amazing," said Easan "what two human bodies can achieve." He thought for a moment. "Maybe *enjoy* is the right word."

I knew what he was getting at, but such sentiments were not expressed in a society based on the extremes of religious fundamentalism, where there was no contact between men and women until they had gone through the procedure of an arranged marriage, and any form of sensuality would be unlikely. The husband might take his wife, she might give herself, but it would be a lucky circumstance for them both to be able to enjoy the resulting sexual act.

It was rumoured that rich and important men visited so called cruise ships, which moved in orbit around bodies in the solar system, and on which all desires could be fulfilled. On the cruise ships men could indulge their sexual fantasies with real women, and for the more extreme fantasies there were simulators of various sorts.

But to start with you had to be well-heeled enough to be able to afford the fare out there, or to have your own shuttle, and the prices were out of this world. Or so it was said.

For most of the males in the ex-earth environment then, it was the drudgery of an arranged marriage. Of course it was the same for the females, and no matter how well off the latter were, such a liaison would be unlikely to provide any way out of their personal prison. My mother occasionally made an effort to start something going for me, but up to now I had been able to avoid it. There were still places in the solar system where low caste workers mixed freely, and so did their visitors. Sometimes it cost, sometimes it didn't.

On the other hand we had recently begun to hear rumours that things were changing, back on the mother planet. There had always been pockets of the old faiths remaining in the more remote areas - despite the existence of the Morality Police, and the penalties if people were found doing anything other than what the state required of them.

If the whispers were to be believed, the population of earth was falling to the point where it was no longer possible for some essential services to be maintained . Hence it was necessary for the human population to produce more children. Despite some efforts, and much noise and fanfare, cloning had never worked. There were human clones but they were humans of very limited intelligence. They looked like adults, but they remained children and they never developed in a way that would allow them to reproduce.

47

Because of these problems it was said that the formerly banned religions had been given freedom to recruit members, or that people were now free not to be bound by any religious laws at all. I could imagine living on such a world with Nadia. We could have our own private habitation, somewhere in the outdoors. Here I was using as a reference the pictures still to be found in our educational media of what things looked like in the countryside on earth. There were pictures of small habitations made out of wood with smoke curling out of tubes in the roof. They were usually situated beside bodies of water, and in the pictures people could be seen fishing. Of course I realised that this was an idealised view, but it was a difficult image to dislodge, and it was easy to add us, and a couple of children.

"We could go back to earth," I said.

"Where did that come from?" asked Easan. "I know we've heard that there are things going on, back on earth, attractive things which we'd like. So you want to do things with Nadia which would not be allowed here, and a way of doing it would be to go back to earth. How are we going to do that? There aren't even any shuttles from here to there, and worse, if there were any it would cost a fortune to buy a ticket."

Easan was probably right. But now I was less willing to accept his view.

"Look at it this way," I said. "Who would have thought we could ever have got close to these ladies? If I'd asked you a few days ago what you thought, you would have told me to stop dreaming and try and get on with life as we know it. I'm beginning to believe that anything is possible. As far as I'm concerned there's a chance we will get back together again, and a chance that we'll get back to earth, and a chance that one day we'll live what used to be called a normal life."

Suddenly there was a crisp female voice on the Commnet. "Cygnus Two this is Salvager. Do you receive?"

"Yes, Salvager, loud and clear," I replied. "We have the

48

intercom channel open to Cygnus Four. Go ahead with your message."

There followed a few minutes of communication while we went through the procedure for establishing the approach, and how and when the Salvager would drop onto the surface and sort out all our problems. At some time shortly before the arrival of the rescue craft we would disengage from Cyg Four and take off to allow the rescue to take place.

"What's that crawler doing there?" asked the captain of the Salvager.

"It's here making sure that we're obeying the law," I answered. "It's the AMC 10 crawler."

"OK, thanks," she replied. The airwaves crackled again.

"AMC 10 crawler. This is Salvager."

"Yes, Salvager?" answered the driver of the crawler uncertainly.

"Crawler," said the captain of the Salvager, making the call sound more like an insult. "If you don't get out of the way we'll incinerate you when we land, and the resulting pile of melted metal will stop us achieving a level. So we won't be able to pick up Cyg Four. Honestly I'm not at all concerned about you and the vehicle you're in, but not being able to land and achieve a level does concern me. So I suggest that you get the hell out of here, pronto."

A voice interrupted the exchange. "Crawler this is the Rig Boss. You can come back now."

"OK Boss. We're on our way!" We could hear the relief in his voice.

The captain of the Salvager spoke again. "And you Cyg Two. You can get ready to disconnect."

"We're ready," I replied. "Just give us the word and we'll get out of your way. But we'd appreciate it if you'd bear in mind than once we disconnect, the crew of Cyg Four will not have much time before their lives are at risk."

"Are you telling me that I don't know my job? If that's the case it may be just as well that we're separated by the law and by our environment."

"No, not at all," I replied, "I'm just a concerned observer. And pleased that we've managed to help. Without us things would be a lot more dire than they are now."

"OK, but watch it," responded the ice cool captain of the Salvager. "We'll be at your location in ten minutes. You make the judgement as to when you unlock, but I don't want to see you there when we start to descend."

"That's *now*," said Easan, and started to press buttons and flick switches. Then he disappeared from view and I knew that he was on his way to secure the hatch to Cyg Four's machinery space. When he slid back into the engineer's chair we prepared for departure. Even in this frontier environment we had a procedure to follow, and failing to do this could well result in disaster. I had once disengaged from a station lock without remembering to switch on the thrusters, and it was lucky for me that the tug just drifted off into space harmlessly while I corrected my omission. So we ticked the boxes and switched the switches. On my instruction Easan reached up and fired up the engines and then the thrusters. Once the power plant was operational I tested the controls, and finally we had a line of green lights on our consoles and the needles of the analogue gauges quivered in the correct sectors on their dials.

I gripped the collective control and eased the tug directly upwards on the forward thrusters. The whole of the casualty that was Cygnus Four gradually came into view, and then the plain on which we had landed and then the whole of the asteroid. We could see the crawler still making its way slowly back along its own tracks towards the rig, glinting in the sunlight, and kicking up just a little dust. When we could see the entire asteroid I adjusted the thrust so that we were once more in orbit. We were back just where we had started.

The salvage vessel floated into view below us. It was a large version of a standard tug. It eased down towards the surface, the captain deploying more and more thrust as she countered the minimal gravity of the asteroid. When it was close enough, and more or less above Cyg Four, it rotated nose up and eased gently down onto the surface. Then the crew deployed its airlock. This was a long flexible tube, the movement of which could be controlled from the pilot house of the salvage vessel. The tube of the airlock snaked downwards until it sniffed out the personnel lock on Cyg Four. Once in position it locked on and the tube became a rigid S shape.

I visualised the air from the Salvager filling the tube of the lock and the green lights going on in both vessels. Once this was achieved Rollo would be able to open the personnel door on the tug and the girls would be able to climb to safety up the tube of the airlock, using the crenulations where climbing was necessary. It would be no problem for two fit young females in the limited gravity of the asteroid.

After a while there was a voice on the Commnet. "Hi Cyg Two, this is Salvager. You will be pleased to know that we have the crew of the tug on board. There's not too much room here, but they're relaxing in our recreation space."

I suddenly had a thought. Were the salvage crew dykes? Would they make advances on my true love?

"Even if they are dykes," said Easan reading my mind, "doubtless Nadia and Rollo are well experienced in shrugging off unwanted attentions. Assuming they want to shrug them off."

"You don't think…"

"No, I don't," he replied. "I was just making a joke."

I glanced through the viewport and saw that the salvage airlock had been recovered and a figure in a pressure suit was down on the surface, cutting off one of the trapped legs of the tug. The Salvager was a big bean can. She stood on eight legs, with big pads to distribute her weight. As well as a conventional latch rail running down one side, her vertical surfaces where covered in pods which housed the necessities of salvage. Once the trapped legs had been cut off, an articulated grab would reach out and drag the tug from the surface and hoist it into a position where it would be safely cuddled in the embrace of Salvager's mechanical arms.

It was going to take a while to get it back into service.

"OK, Cygnus Two," said the captain of the Salvager. "What are you hanging about for? There's nothing more you can do here."

And that was it. Of course, even though we were still doing our own thing, and despite the fact that there was nothing we could do, we still had to ask the rig for permission to depart. As I was about to call the rig, their control room operator came up on the Commnet. "Cygnus Two this is AMC 10. You have permission to depart the field." I thanked him and put the hammer down.

As soon as we set course for the base we would be going into the unknown. All of us had made mistakes in the past, or had been blamed for other people's, but in reality there was seldom much that could be done to us. We were already living an isolated existence, and we were highly skilled. The skill meant that the company could not afford to lose us, but they *could* send us to even more remote parts of the solar system, and they could give us older, less well equipped and less reliable tugs. This was the usual trick. Cygnus One was famous for its lack of comfort and difficulty in operation. Although it would seem to the uninitiated that Cygnus One must be the tug that had been built immediately before Cygnus Two, this was not the case. They had got up to Cygnus Eight, and all of them had been lost or scrapped before the second Cygnus Two was built, but for some reason Cyg One just kept going. I would not have put it past them to have kept it going just to punish errant tug crews.

Regardless of the vessel involved, the crew would be

sent to some remote location, and now we had something to lose. I had come to rely on my somewhat distant interaction with Nadia, and now that we were closer, it would be even more difficult if we were sent to different places.

"Hi Salvager, this is Cygnus Two. Have a good trip back," I called. Of course this was not a message for the Salvager, it was for Nadia. I just hoped that she had been in a position to hear it.

It would take time for them to cut off the legs and recover the damaged tug, and doubtless there would be some sort of enquiry, maybe involving both tug crews. So we would have to await our fate. I took a bit of comfort from skimming a couple of small asteroids, leaving them tumbling in our wake. Then we broke out into clear space and I set the cruise control and relaxed.

I looked out at the stars twinkling in the blackness. They were clear and bright. Here and there I could see clouds of stars, galaxies - close in astronomical terms, to our galaxy. The Magellanic Clouds; the Tarantula nebula. They were signposts, but not waypoints on our voyages. They were, all of them, beyond the reach of the space craft which had so far been developed. Even the more distant planets of the solar system were beyond the operating envelopes of commercial vessels, although exploration ships with brave and foolhardy crews had made it to the Kuiper belt, and had returned.

There was a king's ransom in ore in the area, so it was said, but the transport costs would be unacceptable. Nevertheless in the wake of the exploration ships, survey ships would follow, and beacons would be placed on all likely asteroids and dwarf planets in the area. And eventually the commercial arm of Acme, or another mining company, would find its way out there. Some of us would be given the task of acting as the power and directional capability for a rig, and would spend a very long time in transit getting it out to this distant location. Assuming they were still using conventional mining techniques, they would eventually dig the stuff up, and they would find a way of getting the ore carriers out there to pick up their cargoes. Indeed, this might be the most difficult part of the task. Although it is possible to carry out the exploration, and then the survey and even the mining, getting the cargo carriers out there within the lifetime of the crew would probably be impossible.

For me there were no final words from Nadia Abdull, no final thoughts, no promises to meet again, no reminders of what had been. We both knew that we were already in enough trouble. For the moment our memories would have to be sufficient.

CHAPTER 5

The Eugenia Base Operations Manual - Introduction

Despite its large size (214 kilometres in diameter), Eugenia proved to be of limited value as a source of minerals, and the first mining rig spent some years extracting various ores from below the surface, before moving on to the asteroid's own satellite. This resulted in a complex of shafts and tunnels which have been adapted for human habitation.

On the surface a vehicle port has been constructed, consisting of an upper and lower hub each provided with twelve spider arms. It is intended that the lower arms will be used for berthing freighters and the upper arms will be used for tugs. There is limited gravity on the asteroid, so the arms are of suitable strength to be able to support the classes of vessels licensed to work in the area.

It is possible for embarking and disembarking crews to be directed to either the male or female section as appropriate, under the control of the main control centre, without meeting with the embarking or disembarking crews of the opposite sex. The crews are routed to either the male or female living quarters by means of remotely operated partitions in the hub itself.

The living quarters themselves have been developed from the shafts and tunnels left by the mining operation, and this has resulted in the construction of two areas, each provided with seventy-five single and two berth cabins, together with recreation areas and food preparation facilities. There is no regularly-used connection between the two areas, and access from one to the other is normally achieved by a monitored throughway in the hub, directly under the authority of the control room. There is an emergency connection, but its description is beyond the authority and scope of this document.

Eugenia is one of the two emergency base stations in the sector, and hence the main control room is provided with facilities to monitor and assist with any foreseeable emergency as defined by SOLIS (Safety of Life in Space) regulations.

Evening found me in my room in the base lying on my bunk, looking at the ceiling.. Above me on the surface, Cyg Two was snuggled up to the access lock on the end of a spider arm. The tug port was like a starfish on the surface, each arm supporting, and providing access to, a tug. But the main part of the base was underground, in the old workings of the first asteroid to be mined by the Acme Mining Company.

The tunnels in use had been tidied up with individual rooms cut out of the sides and surfaced in a laminate to give them the appearance of home. The furnishings were sparse, a bunk, an easy chair, a desk and a view screen.

I was thumbing through the channels, trying to find something to take my mind of my situation, when there was a knock at the door and Trantor walked in without taking the time to be asked. He dropped his bulk into the chair.

"What do you want?" I asked without ceremony.

"I want to help you get through this enquiry," was the response. I had a job to keep a straight face. Trantor's motives only ever related to self-preservation.

"Here's the situation. It's important for Cygnus to keep this charter. It's long term and it's good money for the Company, so we want you to come out of it OK. But there is no way they're going to keep you here, so we're looking for..." he hesitated for a moment, "a little favour from you. What we are asking is that you don't drag us into it. Don't start talking about the gas bottles. If Acme find out that we failed to follow their rules, they would have a valid reason for cancelling our contract."

"What's in it for me?" I asked.

"Well, we already went along with your plan for the

rescue..."

I interrupted "What do you mean, went along with it. It was the only way of saving the lives of two of your employees. Had they died there would have been an enquiry, and Cygnus would have been on the receiving end. All I did was shortcut the decision-making. You would have had to do it in the end, but by then it might have been too late. So, I'll ask you again. What's in it for me?"

"OK," replied Trantor. "This is it. Macgregor has told me that if you can keep the Cygnus ships on this charter he will guarantee to find you work elsewhere. There's a new sector opening up and they're bidding to supply the tugs. You'll get another job, and the company will keep you on pay until you do."

"And what about the others?"

"They get the same deal of course," said Trantor. "But we have a problem there. All means of communication with Nadia Abdull would be monitored and we can't take the risk of being overheard. I could get to see her in the crew briefing room, but it's monitored, so you're going to have to get to see her yourself."

My heart leapt and I sat up. But I didn't feel any happier. There was no legal way I could get close to her. He went on.

"There's rumoured to be a way into the female section. I don't know anyone who's been there. But you could find out."

I knew the talk. There were always a few macho types who boasted about having found their way in and what they'd done when they got there. I had given the tales little credence since they mostly seemed to involve numbers of leggy blondes clad in body suits or less, carrying off the intrepid explorer to a dormitory and collectively engaging in a variety of stimulating activities. Pressed as to the route they would clam up. In addition there would have to be some sort of heating system in the women's section to allow anyone to walk about in a state of undress. One of the major complaints about underground Eugenia was the low temperature.

However, I did recall one of the base maintenance engineers looking a bit thoughtful during one of these flights of fancy and felt that he might have some useful information to impart.

"Hey Sully, what about a coffee?" asked Trantor. I grudgingly got up and poured him a cup. The perc had just finished brewing. One of my only luxuries was coffee. It cost a fortune, and took up valuable space in my baggage when I came out on tour, but what I brought usually just lasted if I could avoid freeloaders like Trantor.

He accepted it. "My, this is great." It *was* great. At least he was right about something.

"OK," I said. "I'll try to get to Nadia Abdull or Rollo Vespasian. But even if I do get in there, I'm going to have to start asking someone for information, and I might just ask someone who's going to report me." A sudden thought occurred to me. "What if Nadia Abdull would rather report me than keep her job with Cygnus?" I was not supposed to know Nadia.

"As for Nadia Abdull," he replied, "you're just going to have to trust to luck. She's a career tug driver and I think she's got ideas of higher things. There's a lot of scope for females in the management now that we're supposed to give them the opportunity, and with the increase in female pilots there's a lot more work for them to do."

I had not really considered the possibility that Nadia might see herself as a manager, but it was inevitable that, with the increase of female crewmembers, there would be such opportunities. Some companies already used female base engineers to look after the female crewed ships, though Cygnus had, up to now, relied on the supervisor system. This allowed male base engineers to talk to the women in a suitable environment. And in the event of repairs being required they could get direct access to the engines through the machinery lock.

Trantor went on. "As for finding her, if you can get in,

there is an emergency list in the central recreation area with the room numbers against the names, just like we have. All you have to do is look up her number and find the room."

"Is that all?" But I knew that I was going to try. "What if I can't get in?"

"If you can't get in then you're just going to have to try to signal her somehow at the investigation." Trantor was getting up to go. When things began to get difficult you could rely on him to be absent.

As what was called "evening" drew in, Easan and I were hunched over two cups of coffee, this time something with it's origins in reconstituted human bodily waste. I tried not to think about it and took a sip.

I asked the question that had been in my mind ever since Trantor's departure. "How do we get out of this one? Somehow I have to get over to the women's section, avoiding any of them who may be genuinely distressed to see me. Don't forget they have morality enthusiasts as well, even if none of them are actually members of the police."

"I don't know about that," replied Easan. "The rumours are that every one of them is a sex maniac, desperate for any man who can make it into their domain. That is if we believe the guys who say they have been there."

"That may possibly be true, but even if it is, I still have to somehow manage to avoid them, and get into the recreation space. And extract information from their room allocation plan, then somehow get to Nadia's room, get her to let me in. Once there I have to convince her that we should all tell the same story to get Cygnus off the hook. Really with little guarantee that it is going to do us any good. Then if I'm successful this far I actually have to get back here without being caught."

I could see Easan was thinking.

"Well," he replied. "What do we have in our favour?"

"Nothing".

"Yes we have. Firstly, we've got Trantor on our side. Secondly there are stories that people have actually managed to do this, and thirdly you desperately want to succeed in this little venture."

I looked sharply at him, but his face was perfectly straight.

Easan got up. "I'll see you later back in your room," he said.

At what passed for the middle of the night there was a knock on the door. I got up and let Easan in.

He was carrying an emergency breathing set. "Grab this and let's get going."

When we arrived at a door marked "Maintenance Personnel Only" my heart sank. I hung back.

"Come on," said Easan. "Think of that body".

I did. All the time bits of Nadia Abdull intruded into my thoughts. At some particularly inconvenient moment I would glimpse a smooth hip, a curve, a curtain of dark hair. Even worse, I could smell her and feel her. Yes, I thought of her.

But somehow I had to concentrate on the task in hand.

We descended a circular staircase until finally we stood in the darkness, our flashlights illuminating the entrance to a tunnel.

Easan coughed. "This is as far as I go. You're on your own now. Remember: follow this passage for a couple of hundred paces and you will come to a door. The door is controlled by a big red button, but if you press it the fire alarms go off in both the male and the female sections."

"So what good is that?" I asked. "Within two minutes the place will be full of people dressed in fireman's suits waving fire extinguishers, and if I make it to the women's section I'll be caught there by some official."

"Fortunately, the red button is not the only way. There is

a numeric keypad next to the door handle, and if you key in the right code the door will open."

I breathed a sigh of relief. "So that's alright then."

Easan went on. "If you get the code wrong, the door won't open, and the alarm will go off. So if that happens get back here pronto. All being well you can get back to your room, and be pretending to be asleep before anyone gets to the scene. And by the way, I've managed to disable the cameras in the corridors between your room and the door, so no-one will see you. In the female quarters they managed to have the cameras removed some time ago, on the basis that peeping toms might have access to the monitors. And the code is one, two, three, four."

"Even I should be able to remember that," I replied.

"So once you get through the door you should find a set of steps similar to this, going up. This is an escape route between the men's section and the women's section which could be used in event of fire in either, although you need the escape sets to get from one to the other, because there's no ventilation down here. So even though there is breathable air in some places, there are pockets where there's nothing. "

Typical, I thought. Mark an escape route and then don't tell anyone about it in case they make use of it. How were we supposed to know what to do if the place caught fire? Find our way by telepathy?

I shone the flashlight, which Easan had given me, down towards the ground and sure enough, there they were, little yellow arrows painted on the faced rock. I put on the escape set and adjusted the air delivery until it was comfortable, then followed the yellow arrows through the darkness. I noticed that there were light fittings on the walls, and wondered what it took to illuminate them.

I followed the arrows until, just as Easan had described, I came to a door made out of some sort of black metal, and beside the handle there was a big red button and a keypad. With a degree of apprehension I punched in the numbers, one two three four, and crossed my fingers. For a moment nothing happened and then slowly the door slid back. I stepped through and it closed behind me. I would have preferred it if the door had remained open, but what could I do? So I walked on, still following the yellow arrows until I arrived at a similar winding stair to the one which I had descended from the male section. I made my way upwards until I came to an access, identical to the one which we had used to enter the area. I took off the escape set and laid it on the second step with the torch, and eased the door open. The corridor was empty. Could I rely on it staying that way while I found out where Nadia was?

There was nothing for it but to make for the recreation space. At that moment I wished that there had been some disguise available to me, but as it was I took two steps out in the open, and a small woman charged round the corner, ran right into me, and bounced off. We stood opposite each other, both stunned into silence.

"Who are you?" asked the woman. "Sully Smith" I replied.

"Come with me, Sully," she said, apparently unfazed by the presence of a male in the female section. She guided me through an adjacent door and closed it behind us.

"This is my room," she said, waving a hand in a circular motion, indicating the space. I looked round. It was just like the one Easan and I shared in the male section, except that there was a vase of artificial flowers on the table. "Make yourself comfortable." She pointed to the chair, and sat on the bed herself. There seemed to be nothing else for it, and so I sat.

"Now Sully, I'm Gelda by the way, I have to tell you that you are not the first visitor to the female section, and as you can see my room is strategically placed to be in a position to receive visitors. So perhaps the first thing you could tell me is whether you are on an exploratory mission, or whether you have a specific objective in being here. What do you do anyway?"

Not knowing whether being a tug skipper was a good thing or not, I told her.

"So maybe there we have it," she said. "Could it possibly be that you are looking for Nadia? We hear that something went wrong out in the asteroids and that Nadia has some questions to answer. She and Rollo came back in the salvage ship. They had to leave Cyg Four in the repair yard. But more importantly, is your visit to the female section purely for administrative purposes or is there something else between you and Nadia?"

Again, having no idea whether the answer would be for good or ill, I answered honestly. "Nadia and I would like there to be something between us, but up to now we haven't had much of an opportunity. But just at the moment we need to talk, so I wonder if you could tell me where I can find her?"

"There's a problem," said Gelda, looking at her watch. "In a few minutes there's an inspection by a representative of the Morality Police. Some of them are very tiresome, demanding all sorts of things of one or more of us, or else..."

"All sorts of things and or else what?" I asked.

"Use your imagination," she replied. "Do you think these people are really believers in a religion which insists on arranged marriages between people who don't fancy each other? As far as we're concerned they are just predatory men, so some-one has to have sex with them or else they tear our rooms apart, supposedly looking for illegal objects."

I was almost speechless, but I managed to stammer out a question. "Well, do you take turns, or what?"

"No, it's not like that. Fortunately for the more sane ones among us there's usually someone who thinks that having sex with a member of the Morality Police will be beneficial in some way for them. And of course it doesn't happen every night. And there are some genuine religious zealots. Honestly, they're preferable, and I never thought I'd hear myself say that. But more importantly this visit is due to happen in a few minutes, so you'd better get back into the passage. I'll give you a call when they've gone."

I left the room and slid back through the door into the emergency passage, donned the escape set, grabbed the flashlight and descended the steps. Then I waited for Gelda to call me. And I waited. Before long I realised that the escape set had a limited life, and that I had to do something. Could I get back to the male quarters, get another set and come back? Hardly. Could I take the set off? And what would happen if I took it off and there was insufficient air for me to breathe? The answer to that was fairly easy: I would die. I wondered why Easan had not thought of this eventuality. If he had, I would have had a monitor to make sure that the air was breathable. At least the flashlight worked, so I shone it on the dial of the escape set, to see that there were only a few minutes left. There was nothing for it. I closed the valve and took off the escape set.

The next thing I remember was the unusual sensation of a mouth stuck limpet- like to mine, and heavy breathing which seemed to be having an effect on my diaphragm. I opened my eyes. "Thank goodness for that," exclaimed Gelda, easing her lips away from mine. "I think I got to you just in time, and fortunately you had left a bit of air in the escape set, or else we'd both have been found down there dead as doornails. What a scandal that would have been! Fortunately the inspector tonight was Ali. He's straight as a die, and just looks in all the rooms and then gets out and on with whatever pleases him."

I looked round. I was back in Gelda's room. "I know what pleases him," I replied. "He's very keen on one or two of the younger crew members in the male section."

"Well, it's an ill wind that blows no-one any good," said Gelda. "I think the best thing would be if you stayed here and I went and got Nadia to come and join us." And with that Gelda was gone, and I was left sitting alone without actually knowing

64

what was going to happen next. Would Gelda return with Nadia, or else would the authorities in some form, open the door and drag me off to the cells? All I could do was keep my fingers crossed and a rein on my imagination.

But my fears were groundless. Minutes later Gelda returned with Nadia, who was looking wonderful as usual. "She took my hand and we sat, opposite each other, her on the bed, me in the chair. "I'll leave you to it then," said Gelda, and was gone.

"This is madness," said Nadia, thinking that I had been irresistibly drawn to her side, without concern for my own safety.

"It was the only way," I replied, and unfortunately I had to tell her the truth. Much as I wanted to spend my time with her, it seemed foolish in the extreme to hazard my job and hers, for a brief moment together. On the other hand, as I explained, this adventure would result, if we both kept our stories the same, in the maintenance of our employment, and the possibility of us being able to spend proper time together later.

She seemed just a little disappointed. Sometimes good sense just can't compete with romance. So after some discussion I managed to convince her that success depended on us bending to the will of the God Cygnus. I was about to get going back to the men's section when I realised that I would need another escape set. Fortunately this did not prove to be a problem. Nadia took one from the stock in their emergency supplies and buried my empty one in the bottom of the cupboard. We expected that when it was checked it would be assumed that it had been leaking. And of course, that would be if they ever got round to inspecting them at all.

Armed with my new escape set I took my leave, put it on and once more descended the winding stair into the passage. Within moments I was at the door, and punched in the code in the keypad.

Suddenly all hell broke loose. Sirens blared, lights flashed and my question about the illumination in the passage was answered. It came on. Desperately I pushed at the door but nothing happened. The code from the women's section was different. Without really thinking it out I hit the red button with my palm and was surprised when the door flew open.

I sprinted the rest of the way along the passage and up the stairs. I wrenched the escape set off and flung it on top of the pile in the emergency equipment cupboard, and made it back to my room without meeting anyone. I attributed the lack of men in the corridors to the number of times the alarms malfunctioned, and as a consequence it had more or less been accepted that no-one would get up until they heard a knock on their door.

I got into my sleeping bag and waited for some-one to knock. When they did it turned out to be Easan, who raised his eyebrows as we made our way without speaking to the recreation space and ticked our names off on the emergency list. Then we sat about with the rest of the guys in the base. Most of us were tug drivers or freighter pilots with the addition of a few controllers and maintenance men. None of the bosses were in sight, so I presumed that they must muster somewhere else.

There was an announcement "This is the Base Boss. We are checking the emergency systems and all control and operational spaces to see what triggered the alarm. Please remain mustered. We'll update you with further information as soon as we have any." The Base Boss was *not*, of course, the boss, although he was the senior administrator. He was outranked by the Acme local manager, the Cygnus representative and of course the head of the Morality Police. I had no doubt that Sediki was at his right hand and that it was the Morality Police who were doing the checking to see what was going on.

We sat silently side by side at the back of the room. I had my fingers crossed, but it was beginning to look good. Amidst much muttering and grumbling the loudspeakers burst into life again. "This is the Base Boss. It seems that the emergency was a false alarm. You may now stand down." With a sigh of relief I stood and joined the queue to get back out of the room, and back to my bed. It was, after all, as far as we were concerned, the middle of the night.

"So?" said Easan.

"Job done," I replied.

Uncharacteristically, he shook me by the hand. It was just as well he had disabled the cameras.

CHAPTER 6

An Introduction to "Why Not Join the Morality Police?"

      Are you a young man with a sense of duty and a strong moral conviction that women have a place in the home, or else that they have a place with other women? Do you think that the gratuitous exposure of female flesh, with no other intention than to inflame the lustful desires of young men is totally wrong? If the answer to either of these questions is yes, then you may be a candidate for the Morality Police.

      The Morality Police exist, as the name suggests, to maintain the moral status of both men and women. The focus of our activities is on the developing areas of the solar system, where there are new challenges for us. We must ensure that the proper segregation of both men and women is maintained in working and rest environment.

      Of course the rules apply to people who are not related by blood or marriage, so a very well honed level of judgement is required. You must be respectful of married women who are in their proper place, but be prepared to take action where women and men are seen to be together in inappropriate situations.

      Out in the asteroid belts, and in the airspace around Mars and Jupiter there are space craft manned entirely by men, and similarly many crewed by women. In order for this to be possible, segregated accommodation is also provided for them at the asteroid bases, and it will be necessary for you, as a member of the Morality Police, to patrol both the men's and the women's sections. Do you have the moral integrity to be the only man in a woman's section as you carry out your patrol?

      There are opportunities for promotion for outstanding candidates. As a Chief of Morality Police in a solar outpost it will be your responsibility to carry out investigations into any perceived violation of the moral imperatives. Together with the commercial management on site, it will be your responsibility to determine the sanctions to be administered, depending on the severity of the crime. In the most serious cases, re-assignment to the Ganymede Correction Facility may be required. Do you have the strength of purpose to carry out the sentencing of malefactors no matter how painful this is likely to be?

If your answers to these questions are a firm affirmative, then contact your local Morality Police recruitment office today.

There was a model of Acme One standing on a small table close to the door. Acme One had been the first purpose-built mining rig to be operated in the asteroids. Before its arrival, Acme and other mining companies had used the somewhat haphazard technique of blasting small asteroids to pieces with high power lasers and then attempting to collect the resulting debris. Like all mining techniques, it had its problems. If the miners were lucky the rock would be blasted into two or three pieces, at least one of which would be small enough to fit into the cargo bay. If not the asteroid would fragment into hundreds of pieces, some of which would hit the ship on their way into deep space. But however crude the technique, it provided sufficient ore to make metal, and the metal made, among other things, Acme One.

Even the builders of the rig thought it had no chance of doing any sort of job at all, and it took Rock Hocguard, then the president of the Acme Corporation, to get it rolling. When he did, the mining business changed for ever.

Acme One was built on Mars, many miles from the asteroids. This was the closest construction yard, and as soon as it was finished, without bothering to christen it, Rock blasted out of the yard, flew it to Phobos and screwed it down onto the tiny moon. It is a fable which is still told in the spaceports.

Acme One was designed to extract the ore and fill up its belly, then take off for the nearest foundry, but it didn't take long for Rock to realise that while the rig was going to the foundry and coming back to the asteroid, no mining was being done, so his very expensive investment was suffering an unacceptable level of non-productive time.

We were seated on one side of a long table in the Acme Mining Corporation conference room. It was an inordinate misuse of space in an environment where every cubic metre of living area cost a fortune. On the walls were holograms of Acme rigs past and present. They looked like nothing more than identical piles of scrap iron on identical pieces of rock, but they represented history and were, in some cases, the only memorials to the mining technicians who had lost their lives for the furtherance of the wealth of the Acme Corporation.

Rock Hocguard understood immediately that it would be more efficient if freighters picked up the ore from the rig and carried it back to the foundry. In this way the rig could keep on digging and storing the results until the freighter returned. His only problem was that there were no spacecraft suited to the work.

Some of the tales about the early freighters were even more hairy than the original rig stories. Up to that time space pilots had been used to cautiously manoeuvring up to a point where the lock of a space port could be extended to make positive contact. Or if they were of a pioneering nature, they might have been engaged in an activity that required them to land on the surface of a big rock, making sure that the nearest object more than half a metre high was at least a kilometre away.

To carry out these fairly simple tasks the embryo space pilot would do several hundred hours on a simulator, so that by the time he came to drive the ship for the first time he would be probably more familiar with it than he was with the controls of his wristwatch.

Then suddenly some madman wanted them to land a ship, on its belly, within five metres of a large fixed object. Close enough to attach a lock and then transfer the ore, and without even doing any simulator time. Then they were supposed to take off fully laden, without knocking the rig over. After that it was all plain sailing.

Rock was not a space pilot, but he bought a second hand mining ship, still fitted with its cargo bay and manipulators, and put in some extra thrusters to provide the right sort of manoeuvrability. Then he got a nutty ex Navy pilot to test it.

The nutty ex navy pilot was one Tiny Pawlak, a name to conjure with. Tiny had been axed from the navy for engaging in unsuitable activities with his ship. He had a tendency to indulge in aerobatics, and sometimes made unscheduled visits to lesser-known space stations, for purposes which were never revealed. Usually he was able to make these visits in some way coincide with a mechanical defect which had to be repaired, until he made a trip with an engineer who would not be swayed from the straight and narrow, and who, despite Tiny's silver tongue refused to be part of his scam, and reported him for engaging in unethical activities.

Tiny was drummed out of the space corps and the next day Rock picked him up and offered him a job.

To sort out the cargo ship, Rock had brought Acme One back to base, and to develop the process they flew together to the Great Plain. Rock landed the rig and Tiny started to practice landing the freighter.

He started as close as his nerve would allow, which is said to have been half a kilometre away, and then worked closer. It took him four days and eighty-three landings to get within fifty metres of the rig, and then the difficult bit started.

Every tug pilot and every freighter pilot knows the feeling, and Tiny was the first to experience it. You have to overcome every bit of training you have received, and instead of keeping as far away as you can from every fixed object, you have to get as close as possible. You need to be close enough for your palms to sweat and for you to feel a severe need to evacuate your bowels. You have to be so close that the slightest error will mean disaster. It still happens to most of us after years and years, and if it doesn't happen any more then it may be time to give up. No-one had ever done this before, and Tiny faced it on his own. On the ninetieth landing he was close enough for Rock to extend the cargo lock, but he was still two metres too far away.

At that point they gave up the battle and Rock screwed up the legs and by dint of moving them up and down in rotation walked the rig close enough to make the connection. And after that it was just a little bit easier, because Tiny knew that if he was doing it right he was going to be scared shitless.

There was a model of the first freighter too, the very one in which Tiny Pawlak had blazed the trail. It was, aptly, named the Acme Explorer.

Now Acme held the licences and contracted others to do much of the mining and freighting, and Rock's son, Jacques Hocguard, ran the company. Jacques was just a name, mostly he was not even a name. He was known as the Rais. An old earth name for Chief, pronounced *ryees*. Other companies and other places might have had their Rais, but if anyone in our world said the word, they were talking about Jacques Hocguard.

Hassan Kyzyski, his manager at Eugenia, had probably never met him. He'd probably never even seen him. No-one knew where the Rais lived. He was just a voice who spoke to a chosen few. Hence it was possible that Hassan's boss, J.T Seabag, had heard him, even if he had never seen him.

However, we could see J.T. He was standing at the end of the conference table sneering at us. He was tall and bald, with a minimal fringe of fair hair just visible above his ears, his baldness almost compensated for by eyebrows so bushy that they looked like a pair of small rodents nestling above his eyes.

His belly stuck out, causing his suit to bulge in a way which, in a woman, would have indicated an advanced state of pregnancy. J.T was glowering at us and his assistants alike, but somehow managing to leave out Carl Sediki, who was sitting immediately to his left.

Next to Sediki was an unnamed scribe, ready to write everything down for his superior. The mopo only used automated writing devices if absolutely essential. Opposite him were Macgregor, who must have flown in, in an attempt to salvage the Eos contract, and Trantor, who was only there for the purpose of saving his arse.

We, Easan and I, sat on one side of the table in the last two places. Opposite us sat Nadia Abdull and Rollo Vespasian. At least there was a little lightness in an otherwise black day. We all wore company coveralls, even Rollo and Nadia. I looked cautiously at Nadia. She looked demurely down at the table her dark hair falling forward, almost covering her face. Rollo Vespasian had taken the other approach. She held her head high, lips pursed, her dark eyes staring into the middle distance.

At that moment we were a stationary tableau. J.T standing immobile, apparently waiting for someone to say something. Macgregor and Hassan taking a sort of neutral stance, acting as if the whole thing was nothing to do with them, and I had to admit that essentially it wasn't. Although someone had authorised the removal of the air-bottles, and someone had sanctioned the third rate upgrade programme on Cyg Four, they must have been confident that it wasn't going to reflect on them.

Carl Sediki was attentive, his black uniform casting an aura round him. He was looking at each of us in turn. To him we were all under suspicion, and no-one was exempt. It might have been the reason that J.T stayed on his feet; at least it gave him the advantage of height.

Trantor was tearing small pieces off the corner of his notepad and sweating into his collar. We all knew the story, but of us all he probably had the least confidence that it was going to work. Each time Sediki's dark eyes stopped at him he seemed to flinch. I found myself praying he would keep his nerve. If any of us failed then the game would be up, and not only would we be had for crashing-landing a tug and breaking the Acme rules, but also for concealing evidence. There was also the little matter of my unauthorised access to the female living quarters. For the last they would lock me up and throw away the key, and for the rest they would just give me a very hard time.

It had not occurred to me that Trantor could be our weak link. I had thought it might be me, or even Nadia or Rollo. I had ruled out Easan. By now he would have re-programmed himself and would be convinced that the story was true, and I could depend on any of us to stand up to Sediki, terrifying though he was. *Our* advantage was that the truth was worse than the fiction. For Trantor it was the other way round. The worst thing that would happen to Macgregor would be the loss of the Acme contract.

Cygnus could go to work in some other area of the asteroids, taking Trantor with them, but we would be in big trouble. The correction facility on Ganymede? Surely not. Why was Trantor tearing bits of paper off his note-pad, I wondered?

The managers studied the table top and did a little writing, and I thought of all the things I might have done in my life which would have saved me from being here. But any of those options would have prevented me from meeting Nadia Abdull.

"Let's get on with this," said J.T.

He cleared his throat. "I formally convene this enquiry into the crash of Cygnus Four." It was obvious J.T was not too used to this sort of thing. There were still a few miners in the management hierarchy at Acme.

He continued, "I formally call on Commander Sediki to summarise the event from the viewpoint of the Morality Police."

I had a bit of a job to understand why we had to go through this, since we had a pretty good idea what the mopo view would be, and anyway, he hadn't even been there..

Although I tried to concentrate, I found my mind

74

wandering, wondering if I had taken a wrong turn. Should I have really made the move to the tugs? After all, after basic training I'd started as a co-pilot on the shuttles. That had been easy. Maybe it had been too easy, because I'd transferred to the freighters and eventually started landing next to the mining rigs and taking on the ore.

That had been gut-wrenching work, pushing the great bulk of the ship up close to the rig and landing within range of the cargo lock. There had been an attraction in the early days. The freighter would hold a little more than the rig was capable of storing, and as a result we often got a couple of days lying dogo on the surface of some comfortable little asteroid.

At the other end it took even longer to unload, so we'd just lock on at the foundry and put our feet up for a while. It sure beat the hell out of dodging our way through the asteroid belts to get to the next rig.

Sometimes we managed a bit more excitement. The controllers who landed the ships, or more precisely told them which locks to connect to and when to move, were all female. They were often married but bored by the fact that their men folk worked twelve hours a day, turning the stuff we brought in into sheets of metal.

I knew guys who had taken it on. Work hard for two years. Make your fortune and then chill out on some lesser moon with more leisure areas and more living space. Pay for it with the money you made on the contract.

If there was an area where the logic failed it was in the fact that the rents on the tiny living spaces cost almost everything that the contractors made. They would probably have been better separated for two years, he in the male dormitory, she in the female dormitory. They could both work. They could both make money and in the end they could clear out at a profit.

Once the initial enthusiasm had worn off, and it had dawned on them that there were virtually no recreational possibilities, the ladies began to see that there were opportunities for excitement, at virtually no risk, with the guys they were already talking to every day.

The girls could set up the codes within the talk down sequences and they could find their way through the airlocks, into the cabins of the freighters when they came off shift. I must have been mad to think that life would be better as a tug skipper.

Sediki got into his speech.

"We, the Morality Police detachment at the Eugenia base, were contacted directly by Mr George Trantor of Cygnus, to tell us that an unauthorised incident had occurred on the surface of Eos 231. The time was..."

He consulted his notes, and the story continued to unfold. Trantor had told him that the ship had landed on the surface, breaking the rules, and how due to the breaking of this very simple law, one of the ships had fallen through the surface. Then all the stuff which eventually led up to the rescue of Cyg Four and our return to the base.

It was pretty straightforward, but omitted the important bits about the bottles, and how the mainframe had demolished the air scrubbers. Instead he went on to say, "Mr Trantor was unable to define why the Cygnus staff failed to obey the Acme rules and also failed to define why it was that the air supply on board Cygnus Four was so limited. It has been necessary for us to accept that the air supply was low, since non-acceptance might have resulted in a fatality. However we need to know, at this time, exactly what caused the air supply to fail, and also why the rules regarding landing on the surface of the asteroid were disobeyed."

This seemed like the end of the intro and I was relieved to see that Trantor was looking just a bit more relaxed. Obviously he had felt that it was possible that someone might have found out the truth and that he would be faced with it there and then.

He had not considered the fact that Sediki might well be going for disinformation, just to lull us into a false sense of security.

"And now," said J.T, consulting a small piece of paper, "we are now going to conduct interviews of the personnel involved. Would you all please leave the room?"

I got the impression that Sediki must have written it out for him, but I'd never heard of the mopo doing anyone any favours before.

In turn Nadia and I went through our story, omitting, as we had arranged, the fact that there were only five air bottles on Cyg Four. Somehow between us we managed to convince the investigators that the ship had lost air at the time of the crash, and somehow they accepted it. The main reason for the success of our story was that no-one actually knew much about the tugs. I thanked our collective stars that Big Jim was out on a job, otherwise as senior rig mover they might well have called him in, and then we would have been hoist.

But whichever way we played it, it was impossible to get out of our complicity in landing on the surface of the asteroid, and just saying, "It was me - I done it", was not sufficient for this little coven.

They wanted to know how we had determined that it was better to be on the surface of the asteroid than to be in orbit. And it did not seem to satisfy them that all we wanted to do was have a quiet night's sleep before we started the job. I made the point that we worked much better if we were well rested. Tired pilots made mistakes. Of course everyone makes mistakes, but if one's reactions are slowed by exhaustion then recovery might not be possible. Surely, I suggested, it might be a good idea not to use tugs on two rig shifts running, without giving them a rest period in between?

Of course fatigue is no problem for people who never get out of their cushy offices, and even some who have been out there forget about the difficulties. All they wanted to know was whether we knew the relevant section of the Operating Manual. Of course we knew. All of us, apart from Easan who had known it already, had spent several hours learning the section by heart. It was next to the bit about how to deal with obscene Commnet calls. The long and short of it was, that as far as they were concerned, we knew the rules and we had flagrantly disregarded them.

After a couple of hours we were called back into the room, and took our seats again. I sensed that things were not looking too grim. Although Sediki and the managers from Acme were looking serious, Macgregor was relaxed, and Trantor almost radiant.

Macgregor cleared his throat. "It has been left to me," he said, "to tell you the results of our deliberations. There are less pleasant places to work that on the Eos asteroid project, and it is often difficult for us to source personnel to do the work. Acme also appreciate this, and so if you are willing to accept an assignment of our choosing then there will be no further sanction against you. There are no choices here, and we are not prepared at this moment to identify exactly where the assignment will be, but if they are willing to accompany you, your engineers can remain with you."

I had not even considered the possibility of not being accompanied by my engineer. I looked at Easan. He nodded.

"As far as I am concerned, and I believe I speak for my engineer as well, we will accept the assignment of your choice," I said. Macgregor nodded in acceptance and turned his watery gaze towards Nadia and Rollo, who were sitting silent and serious on their side of the table. I could not read anything into the expression on the face of my beloved. All I could do was wait to find out what they had decided. "And so will we," said Nadia. I could not resist a fleeting smile.

"In that case, ladies and gentlemen, the investigation is concluded," said Sediki.

We gratefully got to our feet. Now, all we had to find out what it was that we had let ourselves in for.

CHAPTER 7

Io Residents Information Sheet.

Welcome to Io, the latest and best destination in the Solar System. This data sheet contains the information you need in order to make your stay with us more pleasant.

To start with, you cannot go outside. There is no atmosphere that you can breathe, but if you are a guest in the hotel there is an observation lounge from which you can see the full majesty of the planet Jupiter, and the fearsome surface of Io. If you are a worker, well, just try to make the best of it.

Foundry employees are expected to work a twelve hour shift using whatever skill set you have available. You should have been met by your co-ordinator who will have given you some initial instructions, and assigned some accommodation to you, depending on whether you are married, and whether you have chosen to accept combined or segregated space.

The co-ordinator will have instructed you to be present at a transport point thirty minutes before your first shift. Please ensure that you are there. It is never acceptable to arrive late, so on day one give yourself plenty of time.

The foundry is separate but close to the accommodation pod, so there is a measurable interval between your access to the transfer device and your discharge in the work area. On your arrival at the disembarkation point you will receive instructions as to your next action.

The fast transit vehicles minimise your travelling time. Elevators are also programmed to operate at the best possible speed, and will not stop at floors other than your destination unless you command them to do otherwise. The only exceptions are orders from priority personnel whose instructions will always be followed.

There are other automated devices both in the accommodation areas and in the foundry. These are both fixed and mobile, and are carrying out pre-planned and pre-programmed instructions. However, in order to ensure the safety of our workers and guests in all cases their programme can be overridden by the human voice. If you choose to override a robot programme you will be expected to justify the instruction and register your ID.

The passenger departure lounge of the Io ferry port was not the most popular place in the universe. The space was furnished with rows of plastic chairs bolted through to the concrete, and the floor was covered with threadbare magic carpet.

Magic carpet was alive. It was a moss-like growth that could be encouraged to coat any surface and if suitably stimulated by the correct enzymes, took on a particular colour. Of course you get nothing for nothing and to keep magic carpet growing you have to feed it. A cursory pass with a watering can twice a week is not enough.

Easan and I sat next to each other staring into the middle distance. We had already been there for seven hours and there was, as yet, no announced departure time for the Trojan shuttle. Late arrival incoming, the clerk at the desk had told us.

"Just go ahead and enjoy yourselves," he said. We felt anything but cheerful. It was bad enough being sentenced to the Trojans, but being delayed in getting there was something else.

It really seemed to us as if George Trantor had had the last laugh. We had kept our jobs, and the company had extended our contracts, but in return we had accepted an assignment at the current edge of commercial space.

"Why did we sign anyway?" muttered Easan.

"Because we had no alternative," I replied. "We thought we might be working somewhere not quite as good as Eos which was, let's face it, not a bad number. And since you and I found the way through to the girl's section there were real possibilities that we were about to enjoy ourselves. We knew that we might be sent somewhere just a bit more challenging, but how were we to know that Acme had just got the licence for the Trojans?"

The attendant walked slowly past us, watering the magic carpet, but it was too little too late. It was unlikely that it would regenerate.

I looked round the hall. Possibly fifty of us were seated uncomfortably on the plastic seats. Some were lying across three or four. Some were slumped in semi-foetal position. At a desk next to the access hatch the clerk sat idly thumbing through the screens of the information service.

The departure lounge was divided into sections. We of course were in the unaccompanied males section, making up the vast majority of the numbers. Next to us, barriered off by a line of metal grills, was the family section. Here husbands and wives were allowed to sit together. There had been a great deal of hand-wringing in the morality department about this. It was fine for men to be close to their wives, but what about other men being close to women who were not their wives? But in the end they had to give in. They needed people and they needed people to move around. The more this movement is restricted the less likely it will be that the required movement will take place. Beyond the families section, in the far corner of the lounge sat six women, their heads close together as they talked. Women by themselves were the smallest category so I assumed that two of them were Nadia and Rollo, although it was only just possible to see their shadowy outlines through two sets of grills.

The Io spaceport was a home for travellers from hell. It looked more like a derelict warehouse than a people transit terminal.

I looked up at the departure board where the shuttle for the Trojan base was indicated as being three hours late. Shuttles were never on time, the result of optimistic scheduling, and the

Trojans shuttle, which only left once a week anyway, was not a service which would be likely to receive any priority at all. Its only customers were luckless mining engineers and people like us; tug crews with a black mark against them.

At least our stay on Io had been interesting. We had started by relaxing in our hotel rooms watching piped TV and then when we were thoroughly bored we had decided to have a look at what was laughably called the town.

Wandering through the corridors had done nothing for us. The few retail outlets held few items of interest, apart from essential supplies for the inhabitants of this bleak little world, and public entertainment was limited to holo-films whose themes appeared to be restricted to sickening physical violence. I had never been able to understand why it was ok to show humans being blown apart but not to show a female ankle.

Io was the hub of mining operations for the sector. No mining actually took place on its surface, but it had the only foundry. It was the place where the ore, collected throughout the sector, was turned into usable metal. Io itself was a unique heavenly body. It was a hostile moon covered by volcanoes, with lakes of molten lava and sulphur streams on the surface. Its energy came from its self generated power. The moon was so close to the surface of Jupiter that its transition through the magnetic field of the planet generated millions of kilowatts of electricity. It had to come out somewhere.

The foundries used some of it, and the power available had allowed installations to be built that were capable of turning more ore from the asteroids into finished product than we were capable of transporting. Even so, they used just a fraction of the total power available. The station itself used some to super-cool the ceramic tiles which formed its boundaries. The rest came out on the surface as pure energy.

The availability of free power was the principal reason for Io being the centre of civilisation in this part of the solar system. Obviously one of the other Jupiter moons could have been chosen as the site for major financial investment, but even the collective wealth of the exploration, mining and foundry companies could not afford to invest in more than one base, although some exploratory missions were initiated to the other Jupiter moons. All of them were found to be covered in ice, and on both Calisto and Europa the ice was on the move. This was not too much of a problem on Calisto, but the explorers were unenthusiastic about its distance from the mother planet. The fact that it had been there for billions of years did not seem to re-assure them.

The Europa expedition was taken by surprise by the movement of similar ice fields. It was known that there was interaction between Io and Europa, essentially a tidal effect, and that this was moving the ice fields, although it is difficult to imagine how ice 50 kilometres thick could be affected by anything. The Europa expedition landed and set up shop on an ice plain. It was cold, but explorers are used to that. They built their little houses, inflated and solidified the domes, and started to drive about in their crawlers. There is always a bit of excitement when explorers find water, and on Europa, mixed up with the solidified carbon dioxide, were oceans of ordinary H_2O. It is very useful for fuel, and as a result they began to do serious analysis. They scooped and drilled and assessed, but to their surprise they found that the ice was moving differently from the way the experts had predicted.

According to the news feeds it had been almost too late when they embarked on the transits and got into the air. From there they were apparently able to watch the ice fields splitting and grinding together, within no time at all engulfing the base and reducing it to shards and shrapnel. I had met one of the explorers at Eugenia. He had been so traumatised by the event that he had opted for a change in direction and become a tug pilot. He had a slightly different take on what had happened which was not really a surprise.

The seismologist in the team had detected some excessive movement quite early on in their visit, but he had been told that he must be wrong. And anyway they were there for the duration, and when the ice started moving, if it started moving, there would be plenty of time for everyone to get away. So when it came to it, everyone was asleep. The ice started moving so fast that it was difficult to stand up. Everyone somehow managed to get on their feet, get dressed and prepare for evacuation as the domes, in which they had been living, cracked and disintegrated.

My contact had had the misfortune to see some of his colleagues lose their footing, slide down an ice slope, and disappear into a crack in the surface. There wasn't even any point in going to look for them. The crack could be a canyon fifty kilometres deep. Of course none of this was broadcast to the solar system as a whole. The exploration and mining companies kept tight control on what was released to the general public, and the last thing they wanted was people raising questions about safety. Of course if the expedition leader had taken notice of the seismologist, no-one would have thought anything of it. Even the most obtuse senior management were aware that nearly everything we were doing out there was dangerous. It was just a matter of how dangerous. But you could not stop middle managers from wanting to make names for themselves.

On our way to Io the pilot of the shuttle did a fly-by of Europa and those of us who had window seats had the opportunity of looking down on the surface. Of course we studied it for signs of the base, and an indication of the catastrophic movement of ice that had been the cause of its loss. Either we were not looking at the right part of the surface, or else the ice had completely covered every aspect of the disaster, and had welded itself together seamlessly.

Europa disappeared behind us, and it was not long before we had covered the 300,000 kilometres between it and Io, possibly the most famous base in the whole of the solar system. From my window seat I had a grandstand view, and was astounded as the moon came into sight. It was dwarfed by the vast bulk of the Jupiter itself, visibly spinning. One rotation of the enormous planet took under half an earth day. You could see it moving.

As we closed on Io it became possible to see the base itself. From a distance it looked like a pearl on the flesh of an oyster, but as the shuttle gradually drew closer it took on a form of its own.

The station was embedded in one of the few areas of solid lava, cooled to a habitable level, at the pole. The rest of the surface glowed and flowed as the volcanoes under the surface spewed out magma, and the sulphur pulsed in the extreme heat. Very early in the exploration of the solar system it had been evident that the atmosphere of Io was actually made up of sulphur particles. The addition of further particles from the surface just maintained the status quo, as vapour drifted off into space.

From my porthole in the shuttle the base looked like a giant metal egg embedded in black basalt. The metal above the surface was the exposed sector of a vast ovoid, which completely encased the human habitat. The foundry was another egg and on top of each, a column rose hundreds of metres into what existed in the way of the Io atmosphere. On the top of each column was a pinwheel, allowing a number of ships to berth: passenger craft on the accommodation unit; ore carriers on the foundry unit. I noted that there were six ore carriers berthed at the foundry. They were very large bean cans, crenulated from stem to stern, with the engines sticking out on spars at the aft end and the thrusters in pods distributed round the body. Each was fitted with a single large lock which attached it to the spar, and I knew from my brief period as an ore carrier driver that the nodules of metal were trundling on conveyors from the holds of the ships into the maw of the foundry. The length of time they would remain attached to the lock, and therefore at rest in one way or another, depended entirely on the speed at which the ore was discharged, and therefore the more modern the ship, the more rapidly the discharge, and the faster they would be back on their journey to the asteroids.

The shuttle approached the top of the accommodation spar and there was a vivid flash and a faint explosion as it discharged the static which had collected during its trip through Jupiter's magnetic field. As usual when other people were doing the driving, I checked out their technique. The shuttle approached its docking spar, slowed and then came to a stop a long way off. The pilot was a chicken, but then he didn't do this very often, so he might be forgiven. I sensed that the computer had taken over, and very, very slowly the ship eased in until it was within range of the lock. It was like watching paint dry. But finally there we were. The lock extended and attached itself to the access of the shuttle, and we heard it crank. We had arrived.

Io was busy. It served as transit point for the whole area and its foundry worked for twenty-four hours a day, producing finished metals for the rest of the solar system. As a consequence there was a large area of accommodation for the foundry workers as well as a few hotels for the transit passengers. It was difficult to identify one from the other, one steel passage from another, one steel door from another. Io was an ant heap, and temporarily we were a couple of ants. I could almost feel the mass of humanity burrowing in the tunnels beneath me.

Having found nothing that would even remotely entertain us in the public areas of the Io base, we had returned to our hotel's recreation space and relaxed with some up-market recycled waste coffee. We were half way through our second cup when a little man in civilian coveralls sat down beside me. He had a light growth of beard and despite his youth his hair was going, which did not stop him growing it long at the back and tying it in a ponytail. His bald spot stuck through the remaining hair like the sharp end of an egg.

He leant towards me and addressed me conspiratorially.

"Hey, you guys on your way to a mining base?"

"What of it?" I said.

"If you're looking for a good time here I can help," he replied.

I said nothing but Easan leant over in a manner which indicated that he wanted to know more.

"How's that?" he asked.

"Well, I'm here because I'm in the entertainment business. I don't actually do the entertaining myself but I arrange for guys like you to be entertained. It's just a mite unofficial but the enjoyment is just the same. Believe me it's absolutely safe. We have the local mopo in our pocket. In fact some of them are our clients. Let's say that what we have is a club, and occasionally there are vacancies for new members.

"What sort of entertainment is it?" asked Easan.

"It's a club which can provide you with something to make you feel better, and someone to make you feel even better than that."

"No, I don't think so," I said. "We'll just sit here and enjoy the scenery. Thanks anyway."

"You want guys - boys, anything, just ask. Let's face it, you're going to be a long time at the end of the solar system."

"Imran! What sort of perverts do you get through here?" I cursed.

"Hey, hey," said Egghead. "In our business we've got to cater for all sorts, and let's face it, sex with other guys isn't even illegal. You heteros are the hardest to cater for, but we do have the means. It's been hard, but we've got it together.

Anyway, do you want to join the club? Yes or no? If you don't then I'll have to go and look for another couple of members. I just work here and the boss likes to have a full set of clients on the premises all the time."

Easan looked at me. I could tell that he wanted to go, and I was so bored that I was game to try anything. After all, if we didn't like it then we could always leave and come back here.

"Fair enough. Let's go." I said.

"You won't regret it," Egghead replied. "Follow me."

We followed him into the lift and stood waiting for something to happen. When nothing did, Egghead pressed a button and we descended through what I knew to be the bedroom levels of the hotel. We reached the bottom, the doors opened, and Egghead led us out into a service tube. We wended our way through pipes and cables and stepped over piles of debris, and occasionally over a body lying across the corridor.

"Why are we going this way?" asked Easan.

Egghead paused momentarily. "If we go across the upper levels we eventually get to a checkpoint. It's possible to make the move across the great divide but the Morality Police and the local security don't like it. They don't want the passing trade seeing what it's like down there, and actually they don't like the locals getting a view of the outside, no matter how small. Once you're in here they like you to stay.

Guys like you they do feel a little different about. They wouldn't stop you crossing but sure as hell they'd want to know why. And of course there's always the chance of getting lost."

"If we were going to get lost, how are we going to find our way back?" said Easan.

"That's my job, to make sure our customers make it back to where they came from." Egghead came to a small door, pushed it open and beckoned us to step through into the other world.

On the other side a steel corridor curved away in both directions as far as the eye could see. This wasn't too far. The lighting wasn't bright and a light mist obscured the distant vision.

"Why is it misty?" I asked.

"That's probably human skin," said Easan. "Most dust is human skin, you know. Probably the AC is overloaded and is pushing it back through the vents. They could do with a few less people in here."

We walked down the corridor until we came to a lift entry. Egghead pressed the call button and almost immediately the door opened.

"Good day, gentlemen," said the lift "To which level may I take you".

"Forty-two," said Egghead.

"Forty-two, thank you sir," said the lift. "I am going to rise to level eighteen and pick up a passenger."

"No way José," said Egghead. "You get the level forty-two right away."

Despite Egghead's protests, and the fact that he seemed to be randomly pressing buttons on the control facia, the lift went on its way upwards.

"Imran!" exclaimed Egghead. "Eighteen's a priority deck. When we get there and the door opens just try and look as if you live here."

"What's with the talking machines?" said Easan.

"Oh, its part of the facility to make the locals feel looked after, so they say, but I think it's to stop us reading. The less we read the more compliant we become. There's not many of us readers left I can tell you."

We became silent as the lift slowed to a stop at deck eighteen. The door opened and in front of us was a man in mopo uniform with the insignia of a colonel on his shoulder. Behind him we could see signs of luxurious accommodation. The corridor was faced with magic carpet, in well-maintained condition. It formed an attractive pattern of coloured geometric shapes.

The colonel looked us up and down. "Good day sir, to which level may I take you?" said the lift. "Level two," responded the colonel. And unhesitatingly the lift set off upwards again. We tried to give the colonel as much room as possible, without actually appearing to shrink away from him, as one might upon detecting that someone had a seriously contagious disease. He in return looked us up and down with a complete lack of interest. Colonels did not go in for arresting people met randomly in lifts, but they could still be pretty scary. The lift stopped at level two, and the door opened. It was the control room, and we had come up right in the middle of it. The space was filled with guys doing stuff which related to the operation of all the craft in the sector. They were mostly hunched over consoles speaking softly into microphones, switching switches, checking dials and occasionally talking to each other. The mopo had an interest in everything that happened, although I don't think that the Colonel's duties extended to overseeing what went on. More likely he was just stretching his legs in a place from which the majority of the population were barred. As if to confirm my impression the two mopo minions who were on duty sprang to attention as soon as they saw him. The colonel nodded in a way that acknowledged our existence as fellow travellers, even in a lift. And then the door closed, and we were on our way down again. Egghead drew a square of linen out of his pocket and mopped his brow.

We were soon making our way along another featureless, stainless steel corridor, punctuated only by well-fitting doors, when there was a whirring noise and a mechanoid more or less filling the corridor rounded the curve and swished to a stop in front of us.

Egghead squared up to it. A couple of small lights blinked on the gunmetal front of the machine. Its oval bulk filled the space.

"Good day sir," said the machine. "I am currently engaged in the sanitising of this space and I would be grateful for your co-operation."

Egghead said nothing.

To make use of the time the cleaning machine sprayed the roof above it and gave it a quick polish.

"Back up, dirt bag," muttered Egghead.

The machine tentatively extended two small sets of bristles and scoured the joints in the steelwork close to our feet.

"I respectfully suggest sir," it said, as it retracted the bristles and extended a small vacuum nozzle, "that perhaps it might be more advantageous for us if you moved back to the first alcove."

I remembered seeing some small niches in the walls between our present position and the lift.

"More advantageous for you maybe, cesspool," said Egghead, "but what's in it for us?"

"Well sir," said the machine. "If you'd be good enough to move back then I might be able to maintain my schedule. If I am then allowed to continue with my task, and if I make a two point four per cent increase in my speed, I will still return to the depot for my maintenance period at the commencement of the night shift. This will ensure that I am refurbished, emptied and refilled with cleaning fluid in time to resume my duties at the beginning of the next time period."

"Come on," I said. "Let the poor thing get on with its job."

"Who asked you?" said Egghead, turning briefly to me. "This is between me and that."

I got the feeling that this little scenario had been played out before.

Egghead turned back to the cleaning machine.

"Look pisspot," he said. "Just move back and let us get where we're going."

He kicked it, but there was no sign that his violence had made any impression.

"Yes sir. Thank you for your attention," responded the machine, and withdrew its vacuum nozzle. "I will comply with your requirements, but I would be grateful if you would register your identification card so that I may report your lack of co-operation."

Egghead produced an ID and slashed it down the slot in the front of the machine.

"Won't someone do something about that?" said Easan.

"Not a chance," replied Egghead. "For a start it's false, and in any case it's just a try-on. Even if they had the means, there's no time for them to take the information out of the machine. Even if there's someone available to do it, the system just can't cope. By the time they've worked it out we'll all be long gone."

I thought I heard the machine sigh, but it may just have been the swish of the brushes as it moved back down the corridor, allowing us to move forward until we came to a steel door identical to every other steel door on this level and every other level. It was distinguished only by a small fluorescing number which was unique to it. This was our destination.

Egghead pressed the bell and I saw the entry video refocusing on us. He looked up at it and smiled, exposing a row of yellow teeth.

The cleaning machine waited, whirring gently. I imagined that it must be calculating the necessary increase in speed that would still allow it to maintain its schedule.

There was a bleep indicating that the door was unlocked and he pushed us into what can only be described as a people lock. Then the inner door opened and we were inside.

CHAPTER 8

Instructions for making your own alcohol (From the Interweb)

The first thing you need if you are going to distil alcohol is a still. This is a vessel into which you can put the source component of the alcohol, connected to a tube about six metres long ending up in the collection, or target, vessel. The target vessel should be glass so that you can see if the liquid is free of contamination.

The connection to the tube starts in a funnel with a diameter of about ten centimetres, reducing to the one or two centimetres required for the cooling section of the still. For this you need to source some copper or similar metal or alloy tube, which can be bent into the required shape (See diagram on page 3). To bend the tube you need to fill it with sand or something similar and then find a larger pipe of suitable diameter, then bend your sand-filled pipe around it. You should expect to make about twenty complete circumferences, if it is to do any good.

Once you have the hardware available you should get access to suitable vegetable or fruit matter and turn it into what is known as "the mash". Grain or potatoes are most suitable. To this water, yeast and sugar should be added and the whole kept warm by some means for seventy-two to ninety-six hours until it stops bubbling.

Now you can boil up the mash for the production of alcohol, which will be named differently depending on the source vegetable matter. The snake has to be kept cool during the operation, which may present problems in some environments, particularly since the container has to be kept hot. But water can be used and re-used, and even once used for cooling it can still be drunk, although it will have a slight metallic taste.

Some points to consider are the fact that at the very start of the process some of the alcohol produced may be contaminated, and towards the end the liquid will hardly be alcoholic at all, although this liquid can be returned to the boiling vessel to be distilled again.

Since this activity is completely illegal, and the liquid produced banned from use or possession, some precautions must be taken both during production and the subsequent storage.

As my eyes became accustomed to the gloom I saw that we were in a room about the size of the recreation space of a medium sized unit. Through a large doorway there was a similar sized area. The space we were in was empty apart from a thin table along one wall on which were placed numbers of glasses and bottles, and behind which stood a tall dark woman dressed in bright red body suit which was cut low at the neck to expose an elegant, but possibly illegal, cleavage. She was probably about forty although it was difficult to tell in the semi-darkness.

Egghead ushered us forward.

"Hi Moma," he said. "I brought these two guys. They're on their way to a mining job and they want a good time before they go."

Moma raised her eyebrows.

"Well gentlemen, that's our business," she said "But first the entry fee. It's ten credits." Her voice was cool and cultured apart from the faint slurring of vowels which seemed to characterize speech on Io. She had been here for a long time. Had the base been in existence for long enough for her to have been born here? Possibly. It had always been common practice for the new bases to be set up and operated for a few years before anyone was told about them, so no-one would find out if they failed. The Io base must have been really chancy. I had no idea what made the place safe from all that raging electricity, but if it hadn't worked they could had ended up with a whole lot of fried people.

Paying the entry fee did not hurt. There was going to be

nothing for us to spend our money on for the next few months.

"Now, what would you like?" she said. "Beer, wine or spirit. It's all the same price, five credits a glass."

We chose beer. Despite the attractions of the mind-blowing spirit, which was brewed in clandestine stills, drinking it always carried the possible risk of blindness, or even death.

"Go into the other room and sit down, guys," she said. "The girls'll be along in a few minutes."

We went, choosing to sit on a long leather sofa. In the lounge area the light was predominantly red, lit by one wall, which reproduced the moment of sunset on Jupiter. A red sun descended slowly through swirling mists, while in the foreground brown liquid boiled and bubbled. It was a well-known picture.

"Where do you think the women come from?" asked Easan.

It was a reasonable question considering that all the single women on the base would be restricted to the women's quarters, and probably chaperoned twenty-four hours a day.

"I'm afraid they've got to be married," I replied. "Either their husbands are on shift and they know nothing, or they are off shift and are prepared to allow their wives to do this to make some extra credits. If you take any of them to bed technically you're committing adultery."

The official punishment for adultery was death. Sometimes it happened. It depended how valuable the guy was. People with our sort of skills usually got sent to the worst job in the solar system, whatever that might be, and probably had to engage in it for the rest of their lives. But the women took more of a risk. They were less valuable.

"What the hell?" said Easan. "They can't do much worse to us that send us to the Trojans."

"Yeah, but we could be doing something a damn sight more menial than driving a tug."

This may or may not have been true. There was more of

a chance that we would still be driving a tug, but probably at one of those bases which was not yet acknowledged to exist.

In another corner of the room four men sat round a table with small glasses of spirit in front of them. It was too dark for me to see the insignia on the arms of their cover-alls. The six of us made up the whole clientele.

I surmised that the club was composed of two family living units. Each one would originally have consisted of a living area, two bedrooms and a bathroom, so at most there would be four bedrooms available, one of the bathrooms would have probably become some sort of a changing room and we would still be able to use the other.

I wondered how they had managed to get hold of the two living units. It was either achieved by some bureaucratic slight of hand, or else there were two families somewhere crammed into one family's space. Everyone would be getting a pay-off, bringing them that bit closer to getting off the moon and back to some sort of civilization. The place probably operated round the clock on a shift system and it was not too hard to do the mathematics. In any way it had to pay well.

The sound system struck up some trance music, which filled the rooms with its sounds, then one of the doors opened and the girls filed in.

They lined up along the wall opposite us and stood there waiting for our approval or comment. There was no social interaction here. You chose the one you wanted and then got on with it. With any luck you could be back in the alleyways in an hour and your place would be taken by someone else.

The girls were clad only in underwear, exposing what were, in most cases, their ample charms. The cheap elastic available in the base cut into bulging waists and made lines across large bosoms. Four of them were dark. One had hair sprouting from her armpits. A fifth was a blonde with wide hips and narrow shoulders, betraying her north European origins. She smiled at me and pouted a little.

The sixth was young and oriental. She had short shoulder length hair, which shone even in the dim light. The slanted serious eyes looked at a point slightly above our heads. She wore black briefs and a black man's vest which fell almost straight down her front, only the lightest mounds showing the line of her breasts and sharp points outlining her nipples.

"Wow, look at that," said Easan.

"Get in there before anyone else does, then," I advised. "But remember the score if you get caught. Apart from anything else I don't want to be stuck with a new engineer."

Easan got up and went over to her and they engaged in brief conversation. He returned to the next room and paid Moma, and then came back, put his arm round the diminutive Chinese girl and disappeared in to the nearest bedroom.

The blonde looked hopefully at me and made hand signals to indicate some of the things which we might do together, but I shook my head. I did not want to do anything to defile the memory of Nadia Abdull.

Gradually the four customers at the table chose one each of the remaining five until only the blonde and I were left. In some of the rooms they must have been doubled up. Well, there was no accounting for taste. Moma sidled in from the next room and sat down beside me.

What's wrong with you, sunshine?" she asked, looking at me under arched brows.

"I'm saving myself," I replied, "and I'm not interested in getting done for adultery."

Moma laughed gently and tossed her mane of dark hair back. She was still an extraordinarily attractive woman.

"Well, I suppose that explains something. You must be one of those really unusual people who've actually managed to conduct some sort of romance in this god-forsaken universe. Can you imagine what it was like when anyone could do it? Go out, meet a girl or a fella, hold hands, walk out in the moonlight, kiss and even, if they wanted, go to bed together."

I frowned "When was it like that?" I had difficulty imagining such a world. "When was it any different from how it is now? We've always had the Morality Police. What else could there be?"

"You mean you've never heard of any of the old religions?" asked Moma, seeming surprised. "What about the Jews, Buddhists, Hindus, Mormons? No, I can see you haven't heard of them. Perhaps I have because I'm a bit older than you, or perhaps in places like this people have longer racial memories. I don't know, but I've heard of them all, and I've read about them in books".

"Books?" I gasped. No-one had any books any more.

"Yes, I've still got a couple. No-one bothers me so they're quite safe. Practically everyone from the Morality Police on this base has used this place at one time or another. It gives me something of an edge."

"Why do you do it?" I asked.

"Isn't that obvious?" She smiled at me, displaying an even set of white teeth which looked as if they might nibble, but not bite.

"If I didn't do this, what would I be doing - sitting in some married-without children unit, watching the video and waiting for my husband to come back from the foundry, and when he didn't come back from the foundry, waiting while he came back from some place like this?"

I found it difficult to imagine Moma waiting for anyone.

"Lucinda," said Moma. "Go and look after the bar."

Lucinda looked up and brushed her blonde hair out of her eyes. There was no-one else in the place. She pouted to no-one in particular, got up, smoothed the creases in her briefs and sauntered in the direction of the next room. She was only a little overweight, and I began to regret not having responded to her sign language. Moma turned back in my direction and Lucinda slipped from my mind.

"What's your name, anyway?" she asked.

"Sulliman Smith." People who know me call me Sully.

"What do your friends call you?" asked Moma.

"They call me Sully as well."

She smiled once more, revealing the even white teeth, looking a little more as if they might bite. There was real good humour in the smile and a genuine sparkle in her eye. Her body suit was sheer from breast to thigh and un-creased from thigh to toe. A single fold at her waist was its only concession to her seated position.

I found that even Nadia was fading a little. It was obvious even to me that Moma had something in mind.

"Sully," she said, "I sometimes take a little recreation. At my age... " She paused briefly so that I could interject with some suitable flattery.

I said nothing. She carried on gratified. There was no need to say anything and she well knew it. I had no idea how old Moma was, but she carried it well.

"At my age I've passed the need to be coy, to beat around the bush or to deny myself what I feel like and at the moment I feel like you."

I heard myself saying, "Moma, I'm flattered, but I'm afraid I'm spoken for."

"Well," she said, "I've got to say that's pretty amazing. It's not often that I fancy doing something else rather than standing behind the bar, and when I do you've got to be what... spoken for."

She said the words slowly, drawing them out and examining each one minutely. She said them again interrogatively.

"Spoken for?"

"In a world where the contact between men and woman is virtually nil, in fact where I'm providing one of the few means that men have of meeting women, I have to ask someone who's ... spoken for."

I replied. "I'm sorry. I truly am. Not too long ago you would have been my dreams come true, believe me, but I've fallen in love. But you know that, I've just told you."

I was really breaking new emotional ground, not only falling in love and then almost making love to the woman in my heart, but soon afterwards having the opportunity of being unfaithful to her. At this very moment, somewhere in this rabbit warren, my true love was lying in her spartan bunk and, I hoped, dreaming of me.

Moma slid her hand onto my thigh, with a touch so gentle and so confident, that despite all my resolve I felt an involuntary stirring in response.

I turned to her and kissed her, feeling her even teeth gently nibbling my lower lip.

"Hey Moma," I said. "I can't do this. Much as my body tells me to, somewhere up there my woman is lying asleep. Tomorrow we all get in the shuttle to the Trojans. I'm going to be talking to her every day. I won't see her, but I'll be talking to her. If I was unfaithful to her I couldn't even talk to her. Then how the hell could we work together for the next six months?" To her credit Moma sat back and smiled at me again.

"OK Sully, what's lust against love? But if things change for you, don't forget to come back and see me. Who knows what might happen? Sometimes I think it's time I gathered all my credits together and lit out for somewhere else."

"I hear that things could be getting better on earth," I said. "Apparently there's space. They say that the problem on the home planet is not enough people. I should think that there will be plants growing, and the seas will be filling with fish. All we have to do is get there."

"Yeah, I know," replied Moma. "It could be the place with a bit of peace, without the hassle of dealing with the mopo.

Although I can't believe there's any space anywhere. We're this far out and there isn't any here. How much further can we go?"

There was no real answer to the question. We were all twisting and turning, looking for something that was probably going to elude us for the rest of our lives. The best thing would be to give up and try to manage as we were. But the rumours of the changes back on earth persisted. There just might be something in them.

Before we had the chance to consider life on earth any further, Easan reappeared looking pleased with himself. I looked round, and there was the girl looking quite pleased with herself as well. Maybe he had made a hit.

"OK boys," said Moma. "You want to be on the road now? Your guide will be waiting for you outside to take you back. Bye Sully. Remember what I said, and come back and see me if you find a way of getting out of this rat race. I'll be truly grateful."

She smiled and pushed us out of the door.

In the terminal, very little moved. Further down the same row a couple of disconsolate guys in Acme Corporation coveralls engaged in an unenthusiastic conversation about pay and conditions and leave, time on and time off, and all those things which expats talk about, because they have nothing better to occupy their minds.

Easan and I had a tendency to remain silent. Silence was a quality which we had come to appreciate in each other. It made life in the cramped conditions of the tugs that much more bearable. We each must have had signals which indicated that we wanted to talk, but I was not aware of what they were. At least for the majority of the time at the Eos base we had our own small spaces underground while the tug remained attached to the access port. For this job we would have to live on board the tugs, since the Trojan base was actually a space station, supporting only essential personnel.

Behind the desk in the terminal the dispatcher could still

be seen thumbing though the information screens on his console. He had an even worse job than we did. He looked up wearily to see, as usual, numerous pairs of eyes looking expectantly at him. He shrugged almost imperceptibly and, looking down again, punched a couple of buttons before him. The display screens shifted into a mass of interference and when they cleared we could see that the Trojan shuttle was now delayed for a further two hours. The timing for the other two flights scheduled had not changed.

A brief change of expressions amongst the potential passengers effectively indicated their respective destinations. The guys in the Acme coveralls were momentarily silent, indicating that they were going the same way as us.

More women were assembling in the female section and I had entirely lost sight of Nadia.

Easan must have detected a sign that I wanted to talk.

"So what do you think of this new job anyway?" he asked, knowing that we had already discussed it on a number of occasions.

"There's one thing about a new technique, no-one's going to be able to tell us that we're doing it wrong," I replied. "I can't say I'm too happy with any modifications the Cygnus Corporation might have made to existing ships, though. Especially if Trantor has had anything to do with it."

This was a cue for Easan to be able to talk to me about the technicalities of the new type of mining, which was being employed in the Trojans.

"I don't really see that there's much they could have done to make things more difficult than they already are," he said, obviously having decided that today was the day for an injection of further depression.

I saw no reason to discourage him. "How's that?" I asked.

"Well, the Solar Flame and the Solar Flare were turned

102

into tugs to work with the new high capacity rigs. They used to be freighters but they shortened them by taking the cargo bays out. The result is that you've got a large ship of the wrong shape. Cygnus have only added the explosive bolt systems to pin the asteroids, so any damage has already been done. Oh, and they've uprated the forward thrusters to improve the power to weight ratio, and of course there's no nose ring We won't be doing any rig moves so we don't need one."

"That means we don't have to spend hours hanging face down from our harnesses," I said, realizing that this comment injected an unexpected level of optimism into the conversation. Easan continued without responding.

"Even though the forward thrusters are uprated, there is a loss of power to the main engines when they're operating, because they are dependent on the pressure in the main combustion chambers. So, if you're trying to land and you use the thrusters to correct the attitude, the ship might fall to the ground due to loss of main power."

I felt suitably depressed again.

On a good day we would talk about the extra accommodation provided by the larger hull, and how we would have the most space per person in the whole of the Trojans. And how, actually, we would each have nearly as much private space as we used to have back at the Eos base, and that was not counting the recreation space. It added up to an area of total luxury.

But time in the Io terminal was bad for everybody, and it was not worth wasting time and effort to cheer ourselves up only to be depressed again every time we looked at the departure board or even worse, at the dispatcher.

Without our noticing, one of the voluble Acme employees had shifted up to the seat next to Easan and now addressed us.

"Hey, you guys off to the Trojans?"

"How did you guess?" I muttered in a way that I hoped

would put him off.

"I didn't," he replied. "That's why I asked."

I looked questioningly at him to see if he was needling me, but his expression was earnest.

"Well, yes, that's where we're going," said Easan. "Have you been there before?"

"No-one's been there before," he replied. "This is a new job for us. The space station's just been built, and the plant's only just been bolted down. We're the first crew to go out there. It's the danger that attracted me, and my mate there. Truth is I lost a lot gambling and somehow I've got to support my family. There was no choice really. It was this, or..."

I was not quite sure what the 'or....' was. Gamblers lived in a curious twilight world, almost outside the protection of the law. Gambling was not quite illegal, but it was just socially impossible. Everyone earned enough to support their dependents in a moderate way, and there was nothing to spend money on. You could have a pocket full of credits and search for something to buy and not find it. To buy the ultimate luxuries you had to have access as well as cash and that took influence, but gambling was different. It allowed you to spend your money without having to find anything to buy, and if you ended up with nothing, what was there to do? My brain could not quite encompass the problem, never mind find a solution, but this man had.

However, it was not this fat mining man's addictions which had caused both Easan and I to suddenly pay attention to what he was saying.

"What's this about danger money?" I demanded.

The guy in the Acme coveralls responded, pleased at last to have an attentive audience. "It seems that these Trojans are non too stable, and the odd asteroid is likely to catch the rig – well, the processing plant, and if that happens we can end up anywhere if it doesn't puncture the skin."

This was all news to us. Trust Macgregor to give us an

assignment which was not only the bleakest there was available, but dangerous as well. On top of that no-one had spoken to us about danger money.

"Well, good luck," I said to him, hoping he would go away and let us tease the last morsel of distress from this news.

"Hang on," said Easan as the Acme man began to shuffle back along the seats, "what's this processing plant like?"

The man stopped two seats away. "They tell me it's big. There's hardly any gravity and there's a special docking system to stop the tugs knocking it into a new orbit."

"I wonder who designed that?" mused Easan. It always distressed him that the space mining companies tended to work on the limits of known technology, and as a result, untried systems found their way into operation without any sort of formal testing. If this was a new drug, it would be ten years from the time someone thought of it until human beings could consume it, but in mining business anything went.

"Thanks," said Easan dismissively, and the fat man continued his shuffle back along the seats to his original position.

We turned to each other, for once not silent but more or less speechless. I had to admit it was getting worse and worse. We had been involved before in some of the strange automated systems the mining companies had developed, in an attempt to increase the reliability of the docking manoeuvres between the rigs and the tugs. So far none of them had been successful and we had to revert to doing the job by hand. Here we might not even have the option.

Easan shrugged. "We shall see what we shall see."

We looked up to see a small contingent filing out through the departure lock, indicating that at least one flight was operating. The smiles on their faces told us that it was probably a trip home for them.

The word "home" made me think. As the years passed, more and more people were being born in the colonies. Families were being brought up on Io, and it was possible that some would live and die on the tiny moon. We were by now the second generation. The first generation had arrived about twenty years previously, attracted by the thought of getting away from the ant heap that was earth. Now they had children and they were growing up. Other moons, other asteroids and even some space stations were in the same state. Earth's moon, the first space colony was gradually being covered by a creeping growth of alloy shelters. Mars was being terraformed and in a few years it would have an atmosphere. So what was home?

Most of us had never been there, but we still thought of earth as home. It was the earth of the racial memory. We might never get there, but without it we would all have gone mad.

CHAPTER 9

Project Plan for the Trailing Trojans Base (Confidential)

The technique for recovering ore from the asteroids in the Trailing Trojans is unique and untried. The tugs involved will be required to secure small asteroids and take them to the processing facility that will be located at the Trojan Base. The station will include an entry for the asteroids, where they will be broken up into smaller segments and then fed into the facility. The resulting raw metal ores will be sorted and stored in a number of warehouse tanks within the structure.

The station will be provided with standard locks for tugs and transit craft, as well as loading stations for the freighters, which will be required to take the ores to the finishing plant on Io.

The station will be provided with a comprehensive control room, which will have full communication facilities.

There are frequent meteor showers in the area, and there will be occasional incursions by large objects. In order to deal with this problem the control room will be provided with long-range hazard identification, which will automatically alarm when there is an object capable of causing damage on a collision course with the station. When such an object is identified the station will ready its thrusters and move off in the optimum direction without any intervention on the part of the staff. Only if this system fails to operate should manual intervention be initiated.

The station will be provided with the minimum number of berths for the staff, and a number of personnel in transit. There is a small female section and a larger male section, as well as facilities for the Morality Police. Ship's staff will generally be required to progress directly to their vessels once their papers *have been verified.*

It is recognised that the geostationary position, which will be established for the station, is dependent on a number of bodies distant from it, and as a result there is a remote possibility that it may drift off location. The navigation system, and the manual controls will give the staff the best opportunity of recovering the position, and therefore ensuring their safety.

The base looked like a flying saucer, spinning slowly in the sunlight against the backdrop of stars. Round its edge like short spokes protruded a dozen spider arms, and on two of them I could see the Solar Flame and Solar Flare.

They were just bigger bean cans. The latch rails still extended down each side, but at ninety degrees to them was a rectangular structure sticking out. This device had been fitted by Cygnus to secure small asteroids to the tugs until they could be delivered to the processing plant.

I noticed that there were more ports round the nose, indicating that there was commodious accommodation. The rumours were true then.

The shuttle docked without fuss and we were allowed to undo our seatbelts and walk unsteadily down the lock , towards the reception area, in the reduced gravity. As well as the two Acme miners there were others in Acme coveralls, and six women who were quickly ushered through the reception, and who disappeared down one of the access corridors signed "Female Personnel Only". I got a glimpse of Nadia and Rollo. You could hardly miss Rollo, she was nearly two metres in height, and I assumed the shorter female with her was my true love. We followed into the reception area and were duly processed, this time by an automat.

I placed the smart card containing my travel documents and contract into a slot on the automat. It quickly gave me a green light, spitting the card back at me and opening the barrier that allowed me into the station. Easan followed and we stood in the centre of the visitor's lounge wondering what to do next.

If this area was any indication of how the station was built, it was a depressing place. All surfaces were shining metal, with lights set into the ceiling and a roughened surface on the floor. Around the edges, handgrips indicated an expectation of limited stability.

We were ushered down a corridor and soon realised that we were on our way to the Solar Flame. Then it was across the lock and onto the ship.

The Solar Flame. What's in a name? But this collection of alloys and welds and fabric and Plexiglas was to be our home for the foreseeable future. It had not been part of our bargain to get off early, to get leave or to get anything except the standard Cygnus day rate, despite the remoteness of the location and the difficulty, and even the possible dangers, of the task.

So, for us the name was important. The two words that made it up would forever invoke in our memories the atmosphere, the antics and the operations conducted by this ship, the Solar Flame.

Easan stood behind the engineer's seat and appraised the controls laid out in front of him. I did the same. Not too much different from the old ship except that there were more of them, and some of the switches were new. Easan reached forward and shook the thruster control column, which stuck out of the console between us.

"Oh my. More Cygnus mods," he said.

We toured the rest of the ship. The recreation area was large enough for the four of the original crew to sit down. The space was equipped with a holo-viewer and a music system, and with the means of feeding us. Linked with this space were four minute cabins.

Further aft we were equally impressed by the machinery space. It was all nuts and bolts and stainless steel to me, but Easan liked it. Well, he almost liked it. His reservations about the thrusters remained, but he was unable to instil in me the same level of disquiet about them.

Later we went back down the access tunnel to the space station and, in exploratory mood, made our way to the control room. This was not solely a mission motivated by idle curiosity. We eventually made it by following the sign which said "Crew Only". The space was not dissimilar from the one we had glimpsed through the door of the lift on Io. There were banks of dials and switches, and a number of view screens showing various points on the inside and outside of the station. One screen showed the Solar Flare, immobile on the end of its spider arm.

We introduced ourselves to the single control room operator on duty. Of course there was as yet no action at the station, so there was not much for him to do.

Easan asked him about the collection point for the asteroids and the berthing system for the tugs. He responded by directing one of the cameras at what looked like a hole, in what in some dimensions might have been the top of the station.

"Look at this," he said. He turned to the console and pressed a button. We watched the screen and saw two enormous metal arms rise from either side of the hole. On the end of each, at ninety degrees to the plane of the arm, was a long spike.

"When we activate this part of the system, the spikes are driven into the periphery of the asteroid," he said. "And then the mining auger bites into the centre and grinds away at it, until the whole lot is collected in the processing plant. When the processing is complete we ship the product away from the other side."

"So we have to drop the asteroids into that hole. More or less." I said. "And then we have to get alongside those spider arms."

The control room operator nodded. "The computers'll do the work for you. There are sensors on the tugs, and they interface with the ones on the top of the station. You just flick a switch and it'll all happen, hands off."

"And this has been tested?" asked Easan.

"Of course. Well, that was before I arrived," said the control room operator. "They told me that when they brought the Solar Flame and the Solar Flare out here, they tested them with the automatic berthing system."

We were un-enthusiastic about things that had been said to have been done.

There was a sudden crash, which echoed round the station and caused us to duck, although the control room operator hardly moved.

"What the hell was that?" I exclaimed.

"It was just an asteroid hit. We get two or three a day. The station's set up for it. Double skinned."

"What about the tugs?"

The tugs aren't set up for it all," he said. I should think a big asteroid could knock them off the spider arms. Once you get on board I should keep the doors shut. If one does get knocked off, the door to the reception area automatically closes.

There was a voice. "Trojan Control, this is Winged Messenger." It was the Trojan shuttle. Somehow owners had never got over the tendency to spend a king's ransom on building a ship, and then giving it an absolutely stupid name. Winged Messenger was not the worst name out there.

"Yes Winged Messenger, go ahead," responded the control room operator, leaning over the console and flicking the switching for the monitors until we saw the shuttle appear on a screen.

"We're ready for departure. If it's OK with you we'll start our count-down and cast off on zero."

"Go ahead." The control room operator checked a couple of gauges. "Winged Messenger, it's in your hands."

We heard the shuttle pilot counting down and on zero, its

thrusters puffed briefly and the spacecraft dropped away from the spider arm, and out of the shadow. In the sunlight its carapace shone, revealing a multitude of small indents and scars, which must have resulted from its forays to this station over the brief period that it had been operational.

The shuttle's thrusters oriented it towards Jupiter. With a sudden blast of flame it accelerated away from us, and in a moment had disappeared from the monitor. I looked out of the closest viewport in the direction of Jupiter, and glimpsed its silver shape as it disappeared into the carpet of stars. No-one had left on the shuttle.

"How many of you are there on here?" I asked.

"We're a small team. There are four of us, control room ops, ten mining machinery guys, a couple of mechanics who look after the transfer stuff, the base manager, and the mopo man," said the control room operator.

I found it difficult to understand why the mopo should be out here, but I suppose that they had to look after, if that was the right expression, the four women who had got off the shuttle. And anyway they had tentacles everywhere. They were really the rulers of our world. Reluctantly I had to acknowledge, at least to myself, that this might have been just as well. There is, after all, a certain morality required in the employment of human beings, and as well as the stuff about keeping men and women separate, they did monitor the standards by which we all lived. The morality of the Morality Police therefore kept every employer in the solar system on the straight and narrow.

As we turned back to look into the control room a two tone alarm deafened us. The control room operator flung himself towards a stand-alone console and frantically pressed buttons.

"Imran! We've got a meteor shower on the radar, and there's a big one in it. Get back to the Solar Flame and cast off. Get out of the safety zone as fast as you can, and wait for instructions."

I would have liked to ask some questions, but his demeanour indicated that there would not be much chance of getting any answers. Before we could get to the door several burly men in cannoned in and came to a halt in the middle of the room, looking wildly about them. One wore a mopo uniform, one wore Acme coveralls with his name and a label over his breast pocket with "Platform Manager" on it.

"Who the hell are you?" he said. "No, don't answer that, just get to whereever you're supposed to be during this emergency. Go!"

We went. Fortunately for us it was easy to find the Solar Flame. I glanced out of the viewport, and saw Solar Flare dropping away from the spider arm, then turned to our controls. Easan set up the engines and as soon as we heard a re-assuring rumble I called the control.

"In your hands," he responded. I counted down and pressed the disconnect.

I saw the spider arm retract and moved Solar Flame away using the thruster control. Nothing went wrong and so we were able to reach the stand off location, at what we had judged to be a safe distance from the station. Easan switched on our radar. Sure enough there was the meteor shower, on a close approach to us, but as far was we could see we were safe. However, there was no doubt that the station was in the line of fire. The Solar Flare was also visible on the radar, well out of the way of any possible impacts, on the other side of the space station. The man-made objects were distinguished on the screen by small electronic labels next to them showing their name, position and their current activity. Closest to us was the echo from the station. "Trojan Station," said the label. "Sector 228.432. On assigned fixed location." Next was Solar Flare. The label gave the tug's name and position and its current activity, which was "Standing by at Trojan Station." On the limit of the screen was one further echo. "Trojan Shuttle 1, Sector 228.417, in transit Trojan Station to Io."

We took our positions at the view ports as the first of the small rocks of which most of the shower was composed flew past us. Very small stones pattered against our hull.

We watched as the space station fired its thrusters. I had not known it had any until that moment, but as I watched gouts of flame belched from one side. It lurched off in the direction of Jupiter as the shower intensified, and finally a comet about a kilometre across swam into view and passed the position where the station had been only moments before. I had a job to imagine what might have happened had the avoiding action not been taken.

As the shower thinned and came to an end, the station jetted itself back into its previous position. The Commnet crackled into life. "OK, Solar Flame and Solar Flare. You can come back now. Solar Flare, we'll take you first."

"Roger. We'll fire up now," said Nadia. It was the first time I had heard her speak in what seemed to be an age. "Should we come in on manual?"

"No, this automatic system should be fine. They tested it when they brought the ships out here. They tell me it works really well."

"OK. But I'll talk us in just so you know exactly what's happening."

Solar Flare eased itself in the direction of the station with restrained bursts of thruster power. It was one of those moments when it is obvious that any and every action needs an opposite re-action. Any thruster operation will set a tug moving, and in space it will keep going until it is stopped by an opposing thruster action. The only other force which has any effect is gravity, and out here there was none, or at least no gravity which was measurable.

So we saw the Solar Flare moving towards the Trojans station. Nadia's voice chimed in on the Commnet.

"Hi guys, this is Solar Flare. The automatic system has

given us five per cent on the thrusters in the direction of the space station. It's one kilometre away." She then counted down the distance until Solar Flare was two hundred metres off.

"Now we're at one hundred and fifty metres, one hundred metres. The indication shows that the sensors are linked with the ones on the station. It's firing the thrusters to slow us down. We're still approaching the station. We're fifty metres away."

From our vantage point the tug looked as if it was on top of the station, but we knew that the human eye has a problem with resolution from this sort of distance.

Nadia continued. "Now we're thirty metres away. There's no thruster action at the moment. We're still moving towards the lock. I'm not too keen on this. We're twenty metres off." The tug was now so close to the station that if it turned though ninety degrees it would hit the spider arm.

I found myself mentally carrying out the actions that would result in the tug easing to a stop within range of the spider arm. With enough practice the actions became automatic. The hands would move from one control to another apparently without the direct intervention of the brain. Of course this was the traditional technique. I had heard that there were captains who had not been through the same sort of rigorous training that had given Nadia and I our skills. It was said that they could only do what Nadia was doing now, keeping her fingers crossed and hoping for the best, while the auto-docking device placed the vessel in position.

"Oh ho, the system thinks it's too close, it's moved us away again. Now it's trying to stop the movement. Now the tug's stopped, but we're fifty metres off again. Control shall I take over from the system?"

"Solar Flare, this is the Platform Manager. No, don't take over. We need to see it working, and of course it's going to learn as it goes along. This is only the second time it's done the job. Let it go on."

"OK, control, I'll keep my fingers crossed. Yes, it's firing up again. It's doing a bit better now. It's easing us in. Twenty metres now. It's firing the retros. We're slowing down. It's reducing the thrust. We're stationary. I'm not sure whether we're in range of the lock."

"If you are within range and stationary, the lock will extend on its own. So just wait until it all happens for you."

"OK, how many times have I heard that?" replied Nadia, and there was a silence as we all waited for the right things to happen.

"Now something's happening. The lock's extending. It's coming out fast. Ahhh."

Once more we waited in silence, now apprehensive, because a sentence which is terminated in 'ahhhh' usually meant that the speaker was in trouble. And we waited. Of course we could see the Solar Flare at a distance, but could not see exactly what was happening. The ship was close to the station, and that was all there was to it, for us. Of course in these situations all we could do was keep off the air, so that Nadia, or if necessary Rollo, could communicate when it was necessary to do so.

"Wow, that was a bit sudden. The lock really hit us on the side. But everything's OK. There are no holes. Not even a dent I don't think. It was my own fault for trying to do this standing up. It knocked me over. Now I'm standing up again. Hang on, I'll sit down." We heard a sigh. "I think we'd have done better in manual, but we have to obey the instructions. The lock's cranking itself. OK, now it's solid, we're in place. We're going to look out of the windows and watch the Solar Flame come in. You ready for this Solar Flame?"

We were not ready. "Yes Solar Flare, we're ready," I replied. "Are you ready?" I spoke to Easan. "What do you think?" he replied. I realised that I honestly had no idea.

"Solar Flame. On the completion of this broadcast you

should initiate the docking sequence from your current position. Do you understand?"

"Yes, I understand. I'm pressing the button now."

Easan raised his eyebrows, but as I gave what I thought would be the appropriate signal, by swinging my hand downwards, he pressed the button.

We sat down and strapped ourselves in, and watched it all happening. The automatic docking device did something very like it had done to Solar Flare. It rushed us in towards the spider arm at a terrifying rate, and then, realising that it was going too fast, fired the opposing thrusters. We ground to a halt and were soon moving back in our original direction of approach. Of course, humans faced with the same situation and without the experience will always do something similar. It seemed that the computer was learning, because the next approach was carried out at a much slower rate, and sure enough it gradually eased us into a position where the lock could reach us.

We gripped the arms of our seats. The lock whipped out from the end of the spider arm, but did not hit us in the side. In fact nothing happened at all. I undid the safety harness and made my way to the viewport to see what had happened. The computer was still firing thruster pulses to keep us in place, but I could see that the end of the lock was still a metre away from us.

"Control, this is the Solar Flame. Is the position we are being sent to by the computer determined by the position of the station, or the position in space?"

There was a silence while they tried to find out the answer to my question.

"Yes, Solar Flame. That makes sense. That could be why the Solar Flare was hit in the side, and why you're not close enough. Actually it's the station that's not close enough to you."

"I think on this occasion I should take over and do the rest of the move in manual. I'm assuming that as soon as I get close enough the lock will extend into place?" I chose not to wait for a reply before taking action. The last thing we wanted was for the station to lurch sideways into us while we were being held in place by a dynamic positioning system.

I disengaged the automatic system and eased the joystick in the direction of the lock. The thrusters fired tiny pulses, and all at once, there it was. The lock glued itself to the side of the tug and the control cranked it into place. We were back. No matter how many times I did this, berthing a tug remained a high tension activity. Maybe if it ever ceased to be a job to be approached with extreme caution it would be time to give up.

"Solar Flame and Solar Flare, this is the Platform Manager. I'd like you all to come aboard now for a briefing. No-one has ever done this job before so we want to make sure it all works from the off."

A few minutes later were in the station's conference room. Rollo and Nadia were there which was nice. The Platform Manager addressed us. He could have been talking to a hundred of us instead of four, but he obviously wanted to make an impression. Eventually when he had bored us out of our skulls with safety speak, he got onto the important stuff.

"And now, I'd like to show you a simulation of a tug doing the job you are actually going to do. Here we go."

He pointed the mando at the screen and there was a tug approaching an asteroid which was spinning slowly end over end. The tug hovered over the top of it. The simulation began to present in slow motion, which allowed us to see the tug fire a projectile into the surface. Then we saw a pulse radiate from the tug and the asteroid gradually slow down until it was stationary. The simulation was showing us that the projectile was a receiver, which allowed us to apply a tractor beam to stop the random rotation of the rock. The tug closed up and attached itself to end of the projectile which could be seen sticking out of the surface. Then it fired up its main propulsion and made its simulated way towards the space station.

There was a brief black screen and then the tug and the asteroid could be seen approaching the space station. At this point the second tug aligned itself to a position on the asteroid opposite the first, fired its projectile and attached itself to the surface.

"You can see that you might need both tugs to be attached, particularly if it is a fairly big rock."

It was good to see that they had thought this out. A single tug on top of the rock could only propel the rock towards the station, but not away from it, no matter what sort of computers were connected to it. But a tug on each side would provide total manoeuvrability.

"You don't have to do any of this. The automatic system will do it for us," said the Platform Manager.

"So is the system going to be based on a point in space, or is it going to relate to the station itself?" I asked.

"We'll let you know," he replied.

CHAPTER 10

Asteroid Identification Criteria – Manned Survey Ships

It should be noted that the mining process that has been put in place for the Trojans is as yet untried, and that therefore great care is essential when carrying out surveys. In the asteroid belt the criteria required were that the asteroid of choice should be large enough for the installation of the mining rig, with a minimum diameter of three kilometres. Whether the asteroid was maintaining a regular orbit or not was therefore obvious. Dangers for the rig included cratering and punch through, so a detailed survey would be needed. The survey vessel would be required to land and check out the surface composition, and a recommendation posted as to the landing area.

The work at the Trojans will not involve a mining rig. It is intended that the tugs employed for the contract will attach themselves to small asteroids and then, using their propulsion, take the bodies back to the base for processing. This means that in addition to looking for asteroids with a suitable make-up of minerals, they should be small enough for the tugs to move using their main power, and once at the base they must be small enough to be processed. In general the diameter of the asteroids chosen should be less than one kilometre.

When a suitable asteroid is located, the survey ship should identify the composition by using the remote spectrographic sensor system. We require a 70% metallic composition.

If these criteria can be met the survey vessel must then check that the asteroid is static, within acceptable bounds, in relation to the rest of the field. Broadly the chosen body must be in orbit round the sun and have a moderately static relationship with Jupiter. The consideration here is that some small bodies are *actually passing through the Trailing Trojans and may be on orbits taking them to the edge of the solar system or further. It is dangerous for the tugs to attach themselves to asteroids on non-linear orbits.*

Once the body has been shown to meet all the criteria the survey ship should fire a beacon into the surface and move on.

Note: If non-manned survey craft are used for any part of this operation the validity of the survey activity must be ascertained by a manned craft within a 90 day period.

There was something very comforting about cruising through the asteroids of the Trojans with Nadia. We were on our way to a rendezvous with a fragment of rock, which we were due to bring back to the processing plant. From the viewport I could see Solar Flare apparently stationary about a thousand metres away.

I keyed the Commnet. "How's it going Nadia?"

"Not bad. How's it going yourself?"

We were both happy, doing what we liked to do best, driving space tugs about their normal business - well, almost what we liked to do best. If we had to be apart, at least we could still see each other, or the objects containing each other, and we could talk. I wondered why they had let us come to this end of the solar system together.

I had a brief lapse of concentration as a vision of Nadia distracted me from my immediate task.

We could maybe have been a little more personal on the Commnet, but even out here someone could be listening. If they didn't hear it this week on the station, they could hear it later on earth, or Mars or the Moon where all transmissions everywhere would eventually be collected and monitored by the lower orders of the Morality Police.

On the Trojans space station the police presence was limited. There was no Carl Sediki. When they made him they broke the mould, but the local mopo man was never-the-less an unpleasant little git. It was part of the procedure that new arrivals were interviewed by the local police. Easan and I had waited for some hours in his outer office together with the rest. It was a bit of a let down after the excitement of the meteor shower and the moderate interest of the asteroid recovery simulation, but we had waited while the mopo man tried to impress us with how important he was.

We were distressed enough just being there, and this interview was rubbing salt into the wound. However, in the end the wait had been the most difficult part and the mopo man pretty ineffective. That was probably why he had been posted to the end of the solar system. And since we were now stuck on our ship there was not much chance of us meeting him again.

The rock we were due to pick up appeared on the survey screen and a bleep sounded in my earphone.

"OK," said Easan. "There it is".

"Have you got it, Nadia?" I asked.

"Not a sign," was the reply, "We've got some good static. Hang on." I heard the sound of a bang. "No, that didn't fix it. Who fitted this lot?"

"It was part of the original installation," said Easan. "But it was put in to locate the mining rig beacon, not the beacons the survey ships put onto the asteroids."

"How come ours works then?" I asked.

"I fixed it," said Easan. "It's pretty easy, just a matter of adjusting the frequency modulator."

"Why don't you tell Rollo how to do it?" I asked.

"Ask me again in a couple of weeks," said Easan, whose only character flaw was keeping things to himself. "Or alternatively, tell them to send it back to Cygnus for repair, or even get a technician out here. Acme is paying for some sort of back-up after all."

I was horrified.

"What? We might get Trantor! If he comes I'll make him sleep with you."

"Ok, you've convinced me," said Easan. "I'll tell them how to do it as soon as we get a quiet moment."

Our rock hove into view. It was about fifty metres across and more or less spherical. It was spinning slowly. The first thing we had to do was to stop the spin.

"We'll stop the spin," said Nadia on the Commnet.

"OK, we'll stay here and watch," I answered. I fired the thrusters and the ship lurched out of direction in its customary manner, before drawing to a halt relative to the asteroid.

Solar Flare slowed until the bulky silver hull was stationary, with the rock spinning beneath it. We had both been through the retraining for this particular technique. Back in the old days, the rocks spinning fast enough to give you trouble were the ones you avoided. In any case there would be no chance of a mining rig being able to land on this. The survey ships had the advantage of being able to hover above the surface, and analyse what the rock contained in the way of minerals, while the thing continued to spin beneath them. If they got a positive response they would fire a beacon into the surface and move on to their next task, with no further thought.

I made a mental note to apply for a job on a survey ship. Survey ships never did anything interesting. Most of the crew knew nothing about the environment they were working in. All they did was look at screens, and ask the navigators to move to the next asteroid.

Nadia oriented the Solar Flare until the spin of the rock was directly nose to tail, and then there was a flash and the magnetron was suddenly sticking out of the surface. The main rockets fired up and the ship, locked to the magnetron by the tractor beam, was pushed backwards. I saw the thrust decrease, and the rotation of the rock slowed until it was stationary.

"OK," said Nadia. "That's it; we're cutting the tractor.

Come on in."

The rock, now no longer rotating, was the shape of a deformed nut covered with small red dusty nodules. The survey team had picked a good one. It was seriously metallic.

Our instructions were that the ship which had not carried out the tractor operation would land on the surface, and lock itself into place. That was the way the power use was equalled up. Tractor work still took lots of juice and it took a while for the back-up electrics to get charged up.

I powered up a little until we were close to the rock and the Solar Flare, and then eased down. There was no discernable movement. The only heavenly body close enough for visual observation was the rock in our immediate vicinity, but I noticed that our navigation system showed us to be moving away from the beacon on the Trojans station. A thought struck me.

"Hey Easan, where are we going?" I asked.

Easan punched a few keys.

"Well, if we let it, this little nugget'll take us right out to Saturn. We should get into orbit there in about forty days. That is, if we don't do something about it."

"I thought...."

Yeah," said Easan "So did I. The risk assessments they did for this job said we had to avoid taking anything that wasn't actually in the asteroid orbit. This thing's a comet. It's going somewhere and it's not coming back. Don't these survey people know the rules?"

"They must have sent a remote out. I hear there aren't too many survey ships here, and there must be lots of robots. It's not too difficult. They send one out roaming about the swarm, set the parameters and when it picks one the lights go on back at the station. Either they didn't take the time to check the trajectory or else they knew about it and are just relying on us to sort it out. Don't you think we should get back to somebody and ask what to do next?" I asked.

"That's your decision, boss; or at least yours and Nadia's. Why don't you talk to her? You're both going to be in this together."

"No, I'm going to have to deal with this myself I think."

I sat back and looked up at the deckhead. It was covered with small buttons, a couple of stalk switches and eighteen digital readouts. Up above my right arm there was a long handhold. I reached up and found that with my fingers outstretched I could just touch it. There was a similar handhold above Easan's left shoulder. I reached out with my left hand and found that my fingers came up about ten centimetres short.

I decided to test the distress frequency. The test transmitter fired a burst, which would activate our receiver and any other within a couple of miles. I called Nadia.

"I'm testing the distress frequency."

"Go ahead," she replied, a little puzzled.

I pressed the test transmitter and the receiver responded, flashing up a yellow light on my console and on Easan's, and assaulting our ears with the unmistakable two tone warble. There was no other sound like it and we hated hearing it.

"Turn it off, Sully. It's fine," said Nadia. I reached forward and switched the thing off. Silence once more.

Then I put my left hand in my lap and lay my right arm in the control rest, curling my fingers round the stick with which all direct manoeuvring operations for the Solar Flame were controlled. I avoided pressing the deadman button and twisted the handgrip to left and right and pushed the stick back and forth. It all felt OK, and I'd spent enough time thinking.

"To hell with it, let's get on with it. How long is it going to take them to tell us to do it if we call back to base, and how many extra hours does it mean that we have to be out here waiting? It's going to make no difference if we ask. They're not going to tell us. You know how it's going to go. *Well Captain, the decision to connect with any asteroid rests with you, but should you fail to carry out the task we will want a full report.* Hours of paperwork for no return, two days wasted, and what are the chances of it going wrong anyway?"

I had convinced myself.

"Well then Captain," said Easan. "Let's go."

I placed my arm back in the rest and this time pressing the deadman, I manipulated the stick until the ship was only metres above the surface of the asteroid.

Of course, for this job we were not destined to land the tug on its nose, or on its tail as we had habitually done every time we moved a rig. This technique required us to land level with the surface, and to this end we were fitted with four legs, two at the bow and two at the stern, which would allow us to land in the same way as the shuttle transits did. If we were the tug that had fired the magnetron we would land directly above and attach ourselves to it, but in our case we were to land on the opposite side.

I pushed the stick forward and we were down. Pretty smooth for the first attempt I thought, but Easan appeared not to have noticed my brilliance as he leaned forward and fired the securing pins. There were four thumps, and we were attached to the asteroid, like a beetle to a ball of dung. It seemed awfully big. Our eye level was only a few metres above the surface and it gave us a very close horizon. The rock might have been massive. We could not tell.

"What's your orientation?" asked Nadia.

Easan punched a few keys. If he was feeling mean he would give the heading by means of some distant star up ahead. Today he gave the co-ordinates.

I detected a little tension in him, and indeed there was a little in me. We were out here doing crazy stuff with these rattletrap tugs, where-as before this we had spent a few years doing a job which we had come to understand. Every little piece had fitted into place and we had been able to tell instantly if things were going wrong.

With this task no-one knew. Instead of having the rig-mover to guide us we had to do it all ourselves, and we couldn't even see anything except large areas of rock and a small quadrant of the heavens. We had nothing substantial to go on except for the guidance system. We were part of this rock, and somehow we had to bring it in. Additionally, this particular rock was rushing through space in the wrong direction.

Nadia spoke. "OK guys, we're down. Firing the pins." There was a faint thump through the seats of our suits. No air. No sound transmission.

"We have to turn this thing round and then get it going in the opposite direction," she said. And I realised that without me saying anything she had also determined that the asteroid was on its way out of the Trojans, possibly taking us with it, unless we took positive action. Should I have consulted her? No, she had read my mind.

"We'll let Easan do the navigating," she said. "It's not one of Rollo's strong points."

"What's your beef?" responded Rollo, uncharacterist-ically contributing to the conversation on the Commnet. "I got you here didn't I?"

"Fine," I said. "On my mark, power up to twenty per cent. Five, four, three, two, one, mark!"

I pushed the stick forward and the main thrust fired up. There was no feeling of acceleration, indeed we seemed not to be moving, but the instruments indicated a steady increase in speed.

"Just keep it like that for the moment and I'll tell you when to start the turn," I said.

It became visually evident that we were moving as the powered rock gained momentum. Minutes passed while we waited patiently for the speed to build. Eventually I judged that we were going fast enough for us to start to bring it round.

"Go on my mark," said Easan.

"Four, three, two, one, mark!" For some reason Easan never included five. Perhaps he felt that because everyone else did it, he should do something else.

On the mark I initiated the thrusters to push the nose of the ship into the rock and begin to change the direction. The plan was to move in a semicircle, maintaining the forward momentum so that after the change in direction we would be heading back towards the station.

I increased the thrust until I could feel the change in direction beginning to occur. Then I felt a sinking feeling in the pit of my stomach. The steady background of noise from the main drive had reduced a decibel. Then there was some coughing and banging from behind us, and then silence.

"Remember what I told you about the thrusters," said Easan. "Well, there you are."

He was getting his own back for my previous lack of interest. "This is a fine time to be right," I replied, pressing the ignition bar for the main engine. There was a bit more coughing and we felt a couple of jolts. Then more silence, except for the higher level of sound from the forward thrusters.

"Cut everything, Nadia!" I shouted into the Commnet and at the same time stopped our thrusters.

There was complete silence both inside the cabin and outside. Easan and I watched the stars tumbling round before us, one minute we were confronted by the twinkling darkness of the Milky Way, the next by the disc of Jupiter, which was still large in our heaven even at this distance.

"See if you can stop this rotation Nadia," I said. "It's making me sick."

In response I saw a gradual reduction in the speed at which the stars were flashing past and Jupiter began to rise and set on our tiny world less frequently, until finally we appeared to be stationary, with the red mass of the big planet right in front of the viewport.

128

"What now, boys?" said a voice. "Even our navigator can tell that we're going backwards a bit faster than we were when we tied ourselves on." We had of course increased the speed of the asteroid away from the home base.

Easan punched the buttons and looked serious. "We've got to sort this," he said "otherwise we'll be out of the sector and in the gravity field of Saturn."

"So what?" I replied. "We just power it back to the station."

Easan sighed. "Try to think back to your training; to the time you spent on the shuttles, possibly to the time you spent on the freighters. In general we make the transit between the areas of planetary influence in the big ships. The small ships we work on remain within that planetary influence, and it's a big job to make the change because you've got to go for a slingshot if you don't have enough power to get out of the gravitational field."

Perhaps I was being particularly thick but I still didn't quite get it. We had done slingshots before.

"So?"

"This is going to take time. We're talking about weeks. I don't think we have enough provisions to make it, always assuming we can get the timing right. We usually get a bit of help with the slingshots, but I'm not sure the Trojan base is up to it.

And I'm assuming we'll get the clockwork going again. If we don't... The nub of it is, we'd better get the thing going soon, and we'd better send Nadia back or else there might be two of us doing the slingshot, if that's what it comes to."

"No way, boys," said Nadia. I'd forgotten we were still on the Commnet. "We're not going to leave you out here all on your little ownsomes."

I replied. "I think you should go back before it gets too late. I don't know what sort of supplies you've got, but we're not in too good a state. Anyway I'm going to get on the teelink and tell them what's happened."

129

For the second time I found myself getting on the link and giving the person at the other end bad news. This time it was just some control room operator. He received the news with what seemed to me to be total disinterest, and told me to give them an update if anything changed.

Easan disappeared aft through the living area and I sat in the pilot's seat contemplating the forward instrument panel.

If anyone could repair the ship Easan could. It would just take some time and a little patience. I began to turn over in my mind the possible plans to get us out of this fix.

We did have assets. The thrusters would still work on the Solar Flame. Everything worked on the Solar Flare. Our problem was to provide some balance. If Easan got the machinery going soon then it would be OK and we would bring everything home. The problem was time, and we did not have too much of it.

I suppose I should not have been surprised when a silver shape appeared over our horizon. The Solar Flare passed overhead and disappeared behind my right shoulder. Then dust rose round us, and my vision was cut to a couple of metres.

When the dust cleared the Solar Flare was lying beside us. I felt the impact as the pins penetrated the surface. I looked out, and there was Nadia smiling at me from her viewport. She gave me a thumbs up and I returned the gesture.

There was a grinding of metal as the lock found its way over the contacts on the side of our ship and a familiar creaking and groaning as it was cranked. No-one had said anything. This was one of those situations that were not a good idea to broadcast. We had been through this already, and in the case of the Solar Flame and Solar Flare there was no means of isolating the living quarters from the machinery spaces. In any case there was no point in isolation; we needed help.

I went back and worked the lock so that the door was finally open and we had a connection between us and the other ship.

Rollo and Nadia appeared in our living area and we all hugged. The hugging went a bit further with Nadia and my hand strayed down to caress her right buttock. It was smooth and tight. She stepped backwards. "We've got more serious things to deal with now," she said.

Rollo disappeared into the machinery space. Easan would be pleased to see her. She was an ace with an adjustable spanner.

Nadia and I went forward and sat in the control seats. We were briefly silent.

Nadia spoke. "Sully, if we can't get this ship going, we can all transfer to the Solar Flare and get back in that. I know its going to cause a bit of local difficulty, but surely it's better for us all to survive. Why don't you do a check to see how long we've got before we are committed to doing the slingshot?"

I was sitting in the engineer's chair and made the calculation on Easan's navigation station. "If we don't get going in eighty minutes then the ships are going to have to go round Saturn. We're too late now to take the rock back. In any case they should never have sent us here to get it. And we shouldn't have done the job anyway."

"We could hardly have known you were going to have an engine failure," said Nadia. "If it hadn't been for that we could easily have done it. You know that. It's the same old Cygnus problem. Do half a job and hope for the best."

"True," I said, thinking that I should have known better than to rely on the machinery.

"I hope those two are keeping an eye on the time."

Despite the fact that we were rushing through space out of the Trojans and towards Saturn, there was still no real impression of speed. We had the engines on both ships turned off and there was no impact of anything on the senses. Had we been capable of making the visual interpretation, we would have been able to see the orb of Jupiter getting gradually further away. We were not going that fast, but that made it very difficult to get an impression of the urgency or precariousness of our situation.

I was happy. Yet another dream had come true; I was sitting next to the love of my life. We were not saying much, but between lovers there need not be much to say. But we needed to do something.

"Come on," I said. "Let's go and see what's going on back there." It was not a habit of mine to interrupt engineers at work, but this was a bit different. We really needed to know. Sometimes it is necessary to make decisions based on time. If we had many hours there was no need to do anything. We could just sit there, or even do something more exciting, if we were sufficiently uncaring about the fact that our engineers were slaving away. On the other hand we were actually in a situation where every minute counted, possibly every second, particularly since we were attached to a comet.

I came upon Easan and Rollo, shoulders and arms touching, working in the same space on the thruster pipework. Easan grunted words while he continued to work. "There's only one way of doing this. We've either got to cut off the thrusters or the main power. Those are the options. Neither is great."

"You're right there," I said. Without either we were stuffed.

"How long will it take you to fix the main engines after cutting off the thrusters? asked Nadia

"About twenty minutes," said Easan.

"Do the thrusters work now?" asked Nadia.

"Well, they do for the moment," he replied.

"OK," said Nadia. "Don't do anything else, at the very least we can get away from this rock. Get back to the Flare, Rollo. Get back in the seat, Sully, and I'll tell you what we're going to do next."

CHAPTER 11

A gravity assist, or slingshot, around a planet changes a spacecraft's velocity relative to the sun, even though it preserves the spacecraft's speed relative to the planet, as it must according to the law of the conservation of energy. From a distance, the spacecraft appears to have bounced off the planet. Physicists call this an elastic collision, even though no actual contact occurs.

Suppose that you are a "stationary" observer and you see a planet moving left at speed U; a spaceship moving right at speed v. If the spaceship is on the right path, it will pass close to the planet, moving at speed U + v relative to the planet's surface, because the planet is moving in the opposite direction at speed U. When the spaceship leaves orbit, it is still moving at U + v relative to the planet's surface but in the opposite direction, and since the planet is moving left at speed U, the total velocity of the rocket relative to you will be the velocity of the moving planet plus the velocity of the rocket with respect to the planet. So the velocity will be U + (U + v), that is 2U + v.

It might seem that this is oversimplified, since the details of the orbit have not been covered, but it turns out that if the spaceship travels in a path which forms a hyperbola, it can leave the planet in the opposite direction without firing its engine. The speed gain at large distance is indeed 2U once it has left the gravity of the planet far behind.

This explanation might seem to violate the laws of the conservation of energy and momentum, but we have neglected the spacecraft's effects on the planet. The linear momentum gained by the spaceship is equal in magnitude to that lost by the planet, though the planet's enormous mass compared to the spacecraft makes the resulting change in its speed negligibly small. These effects on the planet are so slight (because planets are so much more massive than spacecraft) that they can be ignored in the calculation.

Realistic portrayals of encounters in space require the consideration of three dimensions. The same principles apply, only adding the planet's velocity to that of the spacecraft requires a vector addition.

Minutes later we were strapped in, still connected to the Solar Flare by the lock, but with the doors closed and dogged. We had forty minutes before we were so far away from the Trojan base that we would have to go through the process of taking the slingshot round Saturn. Perhaps we were lucky. If Saturn had not been at the point on its orbit, which allowed us to use it, we would probably have just flown off into the far reaches of the solar system, desperately trying to overcome the impetus we had inadvertently initiated while trying the re-direct the asteroid.

"Hit the thrusters on my mark," said Nadia.

She counted down and on the mark I squeezed the thrusters, raising the Solar Flame off the surface. I concentrated on maintaining a level lift-off, juggling the power when it appeared to fade. I watched the readouts.

Next to us I knew that Nadia was maintaining precise control, ensuring that the slightly more reliable Solar Flare was rising from the surface at exactly the same rate.

"Keep it going," said Easan, reading the gravity module. Once it read zero we would be free from the pull of the little asteroid.

Then he jabbed me in the arm and shouted into the Commnet. "Stop everything!" I shut down the thrusters as Nadia must have done, because we were once more drifting silently in space, but this time we were alone. A thousand metres away the asteroid drifted with us, and as I watched I was sure that I could see it moving very slowly away.

Easan spoke. "OK, now we are no longer tethered to that rock. We might have a bit of time to do something."

I went back and opened up the lock again, and Rollo rushed past me into the bowels of the ship. Nadia slid in after her and came up to me, advancing until her breasts were pressed against the front of my suit.

We put our arms round each other and held on tight. She kissed me briefly and stepped back, running her hand down my cheek.

"I'd better get back," she said.

"When this lot is ready, we really have to go. I'll point us in the right direction. After that, give it the hammer when I give the word. Goodbye for now, Sully, and good luck."

Then she was gone. I went back to the pilot's seat and watched as Nadia edged us round onto a course for home with cautious bursts of the forward thrusters.

Easan had thoughtfully set up a countdown for the last moment after which we would be consigned to the slingshot, from which we might or might not return. On the other hand there was always the possibility that with two ships linked, the combined power would let us out.

The minutes and seconds were ticking away and there was still no sound from the machinery space. I was reluctant to go back and see what they were up to. Whatever it was, I would be no help. It was down to the engineers, and down to us to wait. Meanwhile the two ships drifted on towards the voids of space.

We had all heard the stories about people who had gone out on routine missions and had completely disappeared. There had not been many of them. Even in the somewhat lawless world we inhabited, and the precedence taken by religion, there was still some consideration for personal safety. The fact that Acme had safety procedures which did not work, and that our manuals were written by people who had no idea what they were talking about, were minor points. We were still mostly successful because of our skill and experience.

The company usually sent a safety officer to give us the once over when we arrived at a location. He would go through our papers to check that we were really qualified, and test us on various aspects of tug operations until he was satisfied that we were who we said we were and could do what we claimed to be able to do. Then they would throw in something like this, making the whole exercise pointless.

"How are they going?" asked Nadia over the Commnet.

"I've no idea," I replied. "There hasn't been a sound from back there."

"They're going to have to hurry up. Our clock says seven minutes and counting, and Rollo's still got to get back over here."

I thought that despite the fact that the engineers hated us checking up on them, there was really no option. I had to go and see what they were up to. So, I unstrapped myself from my pilot's chair and made my way back to the engine space. The change that had to be made was to part of the control system. This was not heavy engineering, but did involve the re-routing of hydraulic pipework and the disconnection and re-connection of a variety of electrical and electronic leads.

There was a central walkway from the recreation area between the cabins to the propulsion space. I made my way along it, and opened the hatch to the machinery space. Even though the tug was large, by our standards, the engine room was full of stainless steel tubing, pipework and wiring. I knew nothing about it, but of course it was not my job to know. Easan looked up from where he was crouching over a terminal block.

"How's it going?" I ventured.

"Nothing's going wrong. But I'm wasting time talking to you, we've only got... At this point he looked down at his watch. Six minutes left."

"So what do you think?"

"I think you'd better get back into your driving seat just

in case we can make it," he snapped.

I took his advice, and once back in the seat I called Nadia, and told her that things were not looking good. It was difficult to accept that we were hurtling though space away from what was, for us, civilisation. Our only close reference point was the small asteroid which was the cause of our problem, and when I looked out of the viewport there it was, getting gradually smaller, but still only about a kilometre away from us. I needed to look at the nav system to see what was actually happening. We were storming along, in the very worst direction possible. I watched the numbers rolling. Nothing was going to stop them until one or both of us could apply some thrust. And meanwhile the seconds were counting away.

Of course for us there was now no option. On completion of this work we would have main power but no thrusters, so we would be relying on Solar Flare for direction. There was the option that we could all pile into Solar Flare and rely on it to get us back. But we would then have to face the problem of the mopo. How could we possibly claim that we were segregated for the voyage back, even though there were separate cabins for all four of us? There was, after all, a common recreation space.

But there was still a chance that Nadia and Rollo could get back if we left them to it. I called Nadia.

"If Rollo's not out in one minute I'm going to get back there and pull her out, and then you get the hell out. We'll take our chance."

"Don't be silly," said Nadia, "We've chosen that you should have main engines so now you've got no thrusters. How the hell are you going to change direction? Either going straight back, or taking the slingshot."

"We could reverse the modification, change direction, and then re-connect the main drive." This suddenly seemed like quite a good idea.

"Don't be completely stupid. You couldn't make even the

simplest course corrections. We're all in this together. But you'd better tell them to get moving, if we are even going to have a chance of making it."

I was just staggering out of the pilot's seat when Rollo and Easan flung themselves into the pilot house. Rollo waved and flashed her white teeth and then disappeared down the airlock. Easan whacked the lock button and flung himself into the seat next to me. The clock was showing thirty-five seconds, thirty-four seconds, thirty-three seconds.

I did not dare speak in case I interrupted the countdown from the Solar Flare, but I gripped the control handle and watched Easan flicking the switches to set up the ignition sequence.

When Nadia started the count I could see that the sequence was going to put us outside the window, but there was nothing to do but wait and hope for the best. I was therefore unsurprised when she stopped at two.

"Sorry boys," Nadia's voice was steady as always. "The sequence is going to take longer than the time we've got. As she was saying it the clock passed zero and went into minus numbers.

"There's no point in using all the thrust and not getting to where we're supposed to be going. If we do that we're not even going to be in a position for the slingshot."

Easan grunted and flicked the switches over his head. We knew she was right.

I called the base and got the same bored control room operator who had been on duty at the time of my previous communication, and told him that we needed some help. This was something of an understatement.

"What do you need?" he asked.

"We can give you our current speed and direction and what we need are some calculations for a slingshot round Saturn. We're out of the planetary influence of Jupiter and there's nothing else to do. It's either that or get a salvage ship out here pronto."

"OK," said the CRO. "We'll see if there's a salvage ship

in the sector and meanwhile give us the data and we'll do the calculations."

"Oh, and by the way," I said, "this slingshot's going to have to be for two ships locked together. One of us has no thrusters."

By this time I saw little point in trying to protect Cygnus. They'd done little for us except get us into deeper and deeper shit.

"Just send us the data and we'll get on to it," said the CRO, "and we'll let you know about the salvage ships. Don't do anything until you hear from us."

I imagined that the lines would be red-hot all round the sector, particularly on this job. The whole thing was a bit on the edge, and to have the two ships lost in the first few weeks of the new operation would not look too good for either Cygnus or the local Acme management, or the briefcases who had sanctioned the development. The downside was, that no matter how concerned they were, we were on the edge of inhabited space and we all recognised that the further away we were from civilisation, the less likely it would be that anyone was going to be able to do anything to help us.

I thought of Nadia Abdull. If we had to do the slingshot it was going to take a hell of a long time. So long that we might never come back. But if we had to go, then there were worse ways.

Easan had finished sending the position data and I roused from my reverie. I grinned weakly at him but he did not grin back.

"I know what you're thinking," he said.

I grinned again. No matter how pessimistic Easan chose to be, things could be worse than going on a slingshot, which would allow me to live out the rest of my life with Nadia Abdull, however short that life might be.

"What if anything happened?" he said. "Like the lock breaking up. We can hardly afford to have two pilots on one ship and two engineers on the other."

I stopped grinning.

"That is not fair," I said. "Here we are, on the edge of disaster, and you're telling me that we have to stay here and they have to stay there, just in case of some sort of mechanical malfunction."

"Let's face it, we've had plenty," he said.

The Trojan Base came up on the Commnet.

"Hello Solar Flame," said the CRO. "Here is our message."

"Shoot," I grunted. I already detected the mopo in the four words.

"There are not, repeat not, any salvage ships within range of your position. However the slingshot can be carried out and will take place in two hundred and ninety two hours. We will instruct you when to carry out the firing sequence. Presently your speed and trajectory are satisfactory. Did you receive?"

"Affirmative."

"We are also instructed by the Morality Police to caution you against any entry into Solar Flare, or for the crew of Solar Flare to enter your vessel." The CRO made the words sound like sexual violation.

"You may be assured," I replied in my best formal speak, "that there is not the slightest possibility of any contact between our crews. We are only too well aware that apart from any moral concerns, it would be dangerous for either of us to consider opening the airlocks due to the possibility of the tube disintegrating."

I saw Easan roll his eyes skyward.

I turned off the Commnet. "How long is two hundred and ninety-two hours anyway?" I asked.

"Long enough for you to work it out," said Easan.

Nadia spoke,."OK boys, I got the message." I glanced through the view port and she waved at me. I gestured my distress, and she put her hand to the side of her head to indicate thinking. I hoped she could think of something. I certainly couldn't.

"One of us can get a few zeds," said Easan, heading for his cabin, and leaving me with the thought that despite the extreme seriousness of this situation, either it was not having the relevant impact on us, or else we just didn't care.

I was doing the mental arithmetic to convert two hundred and ninety-two hours into days when I was interrupted by the distinctive two tone of the distress receiver.

I called Nadia. "You testing your distress system?"

"No, what about you?" she replied.

"No. We must have got a real one, and we're in great shape for dealing with it."

I reported the distress to the CRO back on the base station. He said they were getting nothing there, so we must have some sort of an echo. In any sector if one person gets it, everyone does.

I roused Easan. If anyone could sort this out he could.

He slid into the engineer's seat without a word and started work on his console. The faint warble continued despite the passing of time, and the related indicator lights glimmered on the console. Easan looked up.

"We've got a real signal, but the beacon is very short of power. That's the problem, and that's why they can't get it back at the base. I'll see if I can get a direction and distance."

What would I have done without him? We were equipped with a receiver which was intended to locate survey beacons, well known for their tendency to lose power or to malfunction in other ways, hence the sensitivity of our equipment. It was expensive to send out survey ships, and once one had located a suitable asteroid they did not want to lose it. They had stuck a beacon on it, so no matter where it went we would be able to find it. Within minutes Easan had tuned the survey beacon locator to the distress frequency and analysed the result.

"This ship is only a few hours away at full speed. But the beacon has almost run out of power. If we're going to do anything about it we have to go now."

I thought about the variety of problems which we were currently facing, but my training would not allow me to ignore the warble and the faint yellow light.

I sighed. "Get a fix on it, and let's go. You ready for this Nadia?"

"You bet Sully. Who knows, it could be our passport out of this mess."

Easan gave Nadia the co-ordinates and she set us up on a suitable course, then gave us instructions to push up the thrust. On her word I eased the throttle forward. This was a new deal for two old freighters. They were held together solely by the lock, and there was nothing else for it, but by keeping the thrust balanced the bending moment on the lock would be minimised. I found myself sweating as Nadia gave the instructions, and I in response edged the throttle forward. It was obvious to us as time passed that just for once the gauges on both vessels were in synch, and as we passed seventy per cent and eighty per cent our trajectory was obviously matched.

"Shall we go to a hundred per cent?" asked Nadia.

Easan looked at me, horrified, and shook his head. "OK, we might was well," I responded.

As the thrust reached ninety per cent, Easan opened his eyes and stopped trying to pull his hair out, while shaking his head from side to side.

At ninety five per cent he was showing interest, as neither of us could really believe that these old vessels had the capability to reach maximum thrust.

"What have you got there now?" asked Nadia. I pushed the throttle bar against the stop and took my hand away. The needle crept up to ninety-eight per cent and stopped. "Ninety-eight," I responded.

"Same as us. Just leave things how they are. I'll let you know when we're going fast enough to cut it."

Easan looked me in the eye and crossed his fingers. Full thrust might have been fine when the ships were new, but after countless years in the solar system, not to mention the Cygnus modifications, there was no knowing how long it would go on for. It struck me that if the engines failed on one of the ships, the change in the thrust would be sufficient to send us both cartwheeling into the unknown, and would probably break the lock. I crossed my fingers as well.

There would not be much we could do without power, so it came as a relief when Nadia called, and asked us to cut the engines. On her mark I pulled back the bar into the upright position and in response the engines became silent, and we could relax and wait for our next excitement: the approach to what-ever it was sending out the distress.

Many hours after we had started out, we were straining our eyes for a sight of the casualty. The warble of the automatic distress call was only a little louder, and the yellow light flashed no more solidly. We were looking for the strobes on the ship in distress, which always accompanied the call. We saw nothing.

"How far away are we?" I asked Easan.

"We must be close," he replied, "It's somewhere ahead of us, only a few kilometres away. Better slow it down, guys."

Nadia fired the retro rockets and immediately we began to spin. There was little we could do until she had juggled the thrusters and we were once more facing the same direction, as we had been to begin with, but now more or less stationary.

"Anybody see anything?" asked Nadia.

We strained our eyes, sweeping them across the mass of stars populating the infinite.

"Hey, I can see something," said Easan. "Look right ahead. It's there."

I looked ahead, but could see nothing. There were no

strobes.

"Keep looking. Look at the stars," said Easan.

I looked at the stars, then turned my head away and concentrated on what was visible at the periphery of my vision. It was an old trick but it worked. I got the impression that there was an area of darkness; something blotting out the distant tiny pinpoints of light; the distant suns and distant galaxies. A closer area of blackness.

"Yes," I said, "There's something there. See if you can pull it up on the radar."

I had not resorted to using radar for as long as I could remember, but here I was using it for the second time in only a few time periods. It was not much use in the asteroid belt, the screen was always full of objects, but here there was just one massive echo. It was close. Curiously there was no attached electronic label to show us what this vessel was, why it was there and where it was going.

"I've got it on the screen. Why doesn't it have an electronic tag?" said Nadia. "I'm going to get closer. You lot do nothing. I don't want to end up going round in circles again."

"No problem. Go for it, ace," I replied.

We watched fascinated as the dark shadow became larger. It was black. Not a glimmer of light. Little reflection. Nadia kept on closing in with an increasing level of caution, until the vast shape seemed to fill the viewports.

"Wow, how big is that...?" said Easan.

I looked down at the radar. It showed us still a kilometre away. That was close by our standards, but the object ahead was the size of a space station. Easan went through the process of darkening the cockpit, reducing the light from some readouts and extinguishing those which were unimportant or unused when doing anything other than attaching ourselves to asteroids. In the resulting blackness our eyes gradually adjusted to the new conditions, allowing us to get a view of the object.

It seemed to be composed of a mass of long tubes, or clusters of small cylindrical units, welded together like a bundle of drinking straws tied with an elastoband. There were shapes and excrescences all over the bundle, and the whole terminated in a vast ball at one end.

It was slowly tumbling end over end.

"Never mind how big it is," I said. "What the hell is it?"

Easan responded. "It must be a ship, because sure as hell that's where the distress is coming from, and if the distress is coming from that, then that means there are people on it, or at least there have been people on it, and its up to us to do our bit and rescue any survivors."

"Yeah, yeah, you don't have to tell me, we've not got much to lose anyway. And, whatever sort of ship it is, if it can be fixed, it can take us to where we want to go. We could save ourselves a slingshot."

It seemed extraordinary that there had been no reports about the loss of this extremely large vessel. At the very least it should have justified a mention in our pre-trip briefing from the Platform Manager. There were not that many very large craft out here, although there had been some speculation amongst the space community that the mopo had had a prison ship built. I had a job to see why they would need to extend the existing correction facility on Ganymede, but there might have been something in it. It would after all be mobile, and could find its way around the solar system collecting and depositing members of the criminal fraternity with an absolute minimum use of power. It would just be hard luck if it came to your turn to get off and you were light years away from where you wanted to be. But we had no way of finding out exactly what it was unless we went on board. In any case, would there be anyone alive? I did not like to think of the conditions that would exist on a ship full of convicts on which the power systems had failed. You can do nothing without power. On a ship like that even the air will run out after a time. But without air the bodies would not decompose, so it would not be all bad.

I called Nadia on the Commnet. "Try closing in a bit. It must have some sort of access ports."

"Maybe," was the reply. "But we've got to stop the spin before we can do anything."

"So, what's the problem? You've got the kit for it. It should be child's play for an old hand like you."

"You're right," she replied. "Make sure your lock is closed, we're going to disconnect. We'll be back for you when we've finished."

Sometimes I could bite my tongue off. That's the trouble with women; always too eager to prove they're better than you. If asked, I would have been pleased to tell anyone that Nadia was better than me, but she had to keep proving it.

There was hiss as the lock disconnected and then there was the shape of Solar Flame, balanced on the incandescence of its rocket thrust, powering towards the dark object.

"Hey guys," Nadia's voice came in over the Commnet, full of excitement. The adrenalin was beginning to flow. "I don't think it's a good idea to use the magnetron if it's got people in. We might make a hole into something important, but don't worry, I've got a better plan."

My heart sank. "OK, let's hear it."

"No, no. You wait and see. Just sit back in the grandstand and watch an expert at work."

We watched as the little ship rose above the great tumbling object. A small silver shape twinkling in starlight.

CHAPTER 12

Prosthetic Limbs Inc. – We'll Give You a Hand

What bad luck. You've had an accident. Lost an appendage. Sadly this happens - and worse, you could not recover the one you lost. It could have been mashed up into pieces. It could have drifted away into space out of your reach. Or maybe it was lost in the trash. These things happen. Of course if you had the money you would just get out there and buy a replacement, but they come at a price. You could afford a finger maybe, but a whole arm, or a leg? You have to have a lot of credits to buy one of those.

Fortunately PLI can help. Our prosthetic limbs are almost indistinguishable from the real thing. Our surgeons will carry out the necessary operation to fit the connectors, and our construction department will measure you up for a precise match with the remaining appendage, which we can use as a pattern.

Our arms when connected completely replicate the operation of a normal arm and hand. The elbow (if necessary) will flex through one plane, the wrist will operate through two planes and the opposable thumb and fingers will allow you to grasp anything in just the same way as you used to with the real thing.

There are even advantages to having a PLI limb. Hands can have a grip far in excess of that possible with normal muscles, but don't worry. You get feedback, so you won't crush anything you don't want to.

Although we specialise in hand/arm combinations we also offer a range of legs, and if you have had the misfortune to lose two legs don't worry, a matching set of PLI limbs can give you a manoeuvrability and a speed over the ground which is just not possible with normal human legs.

The cost. Don't worry about it. We offer payment terms you will be able to afford. In fact you can hardly afford not to. Don't be armless or legless. Contact us for an appointment at one of our conveniently situated clinics.

You can rely on PLI

We watched as the small ship seemed to skip over the end of the rotating shape and then positioned itself so that it was lined up to take the impact next time an end came round. The retro-rockets and the main engines fired up.

The end of the big ship advanced, until the ball forming the larger termination was almost touching the Solar Flare. Still almost in contact, the tug eased backwards, but I could see that the rotation had been slowed.

"Wow, that's pretty good," said Easan.

"It must have taken some nerve. You fancy having a go at that?" I asked.

Finally all movement ceased and the big ship was still. The black bundle of straws stretched across space in front of us. I could now see that the band holding them together at one end was a ring, on the surface of which were numbers of airlocks. From this distance they looked like rivets. There were lots of them. Ahead of the ring the ball stuck out, studded with viewports, just a little blacker than the blackness of the metal.

"That thing has artificial gravity," said Easan. "The ring and the nose stay as they are while the rest spins round. It's the best of all worlds. The back part contains all the passengers who get the impression they're standing on the surface of something, while the front bit stays put and allows people to look out and operate all the systems and do the sort of things you and I need to do, unimpeded by some form of spin."

The little bean can detached itself and headed back towards us.

"Did you like that?" said Nadia.

"Not only good, but modest with it," I replied.

"I can't help it. It's part of my sweet nature. You guys get yourselves ready. We'll lock on again and I'll take you up there. You'll have to make the attachment with your lock on the other side. Ours isn't quite up to it at the moment. Once you're locked on we'll detach and move to the next one. Then we'll see what goes down."

An hour later we were attached to the lock on the black ring and Solar Flare was locked on next to us. The sheer bulk of the ship was awe-inspiring.

"Send Easan to open up the ship. Someone is going to have to put a suit on, and we elect him."

Easan looked surprised, but suited up, and with my assistance was soon locked out of the Solar Flame and in the space between the two craft.

He made his way to the lock to which the Solar Flare was attached within sight of our video camera. Space-suits had not changed much since man had broken free of earth's gravity. They remained white in order to reflect radiation, with a hard helmet and a silvered visor to protect the head and eyes of the wearer. They were fitted with a pack on the back, which provided life services. Possibly the only thing that had really changed was the length of time the wearer would survive.

It was practice for anyone by themselves to speak constantly to assure those elsewhere that they were still OK, so as I looked at the video screen, Easan in his white suit hove into view, talking as he went. The commentary indicated that he was opening the ship's lock to the Solar Flare. It took time. There was no power and he had to do it all by hand. The little wheels they provided for the task were seldom used and were always difficult.

Eventually, after he had carried out the same job for the Solar Flame, he gave us the go ahead. "Right Sully, you can open our lock now, there's air in there. It's a bit stale I think but not too much wrong otherwise."

"You get that Nadia?" I asked.

"You bet. Let's go."

I opened the lock and followed Easan along the little tube and out the other end. There was a feeling of space, a lot of it. I tried to penetrate the blackness but could not.

"Who's got the flashlight?"

"I have." Nadia's voice came out of the blackness.

"Switch the bastard on then," said Easan.

Nadia switched on the flashlight. We gasped in unison.

The inside of the ship was like the dark spaces you go to in dreams, the sort of darkness which seems to stretch to infinity at the same time as it encloses you like a skin, covering you so close that it mirrors every move. I raised my hand slowly until it was in front of my eyes. I could see nothing. If it went on long enough I would have thought I was blind.

Then we switched on our headlights and the narrow intense beams cut across the space, illuminating small circles of the bulkheads, deckhead and deck. It seemed necessary to keep them moving to stop the blackness encroaching. I think we all had the feeling that if we steadied up on anything the darkness would catch the beams and throttle them.

I felt something curious underfoot. It was like standing on a small fur covered animal. I jumped to one side and appeared to be standing on two more. Now stationary it still seemed as if I was standing on something and looked down, illuminating my feet with the beam. The fur was grey and seemed to extend out of sight. I realised that it was real carpet. I crouched down and ran my fingers through the pile. It responded by lying flat under my palm and then springing back into the upright position as my hand passed over it. It was wonderful stuff. Magic carpet did not deserve the same name.

"Wow, has anyone felt this?" I said unguardedly.

"Not now," said Nadia. "I'm busy.

"No, no. Feel this stuff. It's carpet," I protested.

Everyone reached down in unison and ran their hands over the surface. The torch beams concentrated in tiny circles of light on the grey of the textile. Someone stretched out and rolled on it. The activity was completely silent but the headlight beam circled. I could not see who it was, but I suspected Nadia.

"Come on," said Easan, always practical. "Let's see if we can get somewhere. I think we should move on and try to find out what's going on here. I get the feeling that there's some sort of a time line, even though we have no idea what it is. We don't know how long this thing has been here and we don't know what it's running out of. Already there's no light and I suspect that we're breathing air which is present only because the ship is vast, and there aren't many people in it. At least not live ones. On top of that we don't know where it's been. We don't know why it's here and worst of all we don't know where it's going."

Nadia responded with the positive view. "Whether there are people or not, and whereever it has been and might be going, we can fix it. And when we've fixed it we can get it going anywhere we want to. It is so big that there's more space here than any of us have ever been in, in our lives. In short this is the opportunity of a lifetime."

"Do you think there might be bodies on it?" I asked.

"There might be," replied Easan.

"Hey guys - you listening to me or what?"

We turned to Nadia. "Were you listening to me?" she said. "I said - this is the opportunity we've all been waiting for. This is it. Space. Success. Freedom. All here; all on this ship. All for us."

"No, you didn't say that," said Easan. "You said something about fixing this thing and going where we want..."

"So," said Nadia.

"Well I'm afraid I don't believe that," said Easan. "There is no way this thing doesn't belong to somebody, and even if they aren't here, sure as eggs they'll be back to claim it. And we will get done by all forms of the law and end up somewhere extremely unpleasant."

Easan was in a surprisingly pessimistic mood.

"You wait and see," replied Nadia. "Come on, let's get on with it. We'll soon find out what the score is."

We made it to the centre of the craft. None of us had been on anything this big, but the general concept was similar to the shuttles, and once in the centre we knew that we would get some indication of where to go next.

Soon we were standing in a drum with the tubes to the airlocks radiating from it. Centrally placed in the flat surfaces of the drum were two circular doors. They were both closed, and it was obvious to us that since none of the ship's systems were operating they would not open for us simply by pressing the buttons set into the bulkheads on either side.

There were also the small hand wheels, provided for just such situations as the one in which we found ourselves. The lights flashed back and forth as we all looked at them both, eventually all beams centering on a plate on one of the doors which said "Crew Only".

Then the beams shifted to one side as we illuminated the safety wheels. Easan stepped forward and began to grapple with one, but as usual it would not move. The emergency systems on all ships were notoriously unreliable.

"Out of the way, weakling," said Rollo. "Let me have a go."

Easan willingly stood back and we spotlighted Rollo as she hunched over the wheel. Even after she had got it turning, it seemed to take forever to complete the task. When Rollo stopped for a breather Easan had another go at the wheel, and this time was able to turn it. I made a mental note not to cross Rollo. She was obviously much stronger than she looked.

Eventually Eason stood back and pulled at the handle in the middle of the door. Slowly it swung open exposing a tube only illuminated in the most rudimentary way by our headlights. We made our way along it. There were doors off at either side, all of them closed, so we ignored them and carried on. Our light beams seemed to penetrate further into the darkness, but exposed nothing.

"Turn the lights off," said Easan.

We doused our headlights and saw nothing, our forward progress slowing until we were stationary, straining our eyes in the darkness. Then it was there, a faint glow from up ahead.

"There. You guys see anything?"

We did see something. Light permeated like the first glimmer of dawn; the slight change in the uniformity of darkness that is there but can't quite be seen.

"There's something there," I said.

Of course there's something there," said Nadia. "It's the pilot house. We know it's the pilot house. That's why we've come this way."

I switched my headlight on again and carried on along the tube. The carpet continued underfoot and the handrails along the sides were upholstered in leather, or something extremely like it.

Eventually we came to an open door. I was in front and I stopped at the entrance. Everyone else piled into me and we cannoned into the space, crashing into fixed objects and sending small, totally invisible items flying off into the darkness. There was a lot of noise and then, gradually, silence. We picked ourselves up and stood there becoming accustomed to the faint light which seemed to be coming from up front.

I began to be able to see things. The viewports showed a faint speckling of stars and a reflection off nothing allowed the light from the fiery ball of Jupiter to seep in, even though the ship was pointing directly away from the planet.

The bulkheads began to materialise as banks of control screens and boards, with sectors of analogue dials shining faintly like eyes.

As soon as I could see a clear track I made my way up to the pilot's seats. They were not dissimilar from those on the Solar Flame. I suppose there are only so many ways to make a contour seat.

The co-pilot's seat I could see quite clearly, but the pilot's seat appeared to have something wrong with it. I reached down and ran my hand over the upholstery. It was full of lumps and was clammy in parts.

I switched on the headlight again and found myself looking down at a body. Rollo screamed. I was getting worried about her. That was the second thing she had done out of character that day.

I put my hand down to the neck. There was a faint pulse.

"Come on, help me," I said. "He's still alive. Easan, you and Rollo go back to the ship and get the first aid kit, and while you're there hook this thing up to our emergency system. We've got to get some light on this scene somehow."

"Do you think that's a good idea, Captain?" said Easan, who always became formal if he disapproved of what I was telling him to do. "How can we tell how much of this ship we're going to be trying to light up? What other systems do you think they might have left connected when they abandoned it? It could be just like putting our live to earth."

"We'll just have to take a chance, smart arse. Now get going."

Easan and Rollo disappeared while Nadia and I laid out the body on the deck of the pilot house.

"This guy is short of an arm," remarked Nadia.

I flicked the flashlight upwards. Sure enough, there, sticking out of the short sleeve of a soiled body suit was the stump of an arm. Visible, sticking out of the skin at points round the stump were four stainless steel clips and a twenty-four point connector. It was the terminal for a prosthetic.

"I wonder what happened to the arm?" I thought out loud.

"I imagine that must have been the least of his worries," said Nadia, who had detached a seat cushion from one of the secondary control seats and was placing it under the man's head.

"I don't know," I said "People with prosthetic arms don't normally lose them. Heavens, they're expensive enough. Let's face it, it's only because the real ones are completely priceless that more people don't have them."

The technology for replacing lost arms with equivalent parts from other people had been available for years, but there was the basic problem that not many people died any more from the sort of injuries that made spare parts available. There was rumoured to be a whole business in buying bits from live people for whatever it was that would make them happy, but I had never come across any sign of it. Anyway, the result was very expensive spare parts.

I examined the connections in the stump. "Yeah, I think this one was battery powered. The real business. The batteries must have run down, and with no electrics there can't have been any way of charging them up."

As if on cue the whole of the pilot house was suddenly bathed in light. There were small lights on stalks hovering above the banks of instruments. There were slightly larger luminous sources uplighting the whole of the deckhead and there were long strips embedded into the bulkheads.

Nadia and I stood involuntarily, the better to take in the scene.

"Hell, if the rest of the ship is like this, our batteries will run down in five minutes."

Rollo eased herself into the room carrying a small satchel over one shoulder, and padded across the carpet noiselessly until she was standing next to us looking down at the body. Walking over carpet suited her. It gave her an animal-like quality. She knelt down next to the potential body.

"Easan's gone to switch off a few lights," she said. She undid the clasps so that the kit fell open exposing the swabs, vials, infusers and pseudo stitch packs that made up the standard space tug medical supply.

Rollo pulled out an infuser and checked it against the light.

"Looks OK," she said, "but mind you it should have been changed four months ago. It's way out of date."

"These things are good for years," I said. "Have you ever wondered what happens to all the stuff we hand in? You don't think anyone actually destroys it do you? And what about the new stuff? Do you really think it is actually new?"

"The rules say we have to change it out. It's part of every contract requirement," said Rollo.

"Yeah, that's right," I answered. "It used to be law but no-one made anything out of that. Now the companies make it part of the contract. I think there's something a bit dodgy about it."

"OK," said Nadia, "Get off your hobbyhorse Sully, either the drug's going to be OK, in which case this man is going to recover, or else its not going to be OK, in which case he's going to die. There's nothing we can do about it one way or the other. But if he is going to be OK then we have to be ready to welcome him back into the world."

"Here we go," said Rollo, and placed the infuser onto the skin at the side of the neck of the one armed man. She slid it back and forth fractionally to ensure that she had made contact, and pressed the button. There was a faint hiss.

She lifted the infuser and dropped it back into the medical kit.

"Now all we have to do is wait and see what happens," she said. "Do you think some-one should go and find some water in case he wakes up?"

Nadia padded over the carpet to the back of the pilot

house looking for a water source. There was usually some in the control area of a space ship, although one would not want to speculate too closely about its origins.

I looked down at the man. His eyes were still closed, but I detected slight movements in his finger ends. I felt his pulse. It was a little stronger. Nadia returned with a small squeegee bottle with the usual tube sticking out of the top.

The man was short and stocky, with a matt of hair curling out of the top of his worksuit. He sported several days of growth on his chin, indicating a failure to shave, rather than an intention to grow a beard. His hair was thinning and short. His one arm was muscular and his short fingers were terminated in dirty fingernails. He was not a pretty sight. And although none of us could claim to be regular bathers - after all, our environment prevented it - he seemed to have let that particular part of his personal hygiene process lapse altogether.

"I wonder what's happened to the bathing facilities," said Nadia. "But perhaps it doesn't matter if there's no-one else about to tell you you smell."

"I think we'll just have to put up with it until we can tell him he stinks," I replied, and I prised his mouth open and stuck the tube of the water bottle between his teeth and squeezed. There was no response to this action, but since the water did not emerge from his mouth or dribble down his chin I assumed that it had reached its correct destination.

Nadia took the bottle from me, squeezed a little onto a tissue, and damped his face.

I had a thought, and scanned the consoles to find the emergency beacon. Somewhere it was still going, and the improved electrical supply might have boosted it sufficiently to get the signal within broadcast range of the Trojans space station.

I spotted the communications console and flicked up the switch to deactivate the beacon. As a precautionary measure I also deselected the teelink. No way did we want anybody to switch on somewhere and catch us on their screens. The Commnet was a little more difficult. I was about to address myself to the problem but before I could get to it I heard the control room operator on the Trojan base.

"Solar Flame, this is Trojan base, do you read?"

I responded. "Loud and clear Trojan Base, what can I do for you?"

"You guys find out anything about that distress? We just got it here for a few minutes, but now it's gone. What gives?"

"Sorry about that," I said. "We lost the distress we heard earlier. I must have switched ours on when we were checking to make sure we were not transmitting. Just noticed it. Sorry."

I realised that I was being a little more humble than was customary for me.

"You guys got any update on our slingshot?"

"As long as you just keep doing what you're doing you'll be OK. We'll let you know when to take the next step. By the way, the Base Manager is going to want a report from you. He wants to know how you got into this situation in the first place."

"Well, tell him that makes two of us," I replied. "Tell him it was a big surprise to us to find the asteroid we were sent to wasn't quite in spec. Tell him I'll speak to him when we get back, and before then he's not going to see a hard copy of anything. That's unless he's got a contribution to make to our rescue. In the meantime get him to have a word with the survey department and see what they say about that asteroid. He'll find the rock he gave us was well out of spec. And if he wonders why we didn't report it, well that's something he's going to have to wait for, but don't think I'm going to be too humble about it. And you could talk to Cygnus to find out what their thoughts might be on our engine failure."

By this time I figured I had scared the middle management and created enough friction between bits of the Acme Mining Company and other bits of the Acme Mining

Company and Cygnus, to keep their minds off what we might be doing.

I switched the Commnet off and stepped back. It might be dangerous to talk on it for too long. It was just possible that some-one might check the transmitter signature and see that it was not the Solar Flame sending. Then the shit would really hit the fan, even though it would be unlikely that this ship would be on anybody's records.

It felt odd to be on a ship with no communications. The voices in the air were our lifeblood. They kept us sane. Making us realise that there was some-one out there, beyond our own walls, between us and the stars, wherever we happened to be.

"What are we going to do next?" said Nadia.

"We're going to wait until this man is back with us," I replied.

Fifteen minutes later the man was sitting in the pilot's chair. It was difficult to believe that recently he had been prone on the deck, apparently at the point of death. Then he spoke.

"So who the hell are you guys?" he asked. "How did you find us? Where the hell are we anyway? How are everybody else?"

In reality rather than answering any of his several questions we felt like asking him some, and Nadia asked to first.

"What do you mean...everybody else?"

CHAPTER 13

Welcome Aboard the Evangelina

Our mission on board the *Evangelina* is to provide you with the products, services and stimulation which you have been missing out there in your world. Here you can relax and enjoy the best in food, wine and company at your own pace, in your own way.

The cabin is your own space for the duration of your visit. You can leave it at your whim, or remain in it and call on the services you require. We can provide almost anything. Just call the appropriate numbers listed in the directory.

The holo-viewer allows you to download images for the satisfaction of many tastes. These can be accessed using the channel selector and by consulting the guidance documentation. There is also a total immersion helmet available. To use this helmet it will be necessary for you to input the appropriate purchase order number into the key pad. Orders may be obtained by phoning Information. You will be advised about the cost of this service when you make the contact.

There is a mini-bar in your stateroom, stocked with a variety of drinks, stimulants and snacks. This will be restocked once a day, or more often if you wish, and payment for the items consumed will be requested at the time of check-out.

The *Evangelina* has a number of restaurants available to cater for a variety of tastes, and several bars and other public spaces. You can visit these areas to enjoy the stimulation of being served by our attractive female staff.

Other services are available, and we feel that the best way of finding out about these may be to visit or phone the Information Desk, which is manned 24 hours a day.

If you would like your cabin to be cleaned please indicate this by pressing the "clean now" button next to the access port. Otherwise the "Do Not Disturb" sign will remain in place.

The man with one arm straightened himself up in the pilot chair and looked round. He was getting more alert by the moment.

"Hell, there must be a couple of hundred people on this ship. They're here somewhere. It's big. I don't know where they all are."

I answered an earlier question.

"I'm Sulliman Smith, and this is Nadia Abdull. We are tug pilots. Our engineers are about here somewhere turning the lights out. Who are you?"

"I'm Boxer, and this," he waved the arm about vaguely, "is my ship."

"Well" said Nadia, "It's not up to much. Nothing's working. There's so little power that it wouldn't even operate the distress signal. What you see now is power from one of our ships. It's only little and it's not going to keep this lot going for long. So we're going to have to fix something soon. Have you got any engineers anywhere? No, I suppose you haven't. If you had you would hardly be in this state."

"Bastards," growled Boxer.

"Does that mean Nadia's right? You don't have any?" I said.

"Got it in one kiddo. The engineers are gone. The pilots are gone. That'll teach me for taking on contract people, I suppose. I thought captains always went down with their ships. And that should go for chief engineers as well. Did they go down with their ship? Or would they have done if the ship had gone down. Are they still here? No sir.

Who do you think was first in the lifeboats, taking our

clients with them, and everybody else who they thought might be important?"

"Well, why didn't they take you?" I asked. "After all, you're the owner."

"You're right." Boxer was momentarily reflective. "They weren't going to leave me. They asked me to go with them, but hell, this lot is mine. It's everything I own. I worked for this. How could I leave it?"

I considered how much this enormous craft might have cost. If I worked for a hundred years I could never find the price of a tug, and Boxer owned this. Or then maybe not. There was no way of telling.

Boxer stood. His red worksuit bunched slightly round his ankles, and partially covering a pair of expensive shoes. His left sleeve drooped and just covered the end of his arm. He ran his right hand through his thinning hair. He studied the main console. A few lights flashed. The video screens remained blank. The analogue dials all read zero.

"Can you guys drive this?"

"You bet," replied Nadia. "But first we have to fix it, and fixing it is going to take time. We need air, air-conditioning and services. Then we'll take it from there.

"What are we talking about?" asked Boxer, "Salvage?"

That was a thought. Salvage. It had not even occurred to me that we might actually salvage this enormous vessel and reap the reward for doing so. But there were rules for salvage. Before embarking on such a course it would be necessary for us to communicate with Acme, our charterers and Cygnus, our owners. And once we had got the salvaged vessel back to any safe place where it could be fixed, it would be necessary for an independent authority to determine the value of the service, and therefore how much we would get for the job. I could hardly imagine doing it. And then of course there was the Morality Police. I doubt that even Nadia's chaste communication technique would convince the mopo guy on the Trojan station that we were somehow keeping ourselves separate from the each other.

If you are thinking about salvage there's a bit of difficulty." said Boxer "This ship doesn't exist. I don't exist. That's why no-one's looking for us. No flight plan. No destination. No departure point. So how can you salvage a vessel which doesn't exist?"

"OK, OK," said Nadia. "I guessed as much. Well, you've struck lucky. Our employers won't be looking for us for a long time, and if we don't ever reappear again they'll breathe a sigh of relief. They think we're preparing for a slingshot round Saturn. We've got several days before they're going to think of contacting us. If they do, we can respond, tell them we're on our way, and they'll forget about us for a long time. We're a perfect match."

"Where are we going?" asked Boxer.

"We won't know that until we've powered up the navigation system," I replied. "Unfortunately, the ones on our tugs aren't going to be much use with this hunk of metal next to them. But once we've got everything going we should be fine, assuming the power plant is capable of powering this thing."

"Oh yes," said Boxer "Believe me, this ship was built with no expense spared. It's the ultimate cruise ship... or was."

"Cruise ship!" I echoed.

"Cruise ship - dummy!" said Nadia.

"Yes cruise ship," said Boxer, obviously unconcerned about repeating himself. The Evangelina...."

"Evangelina!" we both echoed.

"Yes, well I had to make a bit of a concession to an investor. Evangelina was the name of his concubine. He put some of the money up and I let him name the ship. It doesn't matter anyway. Call it what you like. After a while people hear the name and picture the ship, or at least bits of it. And what about you? How is it that you guys are on the missing in action list?"

We told him our story, each of us taking a turn at bits of

it while the other checked out the controls and read-outs in the pilot house. There is no way you can avoid doing this once you have been in charge of any sort of space craft. The eyes scan the read-outs and the needles and the LEDs, hands touch the throttle and thrusters controls, and finally you scan the heavens to see what it going on around you. All that was visible from the Evangelina was the Milky Way, filling the viewports with the twinkle of starlight. The stars were reassuringly stationary. Nadia had done a great job of stabilising the ship.

"So you see," said Nadia wrapping it up, "we're going to be sent on a slingshot which will take months to complete, with very little chance of us getting back alive. It was their fault because they hadn't modified the ships properly and in any case they had assigned us to an asteroid which was really a comet. It's looking as if we would be better off with you. At the very least we should get you up and running and take you to a point from which you can get yourself a new crew. Then we can take off and make up some sort of a tale as to why we've arrived back in the Trojans, or the Jupiter complex, earlier than we should have.

"And what about you?" asked Nadia.

"It's some story," replied Boxer. "How much time have you got?"

"It seems to me that we have as long as it takes for our engineers to make it back here from doing whatever it is they're doing. I'm working on the assumption that something pretty serious has happened for it to be in this state."

"The problem, as I said before, is that we are not supposed to exist," said Boxer. Everybody knows we're out here. We're not even alone. Every part of the system has at least one cruise ship. But when things go wrong there's nothing much you can do except grin and bear it.

Sometime, I don't know how long ago now, we had a major engine failure at a time when we were on passage to the Jupiter system. We were looking forward to a good season.

Anyway, we were moving pretty fast when the main power system dropped out, and once the navigator had told everybody where we were going, it was all hands to the boats. Never mind women and children first. They were gone before we could even think. They even left the women behind.

They took care to take the clients with them because the clients were important. If there'd been any left, someone would have come looking. And if anyone had come looking, then the whole story would have come out, and they would have been implicated.

We had the mopo in our pockets, but even they could hardly have concealed the loss of a few major players in the solar system."

"So, who's left?" I asked.

"There's me," said Boxer "And all the whores I think. No-one told them what was going down and I think they were mostly asleep. To be honest I haven't seen any of them. I'm not sure if they know their way to the pilot house. It wasn't even a place I visited very often, so it took me a bit of time to find it."

"What about food? Surely you found out where the food supplies were?"

"I used the stuff in the pilot house freezer. Not much more than snacks really, and eventually I got fed up with trying to find my way from one place to another. When we had power we had some electronic maps to tell us where we were. It's amazing how little you bother to remember when you've always got something to help you. And finally I ran out of water."

"No, you didn't," said Nadia. "I found some in one of the lockers."

"That just shows you," replied Boxer. "I never even knew there were any lockers. To tell the truth I'd got pretty used to being looked after. I guess I just got depressed. But I'll be OK now."

The departure of the crew indicated that this ship was

going somewhere unfavourable, and unless we could fix it, it wasn't coming back. At worst we might be able to return to the Solar Flame and the Solar Flare and still make the slingshot.

To know what the score was, we had to get the navigation system going. In my mind I had this picture of the big black shape rushing through space and taking us with it into oblivion.

"What's in it for us if we sort this lot out?" asked Nadia, always practical.

A look of pain crossed Boxer's features. "Hell, I don't know. I've never been salvaged before, but there's no formal way you can get anything. How can you salvage a ship which doesn't exist? Believe me, if you get this thing back into orbit round any planet in the system, you can guarantee that no-one will acknowledge it. If you crashed it into the surface of Mars they'd say it was a meteorite.

"What if we stay with you and run it?"

I was finding that Nadia had a very direct way of dealing with things. She would have an idea and bingo - it was fact. The rest of us were expected to go along with it. What could I say - I thought it was a great plan, but I could hardly speak for Rollo and Easan."

"Shouldn't we discuss this amongst ourselves?" I asked. "We've already said that we might take off once the Evangelina is fixed, and it has piggy-backed us to a suitable point within the solar system."

"You going chicken on me, Sulliman?" Nadia gave me one of those straight looks. "What's the choice? Take a chance of surviving the slingshot. How can staying here be any worse than that?"

Boxer looked from one to the other.

"I can see you guys have some sort of a problem," he said. "But I should probably make it clear that without you this ship doesn't survive. You can see that, so I'm prepared to give you an interest if you have the ability to run this thing for me. Believe me, we can make big money anywhere. The Evangelina is well known as the best in the business, so once we get back into orbit we'll soon have customers. You've only seen the passageway from the access port to the pilot house, but there's lots more. You'll like it. If I have it right, you've been working for years on the mining tugs, where you have virtually no living space."

He had it right. Cyg Two had a single cabin the size of a shoebox. It had two bunks into which we had to strap ourselves, and the space remaining was only big enough for one of us to get dressed at once.

Boxer continued, "Can you imagine living in a cabin which has space round a double bed, and of course once the gravity system is working, you can walk round? The cabin has a real shower. Some have baths. Tell you what. If you stay, you can have one with a bath."

"And what about pay?" asked Nadia.

"You can be a shareholder," said Boxer. "The four of you. Everyone else will be on salary, some on not much, because they rely on tips from the clients, but you can take a share of the profits."

"Come on Sulliman," said Nadia. "We don't have anything to lose, except our lives if we don't do it. At the very worst if we can't get this thing going we at least have a source of food and a space to live which can keep us going for.... "

"About twenty five years," said Boxer.

"OK we'll stay," I said. "And if the others really want to do something else then we'll programme one of the ships to take them on the slingshot."

"But neither of you are engineers," said Boxer. "So it's either all of you, or none at all. I need the engineers here to fix the ship. "

"Don't worry," said Nadia, "we'll all stay. I'll speak for them. Whenever the others get back we'll convince them that its a good idea and in the meantime... In the meantime you can tell us how you came to own this fantasy."

Boxer took a sip of water and cleared his throat. It was obviously a story he had told before. I straightened up and scanned the dials, checked the engine and thruster controls and gazed out at the Milky Way. Boxer had started speaking.

"It all started on Mars. I worked in one of the foundries, trying to make ends meet and finding it pretty hard. But I occasionally visited a lady who worked in one of the ventilation ducts. Let's face it; life can be pretty frustrating for a single man in a space station. This made me think - if I could find somewhere more comfortable, then I could make a lot of credits, and so could the lady I was visiting. She had a few friends and I had an idea.

There was a guy who worked with me on the night shift. He'd been gambling and he was in hock up to his armpits, so I paid off his gambling debts, and he and his family moved out.

"Where did they go?" I asked.

"What do I care? I was happy and he was happy. Well he might not actually have been happy, but at least he was still alive. He at least had the choice of living or dying. And he lived. His wife came to work for me. They had to try to make ends meet.

I found this route to the women's quarters and managed to get a few of them in. It was just a bit risky but they were prepared to go through the ventilation shafts, and I was prepared to take the risk of employing them.

It was good for me that the Mars Base is a big place, and pretty soon I had three shops going. I sorted out the Morality Police. In the main their morality relates to the good behaviour of others. They seem to think that they have some special dispensation from god to do just what they like. Anyway, with them on my side it really started to go my way."

"But what about the ship?" I asked.

"Ah yes, the ship.

I had a client who used to come to my best place. He said

he was a miner but his coveralls and his fingernails were always clean and when we shook hands his palms were soft. This wasn't too unusual. Lots of important guys used to disguise themselves. It made them feel less vulnerable.

One day he asked me to go on an expedition with him. He called it an expedition but really he meant a day out. He said for me to be at the shuttle port the following day. He told me that he'd got a bonus and that he'd been offered a special trip out to one of the moons and that he could take a guest.

Actually I got on with him pretty well, so I decided what the hell, and it didn't surprise me when I met him at the spaceport that he was wearing some pretty expensive threads. I said nothing but then I found myself in a private cruiser, and before I knew it we were on a black ship somewhere in orbit. I've never really taken to astro-navigation. I can only tell where I am if there's a sign up.

Of course, it was a cruise ship. The guy told me that his name was Jonah, but no-one uses their real name on a cruise ship. I told him my name was Boxer. It's not my real name either, but somehow it stuck.

Jonah showed me round the ship and we enjoyed some of its services. My little places, of which I'd been so proud, were just cesspools. This was total luxury.

The result of this visit was that me and Jonah decided to build our own ship. Jonah owned, a yard amongst other things. Of course it's not actually a yard, it's a small metal planet that allows people to build structures that are attached to it until completed. It was big enough to build more than one ship at a time, so on one side Jonah's crew built commercial vessels, which were sold off when completed, and on the other side the Evangelina gradually took shape. Of course we pretended it was something else. Whether people knew what it was hardly mattered. Even then, the Evangelina was invisible. I wouldn't want to bore you with the details, but the techniques used were just the same as the ones they use for all the other ships that are built out here. It was just bigger and there was more of nearly everything."

I looked round. He was right. Even the pilot house was ten times as big as anything I had ever seen before. The shuttles just had room for the pilot and the engineer, with of course all the gauges, readouts and controls. Here it was possible for all of us to stand about and admire the scenery. As well as contour chairs for the pilot and the engineer there were secondary seats at other consoles for the communications officer and for the navigator, and in an adjacent smaller space there was a bank of screens.

"That's the security room," said Boxer.

"So what about that?" I pointed to the place where his arm had been.

"Ah yes, that." Boxer took a sip of water and went on with his story.

"When I look back it seems strange to me that I didn't have any idea that I was being set up. I thought I had a partner, putting in equal shares and using our skills to make sure that the ship was just what we wanted. But it wasn't the full picture. He'd made use of my money and what I knew and then..."

Boxer was briefly reflective, and then he continued.

"One day I was doing an inspection of some of the furnishings. The ship was close to completion and by this time I was really able to use my skill. That's what I'm good at; making things fit. You could say it's taste. All I know is that when I decide what should fill a space, people like the results.

I was on my way down to one of the lowest levels of the yard where we had stored all the bits and pieces, which the ship needed for fitting out. If you can imagine it, the hull is in orbit, and by this time the construction yard was hanging onto its side. The trick they used was to build the basic pressure hull using robots, and then carry on from there. It is the cheapest way of doing the job."

I waved for him to carry on. We knew all about yards.

We had frequently taken Acme's rigs to one or another to be repaired; a tricky business, requiring even more precision than positioning a rig on an asteroid.

"Anyway, I went down to the lowest level at the end of the day. It was a big space and there was no-one about but me. It was a bit spooky and I suppose I should have been concerned, but that's the sort of guy I was then. Trusting. Come to think of it I still am. Look what happened to me this time.

I found the stuff I wanted and I was looking through the fabrics and furnishings and putting things in place in my mind."

Boxer paused. I had a job to see the squat little man as a fashion guru. He took another swallow of water from the container at his side and carried on.

"I opened a packing case and was thumbing though the materials. They were wonderful stuff. Real cotton, brocade velvet. An absolute joy. Then I heard this noise behind me. I looked round, but there was no-one in sight except for a cleaning robot. You know the ones. The sort which are programmed for the big open spaces."

I did know. They were big box-like machines, running on tracks, set to provide total manoeuvrability. They were fitted with an ovoid sensor unit placed on top of the box which looked something like a head with eyes all the way round. From various parts of the body the cleaning tools could be deployed, depending on what sort of space the machine was dealing with at the time. These machines were similar to the one that had confronted us in the corridors of Io.

When Boxer observed that I had the cleaning machine firmly in my mind he carried on.

"I looked back into the box, but before I knew it the robot was right up behind me. Then it slid out one of its brushes and began to swish it towards me. I stepped back and for a moment the arm stopped moving and I saw that instead of a brush, the manipulator was fitted with a blade. Of course it all came clear to me straight away. This was a take-over bid, and there was no possible defence.

The blade was black and paddle shaped. I recognised it as part of a cutting tool. Hardly an offensive weapon in its proper place, slicing fabrics for soft furnishings, but on the end of an arm it was lethal. I knew it was sharp. These blades are constructed molecule by molecule so that the sharp edge is only one atom wide. It will cut anything. When the blade is in contact the molecules mingle and then mutually reject each other. Cutting is instant and involves no force. Believe me if you try testing the edge with your finger, that's it. No finger.

The robot clicked and whirred like they always do, but for a change said nothing. I suppose it would have been too much trouble to have reprogrammed the speech patterns with the rest of its functions. In a way it made it even more threatening.

I backed off towards the elevator, but the robot was right with me. I had no idea how it had identified me, but however it was done it was working well.

Another appendage slid out of its body. It was a small circular saw. What did it need a saw for? The blade would have been sufficient. Regardless of any logic there was another click and the saw fired up. Soon it was just a blur. The place was full of the sound of it. The air shimmered round it. I was scared out of my mind.

Soon I couldn't back up any more. I was right next to the elevator door, so I pressed the button and held my breath. I had no idea whether the elevator was coming or not because I was absolutely unable to take my eyes off the saw.

The robot moved right up and took a swing at me. I managed to duck and there was a shower of sparks as the saw cut into the service pipe next to me. There was steam. Luckily a random jet caught the robot in the sensors and it rolled back a bit, giving me time to press the button for the elevator again. Of course it could have had fifty floors to come down.

As the robot started towards me again I heard the door open behind me and so I stepped in.

The elevator spoke to me but I was too frightened to answer. It was about to go through its greeting phase again when I got it together enough to ask it to take me to my floor. It asked me if I was having a nice day, but before I could answer the cleaning machine slid over the threshold into the elevator with me. I was not having a nice day.

Of course the elevator immediately started muttering about being overloaded, and how it wasn't going anywhere. The circular saw was everywhere, whirring and humming and swishing as the manipulator swung it back and forth closer and closer to me. At every swing it touched the walls of the elevator showering sparks into the space. I realised that there was a finite time that I was going to be able to keep on ducking it. Eventually it was going to cut my head off.

This model of cleaning machine has an emergency stop in the middle of the forward surface, on the main body just under the optic sensors.

The stop was close to me, only guarded by the saw, which by this time was flashing back and forward faster than my eyes could follow it. It least the blade was hanging by its side. These machines are programmed only to be able to use one appendage at a time.

I carried on backing up until I felt the back wall of the elevator. It told us that it was going to shut down if the weight inside it was not reduced to the regulatory maximum. The cleaning machine took no notice.

By this time I had no option but to go for the button, but as I'm about to reach forward the saw swung across the front of the machine and I had to pull back. Then I had a moment of luck. The saw embedded itself in the wall of the elevator, and though I might have been imagining it, I fancied I heard the machine grunt as it tried to pull it out.

I took my only chance and reached forward towards the button, but I'd forgotten that these things have the capability to disengage an appendage if it stops working.

In a split second the saw stopped moving and the blade flashed up towards me. It was too late for me to pull back and so it cut my arm off just below the shoulder.

I couldn't stop going forward. It didn't hurt. In fact I didn't feel a thing apart from my head hitting the button."

"But how come they didn't sew the arm back on?" I asked. "It would be dead simple, let's face it. Even the shipyard would have had a medical centre which could do a simple job like that."

"Yeah" replied Boxer. "Well, I woke up on the floor. I was looking up at the robot. I could see the button. It was gradually moving out. I knew that once it was back in the start position the thing was going to burst into life again, and now it would take nothing to finish me off.

The bottom of the elevator was covered in blood, but I realised that the cleaning machine was back on the floor and only my head was sticking out. I managed to slide forward until I was clear of the door, and croaked out for the thing to take me to the twenty-sixth floor. That is where the medical centre was situated.

The doors closed. The elevator powered upwards and I woke up in a hospital bed."

"But what about the arm?" I persisted.

"Oh, when the elevator doors closed, the arm was on the outside, and they told me that by the time they got back down to check it out the cleaning machine had cleared it up. They got a few bits back out of its debris container. In fact they said the hand was complete, but there was no arm in between. Just bad luck I guess. But then I was lucky to be alive."

Boxer looked almost cheerful with his fate, and I suppose being short of an arm is not as serious as being short of a life, and somehow he still had the Evangelina.

"So how did you get to keep the ship?"

"Oh, that was easy," said Boxer "I just killed my former partner. Of course we had a mutual agreement that if one of us died then the other inherited his share of the ship. That was why he'd been able to consider having me terminated.

I moved fast. Obviously he had to get down to the bottom deck to see what had happened to me, so as soon as I was mobile - fortunately with modern medicines, after only a few hours - I made it back down to the bottom deck carrying an antique weapon. I've still got it."

Boxer pointed to a drawer under one of the consoles, and when I opened it there was a weapon. I picked it up gingerly.

"It's OK," said Boxer, "there are no bullets in it. I have some bullets. Expensive but effective. I went down to the bottom deck with that, and sure enough there was my former partner sorting through things. Someone had cleaned the lift up, and he must have thought that the job was done. After all we had no direct relationship, so no-one would have told him that I was injured and in the hospital. I hadn't bargained for the cleaning machine, which recognised me, but before it could start up I stepped forward and shot Jonah. The bullet got him in the middle of the chest and threw him backwards onto a sofa. I could see that he wasn't dead. In the meantime the cleaning machine was bowling towards me at full whack, but the gun is a Colt 1911 automatic which was designed to stop a running man. I pointed the gun at the thing and fired. The bullet hit the curve of its body and whined off into the depths of the store. The machine hesitated for a moment and came on. I fired twice more. One of the bullets seemed to have missed altogether but the other one got it in the joint between one of its arms and the body. And as required by its programming, it stopped to assess the damage.

Fortunately for me this process is not purely electronic. The machines need to move the damaged limbs and see to what extent their operation is curtailed, and this is done one at a time. I knew what it was doing. And while it was checking out the limb to which the cutting blade was attached, I dashed up to it and shot it again through one of its eyes. Then I jammed the gun barrel against the joint between the neck and the body and fired again. These shots seem to have destroyed some essential functions because it stopped working altogether.

Jonah was still alive. He was stirring on the settee, so I shot him again. He stopped moving and I checked his pulse. He was dead. I'd taken the precaution of taking some mild hallucinogens with me as well as a wad of fake credits. I planted these on the body with the expectation that any police investigation would discover these and would associate them with criminal activity.

I was still in bandages and I was supposed to be connected to a drip in the hospital. It was almost an alibi, and no-one in the yard was too interested in finding out the truth. They were already breaking the law, building the ship, so how could anyone get the rights of it? All the payments had been made, so all I had to do was take it over.

Over the last few weeks before delivery I'd been hiring the crew and the workers. I got myself a couple of pilots whose record was only just bit blemished, and a couple of engineers who were just a bit inexperienced. The captain had looked extremely good in his dress uniform, which well he might, because in a previous life he had worked on a passenger ship, and as captain of a ship with both male and female passenger compartments he had to have access everywhere. So he had been able to find a way of being friendly with unattached female passengers, and over time had managed to take at least some of their money off them.

Once the police – of both sorts – were on his trail he had to get away quickly, and taking up a post in the shipyard was as good a way hiding out as any. The first mate came with the chief engineer, a girl and boy duo. They never told me how they met, but the girl was scheduled to be part of an arranged marriage, so it was their way of dealing with the problem. My only trouble was working out a way of ensuring that they had the skills they said they did. It was easy enough for the captain. He'd been in the news, and he was quite proud of his press cuttings. Once I had him on board he was able to ask the right questions of the rest of the team. If you're a pilot you have to know how to deal with this lot." Boxer waved his arm towards the controls, dials and read-outs. "And if you're an engineer could you claim to be one unless you can do things with the engines? We sent the engineers to the engine room, and told them to set one of the engines up for trials. I suppose there was a risk. They could have blown us up, but they didn't. They got one of the engines running.

The catering staff were easier. I had them come to the yard and be interviewed, but when they arrived they had no idea what sort of a job they were applying for. Then, if I thought they were suitable I would tell them what it was about. For all of them the advantage is space. This ship is the only place off earth where you have room to turn round. And of course I offered them lots of money. That always helps. We have restaurants and so I needed a chef. That was just a bit more difficult. How many chefs are there, in a world where there is really no provision made for eating? But I found an amateur who had spent a lifetime campaigning for real food, so how could he resist the temptation? I was going to give him all the ingredients to make any dish he had in mind. We even put roast swan on the menu."

"What, real swan?" I asked.

"Not actually real swan, but something that looked like it. With some difficulty I'd obtained some real ducks and some piglets. We've the space for a small farm. Back in the old days on earth, ships used to carry their own livestock, because there was no way of keeping the meat fresh once you'd killed it. Here we kept some because the only way of making it available was to breed our own."

"So somewhere in this ship there are ducks and pigs?"

"That's right," continued Boxer. "And in the food storage there must be plenty of food. Even with no power, the storage will keep it fresh for years. Something to do with enzymes. I never bothered to get to the bottom of it, but probably your engineers will know all about it."

All this talk of food was making me peckish, and before long our engineers had returned from their task of putting out lights with similar thoughts.

Boxer, who by now seemed to be fully recovered, even though it had been only hours since we had locked on, led us to the back of the pilot house and indicated a door. "Try that. It's got the pilot house snacks in it. That's what I've been living on."

I opened the door and inside a light went on. The whole space was filled with plastic containers and plastic bottles. All of them full of something. I picked a container at random and opened it. It was full of small black shiny balls, glued together in some way. I sniffed. A faintly acrid smell filled my nostrils.

"Caviar," said Boxer. "That's eggs of the sturgeon, a rare fish found only in a few seas on earth. Of course it's not real, but it's a fair facsimile and costs about the same as the real stuff would cost, if there was any available."

None of us really knew the state of the seas on earth. Years ago they had gradually become more and more polluted, and fished out. Wild fish had become rarer, and even farmed fish had become extremely expensive. The sturgeon had probably been the first to go.

But times had changed and what no-one expected was a decline in earth population due to disease and birth control, and finally an irrational fear of heterosexual sex, which promoted the popularity of homosexual liaisons. While we knew how things had once been, and what we had been taught in our history lessons, we had doubts about how things might be now. If there were no longer people to go fishing there was every chance that the fish had returned. If there was no longer a need to support

178

billions of people the levels of pollution might have reduced to the point where it no longer had an effect. I began to wonder what we were doing out here if things had improved back on earth.

Back in the food store, I checked out some more plastic containers, as did the others, and between us we managed to get a reasonable meal together, although it was a strange business after years of subsisting on protein pills and soya substitutes.

Boxer identified some of the different products for us. There was "bread", apparently made from wheat, or some other grain, ground up and cooked in an oven. One could hardly imagine the energy use. Boxer wielded an antique cutting tool and produced slices of the product. Then he spread stuff onto the surfaces, enveloped some slices of something and handed it over, first of all to Nadia.

"This is a sandwich," he said.

Nadia made agreeable noises as she took a bite and chewed. And encouraged, Boxer continued with his task, creating sandwiches for the rest of us. He opened another cupboard and from within it produced some glasses. Of course we knew what glasses were, but most of us drank out of a sealed container by means of a straw. Boxer lined up the glasses on one of the worktops and, with something of a flourish, poured a dark liquid into them from one of the containers. We began to understand how important eating had once been for everyone on planet earth. An activity which for us had become nothing more than a means of remaining alive, could be so much more. There was pleasure to be had in the tastes of different foods. When I picked up one of the glasses and took a sip I realised that the same applied to drinks. The liquid slid smoothly down my throat and seemed to warm my innards. I looked questioningly at Boxer.

"That's a Spanish wine "Ribera del Duero". Of course it's not really made from grapes, but it's not a bad imitation. It's alcoholic of course," he said.

It was beginning to become a bit of a history lesson.

Once everyone had the drug alcohol available to them, and in ancient times fermentation had been a means of making impure liquids safer to drink. But its use was against some religions, particularly where water had been purified by means of boiling, rather than by means of fermentation. As those who might be called "boilers" displaced the "fermenters", in the governments of earth, alcohol reduced in consumption. Laws were passed against its use and, so it seemed to some, a whole area of enjoyment disappeared. The cruise ships specialised in providing products, services and stimulants that were banned by law, and this included alcohol. There were stronger drugs available, and means of providing pleasure based purely on electronics. But alcohol had the special property of enhancing the pleasure of other activities. Even conversation is improved by a moderate ingestion.

"You'd better take it easy with the wine," suggested Boxer, "a few glasses of that and you'll find your reflexes have gone all to hell."

Boxer seemed to have finished telling his story. There was more I knew, but it was unimportant to pursue it at the time. We would have a lifetime to get the rest out of this little man. In the meantime a whole new world beckoned.

CHAPTER 14

Supersense Virtuality Equipment Brochure

Supersense would like to offer you our latest products, which will provide you with the ultimate sensory experiences. They may possibly exceed those which you expect in real life, after all, our programmes are not limited by the natural modesty we expect to encounter in the opposite sex. And we cater for all tastes.

Start at the bottom of our range, the Supersense reality shades. These lightweight shades are fitted with the latest vision screens, providing a genuine three-dimensional experience. They are not called reality shades for nothing. Lightweight in place and on the wallet, you will be amazed by the visual reality they provide.

For a more enveloping experience why not try our Deepvision virtual reality helmet? The helmet offers three-dimensional views with full sound effects created by the foremost Foley artists currently at work. It is comfortable to wear and comes with four free programmes. These can be chosen from our Deepvision programme list, excluding the "Whips and Blood" series. The helmet is suitably sized for adult wearers and contains its own energy source. The source recharges itself in only two hours.

For the connoisseur we have the complete virtual reality suit. These suits are not available to buy, but can be hired or leased for extended periods. They come with replaceable genital pouches, which can be purchased in packs of ten, and it advisable that organisations providing their clients with the suit's experience offer genital pouches for hygiene purposes.

For further information about any of our products please call us, or visit one of our agents. Supersense is an Earth company authorised by the Solar System Morality Police to provide non-contact sexual services, using programmes that are entirely digitally generated. No women were used in the provision of these services.

See all. Hear all. Feel all – Nothing beats Supersense.

It wasn't until Easan had got the lifts going that we began to be able to put the rest of the ship together. It was a storehouse of treasures. A world so different from anything any of us had experienced before that we could only just comprehend it.

There was a conference room big enough for us all to sit round the circular table, with padded chairs, which rocked as we leant back in them. And every vertical surface was capable of being activated, to present an infinite variety of scenes, real and imaginary.

Boxer took us to the major client staterooms. They were decorated in the styles of every period from the old centuries, right up to what the present day would have offered had there been been space. If the millions on the home planet, and the outworlds, and the space stations, and the mining complexes on the satellites, had known that anyone lived like this, they would have wanted a part of it. Civilization would have broken down.

Even the crew cabins were large enough to walk about in, with beds so wide that it was possible to turn and curl up and even share. Of course, at last Nadia and I had finally got round to sharing. When it had been time for us all to take some time off from the initial stages of revitalising the Evangelina, Boxer showed us to some of the crew cabins. We were not even thinking quite straight. We were exhausted from the many hours we had spent going from emergency to survival. So when he threw open the door of the captain's cabin Nadia and I both stepped in. Maybe, because we were both captains, but before we had time to consider our situation he had closed the door behind us.

Now that there was no-one looking over our shoulders

we were curiously shy about taking the next step, and stood looking at each other from either side of the bed. I pulled back the covers and saw that, beneath them, the sheets were clean and white. "Here we go, then," I said and shrugged off my coveralls. Nadia just nodded, and after pulling down the zip of her outer garment, allowed it to fall around her ankles, and then stepped forward and stood there in her underwear. Attractive undergarments are not generally available in inhabited space, for either men or women, and as a result I was wearing a pair of utility boxer shorts. But Nadia was wearing a pair of briefs, which only just covered what they were supposed to. I suspected that she had been sewing, and hoped it had been done with me in mind.

Nadia raised an eyebrow and glanced down at the bed. She was uncharacteristically silent, but it may have been that words were unnecessary. My boxer shorts did nothing to conceal my appreciation of her state of undress. I pulled back the covers and we slid into the bed from either side. I picked up the mando, which I knew would operate the lights and the other systems, and pressed a few buttons. Lights went on and off and finally dimmed so that we could just see the bulkheads around us.

We slid towards each other over crisp white linen. Nadia's bare leg hooked around mine and pulled me towards her. Her hair brushed across my face, our cheeks touched and I felt, rather than heard, her breathing in my ear. We helped each other out of our underwear. And then her breasts were pressed against my chest and my hands were sliding over her muscular bits, her sharp angular bits, and her well-rounded bits.

"Here we go, then," she whispered.

When we drew breath, we were lying on our backs naked and breathing heavily, and holding hands. "Finally!" said Nadia. But, after a few minutes rest, her hand drifted back over my stomach and it turned out not to be finally at all.

183

But the job had to go on and despite the limited time we spent actually sleeping, our relationship seemed to make us more alert. We arose at the beginning of every work period full of enthusiasm to face whatever the Evangelina had to offer. And we approached the task we had given ourselves, to put the Evangelina together, with greater enthusiasm.

Easan started off close to home, while Rollo spent much of her time down in the engine room sorting out the hardware. Nadia and I did what-ever we could, checking the navigation systems, setting the pilot house to rights and doing the limited tasks that pilots can do when they are not actually driving. Once we had some of the systems going we were able to nudge the cruise ship back in the direction of Jupiter, from its previous course, which would have taken it into the surface of Saturn.

Easan was dealing with the software. The intermittent power losses and surges from which the ship had suffered had interrupted all its main programmes, and locked up many essential functions. These were problems which a man with access to a terminal, and an intimate knowledge of neural programming, could solve. And Easan was that man. To him this was the best fun you could have by yourself and he went to it with a will. Sometimes we didn't see him for several days and then suddenly some system would burst into life and amaze us with the scope and effectiveness of its functions.

One of his earlier efforts was in the conference room, where all four walls could be made to display a single scene of something. He went to work on the conference room terminal and soon had the walls active. We sat and watched as pictures began to appear before us.

"OK," said Easan "I'll just make a path to the mainframe and we should be getting somewhere. Once I get it reactivated, it should be possible to use the interface in here."

Suddenly a square appeared on one wall and expanded until it was a couple of metres across. Easan punched a couple of keys and the picture changed. It was the interior of a room. I realized that we were looking into one of the staterooms. A naked sleeping woman lay on the vast bed partially covered by a thick quilted down. She was lying face down, her arms flung wide. The picture was clear enough for me to see the muscle definition of her back, and the individual vertebrae getting smaller, until they finally disappeared at the cleft of her buttocks.

"Wow," said Easan, looking up. "This is really something".

"It's nothing," said Boxer "We just need to be able to keep our eyes on the girls to make sure they're OK, and that slut shouldn't be in there. They've got perfectly good cabins of their own. What the hell's she doing in there, messing the place up?"

"Take it easy," said Nadia. "There's no-one here. What the hell does it matter if they spread themselves out a bit?"

"What the hell does it matter? What the..." Boxer looked up. "How many of you guys have ever had to clean up this sort of space? How many of you have ever had more space to put in order than you can cover in two strides? If we're ever going to get back in business this whole ship is going to have to be CLEAN." He said it in capital letters, and I realized that he had a point. Looking round I could see that the conference room was looking a bit shabby.

Boxer grabbed a small microphone and pressed a couple of buttons.

"Irena, you there! Yes, Irena!" he shouted.

The body twitched and then settled back again.

"Come on Irena. Answer me."

"Perhaps the speaker isn't working," I suggested.

"You can be sure it is," he replied. "She's just hoping I'm going to go away".

"Irrrrrena - get your black arse out of there."

There was a brief silence. I looked round to see if Rollo was in the room and was relieved to see that she wasn't. People were not normally defined by their colour. Black people, or people with very dark skins were an exception, and any skin colour other than the normal light brown was considered to be particularly attractive. Black, or as we more often thought of it, very dark, was good and so was a pale milky colour, or what we would have described as very light. Boxer had obviously missed out on some education somewhere. I could not imagine him addressing Irena as "you very dark person."

He went on. "What's wrong with you lot? You don't like the description - what is she, if she isn't black? And as for her arse, that's definitely black!"

"Irena, get your black arse on your black legs and get the hell out of there." The smaller unfixed items in the room rattled slightly in time to the cadences of his voice. The noise in the stateroom, if the speakers were working, must have been awful.

Irena stirred her black arse and lifted herself slowly from the bed, uncurling like an animal roused from hibernation. She stood and stretched with her back to the camera, giving us the benefit of the sight of her muscles rippling lightly under the velvet skin. She she turned towards the camera, gave us a sign with a single finger, and walked out of sight, I presumed out of the room, with a level of dignity that I would not have thought possible for a woman with no clothes on.

Boxer took a deep breath and turned away from the image, now showing an apparently empty room. "Well, I gotta say that all my luck must have been used up when you lot heard my message." He stopped, considering the statement, and then carried on in a slightly different tone. "But I've got to admire you. It's gradually coming together. If we carry on like this, it's all going to get going. Tell you what, why don't we go and have a look at the Simroom?"

"You didn't tell me you had one of those," said Easan.

"Of course," was the reply. "All the cruise ships have got them. Some of the clients like them better than the real thing. You can see why. It's tailored sex, and it feels the same."

Since we could think of nothing better to do, and Easan was eager to get his hands on a new plaything, we followed Boxer into the lift.

After fixing a couple of lift breakdowns on the way, we clustered in the doorway of the Simroom. Boxer stood slightly in front of us and waved his arm about with a flourish.

"This is it," he said proudly.

We were unimpressed. There was nothing here but a space. The four walls were off-white in colour and gave the appearance of being slightly damp. I stepped inside and experimentally ran my finger down the closest surface. It gave a little under my touch.

In the middle of the room was a plinth, approximately two metres long and one and a half wide. It appeared to be covered with the same spongy material, and was about half a metre high. It had the dimensions, but not the appearance of a large bed.

On the plinth lay a suit.

Up in the corners of the space the tiny eyes of video cameras peered down on us.

Easan seemed a little more impressed than the rest of us. He made a beeline for the suit and was soon examining it, attempting to hold it up and look at the headpiece at the same time.

"Careful," said Boxer, alarmed.

"What can I do?" said Easan.

"Well who knows," was the reply.

"So what gives with this?" I asked. "This is supposed to be the ultimate experience. It doesn't look like much to me?"

Easan was holding the suit up in front of him, and I was amazed to see that it was equipped with its own genitalia.

"What you have to remember," said Boxer, "is that virtual reality is not a mind thing. You don't put on a helmet and have something enter your brain and make you think things are happening which aren't. It's a physical thing. You still use all the senses. Touch, hearing, sight and smell. All the suit does is fool the senses."

He had our attention.

"In the eyepieces of the helmet you see things, which of course is easy. This space here can be anywhere, or even nowhere. You can be in the penthouse of a hotel on the shores of, say, the Caspian Sea, or at least the Caspian Sea as it used to be once. You can look out of the window and see water, mountains. You know the sort of thing. We've got quite a few venues. Out in the country by a mountain stream. That's quite nice. And on the beach. That's even better. You may not be aware of these places. Centuries ago, on earth, the edges of the sea were covered in sand, and people used to take most of their clothes off and lie in the sun and splash about in the water. We have photographs... anyway it's quite an exotic environment. Of course all that came to an end when it became immoral to see ladies, other than one's wife, with very few clothes on.

Whatever the rules are, you can't keep the male from wanting to see such things. It's part of our make-up. If it wasn't an attractive proposition, the incentive to procreate would have diminished to the point that there would be nobody left. That's the way we're going anyway, isn't it?

"Yes, we hear the population's decreasing," said Nadia.

"If it is, it's because we're prevented from doing what comes naturally by all this morality stuff. Not to mention the general acceptance of homosexuality. It's considered to be more moral than being heterosexual in this twisted world. Anyway, where was I?" Boxer continued.

"Ah yes. We can show other people on the beach in various states of undress. Of course you can't interact with them; they're just images; and they just do what they do. Then we've got the land battle scene. You're watching it from a vantage point. The women are in uniform. There are lots of guys who really go for women in uniform, but lets face it, what chance is there of that in this world.

To tell the truth the real turn-on of this kit is the space it gives you. In this space, where-ever it is, we can put people, animals anything, and you can look at them. With me so far?"

Of course we were. We were all familiar with the theory, and a means of mass entertainment was a version of this kit consisting of only a helmet. You sat in a seat, put the helmet on and effectively became a witness to some filmic event. But you could only watch.

"So there we are," Boxer continued. "We can look into the lenses of the face-mask and see what-ever the computer puts in front of us. We're enjoying the view. Then we put in the woman. She's a real person who has just been digitalized. She's been scanned in all directions, standing walking, bending, sitting, from the front, the back, the sides, engaged in every expression, pouting, smiling, laughing, frowning, and apparently doing everything that our clients are going to want her to do. Once the basis is there, the computer can fill in the rest.

There is more, but we can deal with that later. This thing can do whatever we think it should, and it all happens to the guy in the suit.

The next thing is touch. Touch is not too difficult either, particularly the you- touch-other-things bit. You put on the gloves and they can stimulate your fingertips, or your palms or the backs of you hand, or the lot at once if you've got your hand inside something."

So we have our lady in your reality. She stands in front of you and you can walk up to her and touch her. They didn't bother with the effect of touching clothing so by the time you get to her she'll be naked. If you just stay where you are you can see her take her clothes off.

At the same time the smelly bit gets to work. There are

only a few basic smells but they make a good impression. There's the fine sunny morning smell for outside, a few perfumes for the lady of the event, oil and cordite for the battlefield and a sort of musky smell for when you're really getting it together.

Of course the really cunning bit is when she touches you. That's what the rest of the suit is for. When you're close you can feel her against you and you can feel her touching the bits she's touching."

"What's this?" I asked, pointing to a wide band covered with buttons on the left arm of the suit.

"That's the controls," said Boxer. "You can change the scene, change the woman and a few other things - of course it's really the same woman, the computer only adjusts the image. And there's the escape button. If you don't like it you can switch it all off. That's the red one on the end."

"But when you're in the suit you can't see outside it," I said.

"That's true, but the computer produces an image of the control panel on your arm, so most of the time you're going to be stark naked with this bracelet on."

"Stark naked?" I asked.

"Yeah." Well there are later models which let you get undressed, but it takes up a lot of memory so ours doesn't do that. You have to be naked to get into the suit and so we figured you might as well start off as you mean to go on.

Anyway, our problem is that there's something wrong with the suit, or maybe the computer, so someone needs to get in there and give us a blow by blow."

"I'll do it," said Nadia brightly.

We let Boxer disappoint her. "No, it's got to be one of the guys - you haven't got the right bits."

All eyes turned to me. I shrugged. "OK I don't mind, but I don't want anybody watching me."

Somebody sniggered.

"No, we won't watch," said Boxer, and I noticed that the others were nodding in agreement, possibly just a bit too enthusiastically. "The screens in the control room show what you're seeing, and give figures for the tactile qualities, but we'll switch the videos off."

I noticed that Easan was grinning.

"Why don't you do it?" I asked.

"Not me," he said. "I've got to do the things with the computer to put it all right. While you're telling us what's happening and we're looking at what you're looking at, I've got to check out the returns from the suit. So get to it man."

I shrugged and gestured to Nadia and Rollo to get out. Easan left with them but Boxer stayed.

I looked questioningly at him.

"You're going to need some-one to help you get into this."

I was not quite sure how much use he was going to be with one arm, but anyway I stripped off and began to pull on the suit. It was like trying to get into a body-length sock. Boxer held the back with his hand while I pulled the legs up to the crotch and went through the process of fitting my genitals into the spaces in the suit. Then he held out the arms one at a time and I slid into them, finally zipping it up the front.

"You OK?" he asked.

I nodded.

"Now it's going to be dark for a bit until I get to the control room and we switch the system on. What we need you to do is to run through the scenarios... you can do that just by pressing the SC button on your arm. Let it run for a bit. The SC is for Scene Change and when you like the scene you've got you can introduce the character, that's CI. Character Insertion. If you change CI then you change the person in there with you, but if there is only one character available in a particular scene then it will change the scene. You'll get the hang of it.

You can change the scene at any time even in the middle of..."

He caught me staring at him.

"...It."

"Yes," he replied. "But if you fancy changing the scene you should do it at about the time the female has got all her clothes off and is walking towards you. After that you might find yourself committed. If you know what I mean."

I was still staring at him.

"If you press the scene change button you'll find yourself at the same point in another environment, possibly with another partner. It's not a bad idea to avoid that.

We need to know that all the scenarios are there, and then there seems to be something wrong with the programme. I think it goes off just when the woman gets to you. Let us know what's going on... just speak into the suit and we can hear you. You can't hear us, but we'll just have to put up with that. OK?"

"Why don't you do it?" I asked.

"Hey," he said, "you can see I've only got one arm. You can't see what else I'm missing."

I wished I hadn't asked.

The headpiece of the suit hung down in front of me and he lifted it, offering it to me. I grabbed the sides with my gloved hands and pulled it down over my head. I was in total blackness.

Suddenly I could see a blue haze. I looked down and there was my left arm, naked but for the control system clasped over it like a gladiator's armband. Actually, although it was a left arm, it was not particularly mine, but with left arms it is a bit difficult to tell.

My other appendages were definitely not mine, and I realised that although no-one had remembered to mention it, one of the functions of the suit was to give the wearer the impression that he was very generously endowed. It hung there like part of the business end of a baseball bat. When I moved, it swayed slightly. In spite of myself I was impressed. Anything was possible in this world.

I pressed the scene change button and immediately I was on the edge of a battlefield. I was looking down from a dune on a phalanx of tanks moving forward and blasting heavy weapons emplacements in the distance. Numbers of minor armoured vehicles were lying on their sides in the sand, smoking gently.

I looked down at my wrist and pressed the character introduction button and immediately a woman was standing on the top of the dune in front of me. She was no more than ten metres away.

She was of middle height with fair hair gathered behind her head. Her eyelids were enhanced with kohl and her lashes were long and lustrous. Her eyes were wide and blue. Her nose was upturned and her lips full and red, though not with lipstick.

Almost at the same moment a man appeared, clad in desert fatigues. He was tall and weather-beaten with light stubble. He turned towards me and transfixed me with a dark stare, then turned his attention to the woman. He began to unbutton his shirt and she gazed at him, a look of terror on her face. I realised that I had something my right hand and looked down to find myself holding a weapon, not dissimilar to the gun that Boxer had shown us back in the pilot house.

This was a moment of choice. I could let it go, and watch the resulting horror, or I was in a position to do something about it. I realised that the choice depended on my sexual preference.

I looked down at my left wrist and pressed "HELP" with my forefinger.

Words slid across the bottom of my field of view.

"WEAPON. DESERT EAGLE CIRCA 1992. AUTOMATIC PISTOL. FIRES HIGH VELOCITY LARGE DIAMETER PROJECTILES. IF YOU WISH TO USE IT PULL BACK THE SLIDE ON THE TOP, POINT AND PULL THE TRIGGER."

I lifted the pistol into my field of view and pulled back the slide on the top with my left hand, arming the weapon. Both the man in front of me and I were transfixed by the heavy precise metallic sound of the arming. It sounded like the locking of a tug landing strut.

The man had his shirt unbuttoned to the waist, exposing a matt of unfashionable body hair. He reached down with his right hand in the direction of his hip, where I could see the handle of a similar weapon. I pointed the Desert Eagle towards his chest, squinting down the apex of the triangular barrel in an attempt at aiming. I pulled the trigger.

There was an ear shattering explosion and a large hole immediately opened up in the man's chest, and small pieces of skin and a film of blood sprayed the air in front of him. He fell to the ground, groaning faintly, and started bleeding into the sand. I saw that the projectile had made an even larger hole in his back than it had made in his chest. His breath rattled in his throat and he was silent. The pistol disappeared from my hand. We were moving onto the next phase.

The woman looked towards me with gratitude. She reached behind her head and took out a comb, throwing it to the ground, and without taking her eyes from me she shook her head. Her hair cascaded down behind her.

She reached under her chin and pulled down the zip of her desert fatigues. The front of the garment opened down to her crotch and she shrugged it from her shoulders and stepped out of it. Whatever footwear she had been wearing had disappeared and she was standing before me wearing only a pair of white briefs. She never took her eyes from my face, and in spite of myself I felt a gradual stiffening in my lower regions.

She looked down and her eyes widened. I looked down. I was not surprised that she was surprised. The thing between my legs was jutting forward, now a larger section of the business end of a baseball club, smooth apart from a pulsing vein down one side and slightly curved upwards, as if taking the shape in order to support its own weight.

As she began to walk towards me I remembered to press the button and suddenly my world changed. Now I was on what Boxer had described as a 'beach'. I was looking along a sandy white shore towards a cluster of pale rocks, which, on the shoreward side, reached for the sky and gradually tumbled until they jutted out of a pale blue sea. The sea and the sky were almost identical in colour and the horizon was broken by a distant white line of surf and a narrow strip of sand.

The beach to my left was shadowed by palm trees, one almost horizontal, with only its tousled head turned upwards towards the sun. The others were slightly higher, climbing up behind the rocks on an invisible hill, giving the impression of higher ground.

There were a few people on the beach and, just as Boxer had said, they were wearing the most minimal garments. Numbers of couples were closing in on one another. I could see what was coming and, not being turned on by the sight of other people humping, I pressed the scene change button without bothering to introduce the character.

I found myself standing at the edge of a pool of water. Or something more than a pool. It gave an impression of depth, and was surrounded by moss covered rocks overhung by boughs, thickly covered with large green leaves. The upper regions of the trees towered out of my sight into a thin mist, which nevertheless allowed shafts of sunlight to illuminate individual areas of the scene.

There was no real impression of space. It was a more enclosed setting, the grass and the trunks of the trees disappearing as if endlessly into an eternal wood. The rocks seemed to radiate warmth and the sun shone.

Quite close to me there were figures reclining, luxuriating in the solar radiation. There were young women, naked except for wisps of muslin, well rounded, with their hair tied back behind their heads. They looked about provocatively and I could hear the sounds of their laughter.

On one of the rocks was the strangest being I had ever seen. He was short and well muscled, with shoulder length curling hair and a beard. To the waist he was normal, but at his hips a gradually thickening growth of hair turned his lower limbs into the legs of an animal, and I was amazed to see that instead of feet he was equipped with hooves. He was also equipped with an enormous erection. I noticed that the tips of a pair of horns poked out from his hairline on either side of his forehead.

As if oblivious of his engorged phallus he was playing a perfect single-note melody on a reed pipe, which he held to his lips.

I felt something in my right hand, and looking down saw that I also was holding a slim reed pipe. I also was hairy from the waist down, and miraculously was standing solidly on a pair of perfect animal hooves, which were black and cloven and shone with an unholy gleam.

I raised my left arm and pressed the help button.

YOU ARE A SATYR, A MYTHOLOGICAL CREATURE, PART MAN AND PART GOAT. SOLE ACTIVITY, PLAYING THE REED PIPE AND HAVING ORGIES. IN HISTORY THE GOAT WAS KNOWN TO BE EXTREMELY SEXUALLY ACTIVE.

The words disappeared. One of the young women reached up and grasped the satyr's organ. Her wistful expression complemented her air of engaging innocence. Her fingers did not quite meet around it, so she sat forward and clasped it with both hands and began to massage it gently. The satyr did not miss a note of his playing.

I realised that it was time for me to press a button, either to invoke my own innocent maiden, or to move on. It was quite difficult to leave this peaceful scene of sexual innocence and my finger hovered over the character introduction button. What was I doing? I was actually getting involved in some form of mechanical masturbation. Somewhat angrily I jabbed the scene change button and was transported again.

I was in a room. It was only possible to tell that it was a room because it contained furniture. There were several other rooms adjoining it and I could see other furniture though the glass walls.

I turned around slowly. Just behind me was a bed. Well, that made a change. It was covered with a cushioned black bedspread.

Through the wall behind the bed I could see serrated rows of skyscrapers ranged away into the distance like endless white fingers pointing to the sky. I turned back and looked out of the window ahead of me. Here the glass ceased. This side of the room was completely open and I could make out a sea, which stretched away to a horizon made jagged by a line of mountain tops. Some of them were topped by snow.

For a change all was quiet, and I could see that nothing else was going to happen until I pressed the character introduction button. I knew roughly where I was in this scene. The period was almost within living memory. It must have been just before the population of earth began to slide into the sea. Having covered all the dry bits with buildings our forbears burrowed underground and set up colonies under the seas. Eventually they made it off the planet. More or less forced into space by the sheer pressure of bodies, and encouraged by the fact that finally there was just as much space in a living unit under the surface of Mars as there was in one on earth.

After I had pressed the character introduction button, a figure appeared on the balcony outside the apartment. She (I had come to assume that it would be a she) was extremely tall and at the moment of her appearance was facing away from me towards the sea. She turned around and I was shocked to see that she was entirely clad in a black latex skin. Even her head, except for two holes for her eyes. In her gloved right hand she held a short whip with a double thong reaching almost to the ground.

She walked inside the room and stood in front of me, swinging the whip from side to side so that the thongs slid round her feet and across her glossy calves. With her left hand she reached up to her shoulder and, grasping a small tab, pulled down across the line of her breasts. The skin slid aside and she stepped out of it. Beneath it she was wearing yet another. This second skin also covered most of her body, including her head, but this one exposed her nose and lips, her nipples and her pubic mound.

Her mouth, the only exposed bit of her likely to express emotion, opened slightly and her tongue flicked around her lips in anticipation.

I remembered that I did not need to participate in just any old perversion, and before she got too close I pressed the character introduction button again. Instantly the shiny black skin was replaced with a matt black one.

This skin belonged to a naked black woman. It could well have been the same one. Of course they were all the same one, only the computer made the difference. This black woman seemed more friendly, but remained dignified and upright in carriage, even though she was clad only in a single gold bangle which encircled her left ankle, catching the light as she moved.

Now I was beginning to get the hang of it and I pressed the scene change button to change the environment once more.

I had to be in the last of the programmed scenarios. I was standing by a stream, which tumbled over rocks and plunged, on the periphery on my vision, over a waterfall. I could hear the water splashing down as it hit the bottom. In the middle distance, over a meadow full of flowers, a line of pine trees cut across the scene.

The woman appeared, already completely naked. Well, what could she have worn in this environment? The computer had done a good job of her breasts. They curved outward in two planes so that the nipples were slightly upturned, pointing directly at my eyes. She turned to the side to give me a view of her flat stomach and... I pressed the button again and we were once more in the war zone. This could get boring.

I let the scene run until once more I had the Desert Eagle in my hand and did not wait long before dispatching the hairy aggressor. Once more he fell to the ground and his blood spattered body leaked red liquid into the sand. Once more the woman turned towards me and took a couple of steps, then looked down at my almost satyr like phallus.

She pulled the zip of her camouflage suit down again and stepped out of it. The white briefs made her possibly a little more sexy than her nakedness had done. Despite the fact that the scene and the events were now becoming familiar once more I felt the thing, as I now found myself thinking of it, stiffening and once more her eyes widened as she looked down. Then she looked straight at me and smiled. As she came closer the briefs disappeared - it was convenient that the more awkward moments of disrobing could be avoided.

She touched my arm and I was transfixed by her gaze. Then I felt her hand sliding down my chest and my stomach and then felt her fingers curl round it and her eyes widen even more then. I screamed. A white hot pain lanced through my genitals.

"She's pulled it off," I thought wildly. The pain continued and I screamed again. My eyes were watering and I pushed her back but she did not release her hold. I glimpsed the control panel on my left arm and desperately hit buttons. The beach and the apartment flashed rapidly before me. I found myself looking into a pair of dark eyes surrounded by black latex. The smile on the exposed part of her face seemed to indicate that she was enjoying the pain, which I was still feeling. I hit the button again and there she was again now gazing lovingly at me without the rubber cover, but the pain continued. I hit the button again and was horrified to find myself being hypnotized by the pale blue eyes of a young man. He was taller than I and blonde and as his face contorted with effort as even more terrible pains lanced through my nether regions, causing me to let out further screams of distress. By this time I was close to forgetting that I was suffering solely from the effects of a malignant suit, and its supporting software.

CHAPTER 15

General Recycling Instructions – All Installations

It should be remembered that it is impossible to sustain life in the off earth environment without an extensive level of recycling. Failure to recycle all solids and all liquids will eventually result in the loss of the food and liquid supply. It is accepted that a proportion of the nutrients consumed should be uncycled, and for this purpose a source of nutrients will have been identified by your employer, or management of the base facility where you are housed.

The nutrients will be added to the recycling plant on your vessel, or at your installation and as a result the system will provide you with a suitable reconstituted food. This will be offered in the form of a paste or, in the case of advanced systems, can be made to appear as traditional types of food with specific shapes, consistency and taste. Liquids will similarly be provided in dispensers. In most cases the types will be limited to water, and some traditional mild stimulants such as coffee and tea. Once more, more sophisticated recycling plants can be programmed to provide any sort of liquid, as long as a molecular structural pattern can be provided.

It is not within the scope of this instruction to offer technical information about the manner in which the process is carried out, or how to repair defective equipment. For this information you should consult the manufacturer's instructions or else initiate a contact with the makers or their technical support company. All you have to know as a user of the system, is what proportion of new nutrient to add, and when to carry out the task. In general it is necessary to keep a stock of new nutrient, in quantities that will depend on the number of people housed in the facility. The vessels and installations can range in capacity from *two persons to several hundred. However, where numbers are likely to exceed fifty, even on a temporary basis, a fully trained recycling specialist must be provided.*

It is one of those facts of life (and death) that the bodies of deceased space people will become part of the recycling process. However, human corpses can only be recycled at major stations, including Eugenia Base, the Io Foundry and its associated facility, or the Ganymede Correction Facility. There are also a number of habitations on Mars and the surrounding stations, and ship building installations, which can accept corpses.

The only thing which allowed me to keep my grip on sanity was the sight of the panel strapped to my left arm, and despite the pain, it became the sole focus of my attention as I desperately bashed at the buttons. Odd scenes flashed before my eyes, populated by shadowy figures, all of them close up and apparently enthusiastic about doing me harm. Then there was darkness and mercifully an end to the agony.

I reached up and pulled the headpiece off, and then the rest of the suit, checking to see if everything was still there. It still hurt, but not much compared with the agony inflicted by the woman, the suit. I glared at the door as it opened, and everyone filed in sniggering.

"You were watching weren't you?" I shouted. They were still laughing, although I could see that at least Nadia was attempting to keep a straight face.

"Well, what happened?" asked Boxer. "You forgot to talk to us. How did it go? What went wrong with the suit?"

"What went right with it would be more like," I muttered. I was still in so much pain that I was unconcerned at having an audience as I pulled on my clothing.

"So, what did go right with it?" said Boxer.

"The scene in the ancient wood. You know. The Satyr

202

one, where there are lots of guys with hairy legs and lots of young women with no clothes on. That seemed to be going OK. In fact I quite liked it. And I got the impression, since I was also a guy with hairy legs, that something nice would happen to me if I pressed the right button."

"And did you press the right button?" asked Boxer.

"No," I said. "I stuck to your advice, and if I felt that I might get involved, for the want of a better word, in the scenario, I pressed the button.

In fact," I said thoughtfully, "the scenario about the battlefield seemed to go pretty well also, until the last moment. But the one in the apartment went badly from the start. It featured a woman clad entirely in latex, including her head, and her next layer was pretty similar and only slightly more erotic.

I dread to think what would have happened if I'd let her get too close. She looked pretty threatening even when it was going as it should."

"How were the scenes?" asked Boxer.

"They were all fine. It was only the people who were iffy. The final bit, where the woman in the battlefield scene was approaching me, was when it went right off the rails."

"What did she do?" asked Boxer, now really interested.

I had difficultly describing it, particularly with the full team listening in, but eventually I managed.

"It's not supposed to be like that," said Boxer. "We're supposed to programme in the client's preferences before the start. There are plenty of alternatives. Somehow you got three of them, with a few variations. They obviously reckon that everyone likes to look when they set up the programme. And why not in this world?

Then masochistic. That's on the border really. If you've got the control panel sussed you can get close to the edge and still manage to keep on the right side. Let's face it, there's plenty of people who like to be tied up. There's quite a few who go for oxygen restriction. Someone modified one of these..."

He gestured in the direction of the suit.

"...To try to cover that, but after it throttled a couple of people they gave it up. Where was I? Oh yes. The homo scenario should definitely not have been there, but there was only one character and he appeared after the programme had begun to fail."

"I though you didn't cater for homosexuals." I said. "Why didn't you tell me about all that?"

"I don't know why that happened," said Boxer. "It must have been someone's personal preference."

"Anyway," said Easan, "I think we've got enough here to fix it. At the time when the woman got hold of you, we registered a pretty high level of impulse in the suit, much more than when she was just touching you. Obviously the programme is supposed to increase the pressure a bit but it seems to have overdone it. It would probably be OK for men with extremely small, er, genitalia."

"Well as far as I know mine's no bigger than average..." I tailed off, realising that it was pretty ludicrous talking about size, and looked at Nadia in the hope of rescue. She just gazed at me with an expression of mild surprise at the turn of the conversation. She obviously considered it inappropriate to make comparisons, particularly in company.

Boxer turned to Easan. "Well the important thing is, can you fix it?"

I answered for him. "Don't worry, Easan can fix anything."

Easan looked pleased and retreated to the Simroom control area, and as we passed the door was happily punching keys and peering into the several screens used to monitor the installation. As we left he shouted after me, "Sully, I'm going to want you back for testing."

"Don't worry," said Boxer. "You'll like it once it's fixed. I never met anyone who didn't."

We returned to the pilot house, which had become our unofficial relaxation area, and collapsed into the control couches to await the results.

"So, what else have you got hidden away Boxer?" asked Nadia.

"It's a big ship," he replied. "I used to have people looking after different bits. I never got to know what was in some of them. I mean, you've got all sorts of services here. The basic necessity is good accommodation, good food, plenty of water and good service. Even sex maniacs expect to have their creature comforts. Then we offered maintenance and cleaning of the guest's ships. That took quite a big team, and of course we had to keep this lot going, and we had to be prepared to do it all ourselves. We couldn't use the ordinary contract services. We weren't supposed to exist."

"Yes, but you must know what you've got here."

Boxer was indignant. "Well, not everything. To tell the truth I was always more interested in looking after the girls. I mean, they're real people. A few left with the deserters." He spat the words out. "But some wanted to stay with me, some were asleep and no-one bothered to wake them up, and some got locked in by others who didn't like them. That's how we come to have so many left."

"Why didn't they look after you, then?" I asked.

Boxer was momentarily pensive, as he tried to grasp yet further reversals in what had been, to start with, a well organised and well planned adventure.

"True. Just after the lifeboats went we were mostly in the same place, collected in the recreation areas. But for some reason most of the caterers who had not left in the lifeboats disappeared. I say disappeared: they must have gone somewhere on the ship, but there were not enough of us to go and find them. So to start with we hung around, but then we started to get hungry and it seems that we all had different ideas about where we might find food. Then the power failed, and it was every man, and every woman for themselves. I was lucky enough to find my way to the pilot house, but there could be some who didn't make it."

"Well, I think it's about time we had a good look round," said Nadia. Indeed, it was only the sheer size of the ship that had prevented us from searching for survivors before.

"It'll take ages," said Boxer. "There are literally miles of corridors. I don't think anyone's ever done a full inventory. When we built it we really had ideas above our station. We meant it to be the biggest, most luxurious, most spacious cruise ship that had ever been constructed. We were going to do more business that any ship ever. What we lost sight of was the limits to how much space any single person can manage. In the beginning a few subcultures developed in the more distant areas. A few workers went off on their own, and set up their own organisations, and then did their own thing.

Then the punters started to go there from the organised areas, and before we knew it we had a whole red light district within a red light district. When we began to see that the numbers in our own reception and pleasure areas were becoming significantly less than the numbers we had registered as having come on board, we had to take action. Of course we waited until we thought that the rival organisations might be in operation and then we made up a small team of my biggest flight crew, hospitality guys and the security contingent. We got in the lifts and went down with our maps. Down on the bottom deck there are the smallest living spaces used by all the least important people, therefore the people with the most to gain from setting up something of their own. Down there amongst the store rooms and the tiny recreation areas it was a different world. When we got out of the lift we heard the distant sound of trance music, and so we drew our stun guns and crept along until we were in the corridor next to the place where the noise was coming from.

We collected ourselves and, on my command, burst

through the door. What a sight greeted our eyes! Dancing ecstatically to the music was a bunch of balding middle aged guys, usual clientele in fact. Dancing with them in what must have been, up to our moment of entry, an extremely erotic manner, were half a dozen nubile young women clad solely in thongs. They all stood there looking at us in surprise, glistening with sweat. Chests heaving. This was most unattractive in the bald headed men but very fetching in the young women. It was almost dark and we had to strain our eyes to see exactly what was going on. The disco lights kept flashing and the music kept playing, until a man in standard catering gear eased his way to the back of the room and switched it off. The navigator reached behind him and switched the main lights on. Everyone in the room, even us, shaded their eyes. When I looked at the girls closely I realised that rather than being part of our upper deck contingent, what's the name for a collective of whores - a gaggle - they were actually members of the catering staff.

The catering manager stepped forward and started taking names. The navigator casually stood in front of the door, which prevented the men, our clients, from getting out. I needed to have a word with them, and when it was all over we had scared the shit out of a group of well heeled visitors, who had not thought of the possibility that they would be vulnerable to blackmail once out of range of my protection. I took a benevolent approach, and I could see that some of them had things to offer. The girls mostly gained promotion to our upper deck services. They joined the gaggle. The catering guy who had been running the lights and the music was added to our team of backroom people. We hadn't really thought about music, or dancing. But they were old fashioned pleasures which had been banned by the mopo, so it was logical that we should provide them in addition to the more serious ones.

Of course, that was only one area. We didn't search everywhere at the time, and now we really don't have the means of doing it. There must be store rooms full of all sorts of provisions that would support a small army for years. There are probably places where the ventilation system has broken down and suffer from oxygen deficiency. If you go into them you might die. I would suggest that if we are going to explore, we should all be wearing oxygen meters. It's only too easy to get into a space and be overcome. You can't breathe, so you try to take a bigger breath, but taking the second breath is the last thing you do. What you should really be doing is holding your breath, and getting out of there. When you take the second breath the resulting oxygen starvation just knocks you down. You fall to the floor, and the next person down the corridor sees you. They rush in to help without thinking about it and suffer the same fate immediately. It's only the third person who realises what could be wrong and holds back until they have breathing apparatus available to them."

This safety lecture from Boxer was a little unexpected, but nevertheless he was making some points which were well taken. We were unused to spaces which were so big that bits of them could be unfriendly. We went back to discussing how we could look around the ship.

"Hey ho," said Nadia, "I'd like to see what else we've got here. How about the computer, since it's working now? Perhaps we could look through all the cameras? That would tell us. What about it Boxer?"

"The first thing that the rebels did was disable the cameras in what they thought might be the most interesting areas, but there are hundreds of them, so they couldn't have got them all. Some are fitted with floodlights where there's not much in the way of normal lighting, so we could give it a go."

Boxer pulled back the seat at the console and sat down. He was a bit of a whiz with the computer, even with one hand.

"Let's start down on the bottom deck. The most distant point from any authority. We'll need to know where the cameras are, so we'll put a plan up on that screen." His fingers flew over the keyboard, and he nodded his head towards a large screen to his right.

We were presented with a set of menus. The menus identified sixteen decks and eighteen divisions forward to aft. All big ships were divided vertically so that in the event of a major failure, the spaces could be isolated to preserve the atmosphere and the pressure in the rest.

"At a guess," said Boxer, "the renegades must have chosen somewhere as far away from here as possible. When we were fixing the unauthorised entertainment we only visited one section. It was just our luck that we found them at our first attempt. So there are another seventeen we didn't visit. They mostly contain service areas, but we could take a look anyway.

I'll select the bottom deck in division fifteen. Of course we can't get it all on the screen and still see the location of the cameras. I'll zoom in a bit. There's a big space at the right of the screen there. That's the recycling plant. It's pretty important, but self supporting. We could have a look and see if anyone went down there."

He clicked on the camera that was shown on the plan and one of the monitors changed colour from being a dull grey into an inky black.

"Yes, that means the camera is on, but the lights are out. So now all we have to do is put its floodlight on. Just a minute."

The space was illuminated by a bright light, letting us see every detail within range of the camera. The recycling machinery created areas of light and shade. The stainless steel glowed as the light washed over it, turning the space into a functional art installation.

We studied the screen. "There's nothing to see there. If everywhere's like this we're in for a pretty boring time," said Nadia. "What are we actually looking for anyway?"

"You're in charge. You asked to have a look. It's not my fault if it's boring, and anyway this is the first space we've looked in. There are hundreds more and anyway, and anyway! What the hell is that?"

Boxer grasped the joystick controlling the camera and zoomed in on a shadow, which was just a bit darker than those surrounding it. The camera automatically focused and over a period of a few seconds the shadow revealed itself to be someone lying prone on the checker plate.

"Oh dear, he doesn't look well. Or it could be a she. I'll zoom in on the head."

The camera tightened up on the upper part of the body and moved upwards, eventually reaching the face.

"It's a girl, well, a woman. I'd be pretty surprised if she's still alive," said Boxer.

The skin of the woman's face was drawn tightly over her cheekbones and her eyes were closed. She could not be seen to be breathing, although she might have been.

"Should we be going down there to see if we can rescue her?" I asked.

"If you're thinking of going, don't forget to take the breathing apparatus. I'll get you a print of the plans with the space marked on it. If you don't have that, you've no way of finding it."

"You're not coming then?"

Boxer shook his head. "You're getting a bit too confident. You think because we've got this far the rest'll be easy, but it won't. There's still lots to do, and once I turn the light out you could forget that the body is there at all. Remember, we can't afford to lose anyone else, including you. And who's going to go with you?"

Nadia put up her hand.

We were beginning to collect the support gear from the lockers in the pilot house when there was message from Easan. He wanted me back in the Simroom to test the suit.

Boxer grunted. "That didn't take long to fix, did it? So now I suppose I've got to go and have a look at this body in division fifteen. I just hope the lifts are working. I'll get the emergency breathing sets, then." He looked in my direction. "We'll see you back here in a couple of hours."

Back in the Simroom Easan and I tested the suit. I put it on again and experienced the strange loss of my senses until the headpiece started showing me the scenes. Since the problem had occurred in the battle scenario, I decided that I would start, and probably finish, there. I had no idea how far it had to go for the satisfactory completion of the test, but there was a possibility that we might have to wait for a while before I could have a go at a second scenario.

I pressed the scene change button until the battle scene appeared in front of me. As before the very unpleasant soldier made threatening advances towards the very attractive young lady. I levelled the Desert Eagle at him, sighting carefully at his chest and pulled the trigger. Again he fell to the ground, bleeding profusely.

Once more the young lady freed her long hair from its comb and shrugged out of the body suit. I was unable to stop myself tensing as she approached. The possibility of impending agony may have stopped things taking their natural course. She looked down, disappointedly. I looked down and could see why she thought I had a problem. I did have a problem. She came closer. I might have moved away, except that's the one thing you can't do if the complete experience is taking place in a suit which you are wearing.

She came close to me until her breasts were almost touching my chest. There was no pain, but then she was not doing anything yet.

"Don't worry honey," she said. "I think I can fix that." I felt her running her hands down my chest, and then down my stomach until they reached the offending organ. She gripped it gently, or at least she seemed to. By now I was having a job to remember that I was encased in a suit. The offending organ was responding to her touch, and there was no pain.

Now, reluctantly, I pressed the character introduction button, which removed the young woman, with her nubile breasts and her beguiling touch. Was this being faithful to Nadia, I wondered? Having sex, or nearly having sex with an avatar? I felt that I would have to restrain myself, if it was possible to do so, and still to do the test, until I had asked her what she thought about it. It was not fair really that males had all these facilities and women had nothing. Nothing I knew about anyway. I had once been on a virtual tour of the old earth city of Pompeii, buried under volcanic ash at the dawn of civilisation. Amongst the many facilities catering for male sexual requirements there was one for women, a marble statue of a youth with a healthy erection. Although the commentary said nothing I assumed that the ancient Romans were more broad-minded than the present day space community.

Since I had yet to get Nadia's approval I pressed the scene change button and found myself in the glass-sided apartment. Again the scenery was wonderful. Waves lapped on the distant shoreline. Mist shrouded the mountain tops on the horizon, and on the balcony of the apartment was a naked woman with her back towards me. This was an improvement. She was black, and as she turned towards me I seemed to be able to detect a similarity in her movements and her muscle tone to the battle girl. Or maybe it was just because I knew that all the characters were based on the same woman.

She came in off the balcony and glided up to me. Her eyes locked on mine and I felt her hands move downwards until they reached their intended destination. There was no pain. As she sank to her knees I reluctantly pressed the escape button, and there I was in the dark. I felt deprived of something important as I waited for Easan to come and release me from the helmet.

Once in the light I hardly needed to confirm that everything was running properly, and the last thing we would have to worry about was some client having his dick ripped off.

He helped me out of the suit and shook me by the hand with enthusiasm. It was only when he fixed something that he became really happy. It must have been the solving of the puzzle that satisfied him.

I told him about the body, and so we both got into the lift and set course for the pilot house.

When we got there Boxer and Nadia had already arrived. Since they did not have anyone else with them I assumed that the person we had found was dead.

"There was no air in the space," said Nadia. "She must have gone in there for something and just flaked out. She seemed to be uninjured, but there was nothing for it but to recycle her. She'd been dead for a while so we didn't have a problem jointing her." Boxer had taken a cutting tool, which must have been like the one that took his arm off, because he was nodding in agreement.

I was reluctant to think too deeply about the recycling business, but there it was. Any form of organic matter could be recycled into any sort of food. We were cannibals, but out in space, what else were we going to be? We could not waste anything, or we would jeopardise our survival.

I told them about the suit, and so having disposed of the immediate problems we persuaded Boxer to resume his seat at the computer, to continue our virtual exploration of the ship.

Almost immediately he discovered an area where the cameras were disabled. If anything this increased his interest and he switched from the plan showing the camera locations to an isometric. We were in a virtual Evangelina.

He pressed the key and there was a corridor. It was brightly lit and clean and had numerous doors on either side. Of course it was only a plan. Who knew what the real thing looked like now? Up in the right hand corner of the screen was a map showing the deck with a small flashing arrow giving the theoretical position of the viewer.

"Try going aft," said Nadia. "I can see a big space down there, it must be something."

"Probably the garbage disposal" replied Boxer.

We made our theoretical progress down the corridor. There was little change in the scene. Boxer turned left and went through a door. It was a storeroom entirely surrounded by shelves, and otherwise completely empty.

"Not much there," grunted Boxer.

"Go on, keep going to the end," I urged. I think we all felt that there must be something worthwhile in the big space at the end.

Eventually we got there.

Boxer eased his way through the theoretical door and there it was. We were mildly stunned.

"Wow," said Nadia, "we have to go and look at that."

CHAPTER 16

Keeping Pigs – An Idiot's Guide

So you fancy keeping some pigs. It seems easy, but there are some things you should know. Firstly, you have to source your piglets: not the easiest thing these days, but persevere. Ask people you know if they know anyone who keeps them. Listen for the grunts. Search out the hidden pigsties. Pigs are not cheap, so in most environments thieves may steal your beloved porkers. On the other hand there are many advantages. Pigs are worth the effort.

Do not overfeed them. It is not a good idea to use human food waste. Historically there was once a time when pigs were fed totally on human food waste. It was called pigswill, but it was found that sometimes human and other animal diseases, which are not eradicated by cooking, can be passed from one animal type to another in food. It is possible that your pig vendor will not have kept to this rule, so ask what the feeding process has been before buying piglets.

Decide what you want to do with pigs. Do you want to breed them and then sell the piglets? If so you will need some gilts and some boars. But do not be too heavy on the boars. Some breeds can be aggressive. On the other hand you might just want to get hold of some piglets and then raise them to an age when you can kill them and eat them. In this case some-one else will have bred them and raised them for the first few weeks. You then buy weaners, and carry on.

You will need a pig environment, which is not too difficult if you are on earth with some outside space available, but will take some preparation if you do not have such an environment available. In either case you will need earth, or something like it. There are a number of ways in which you can *simulate earth, mostly by using rotted vegetable products mixed with plant nutrients, and hydroponic production residues. The number of pigs you can keep depends on the space available, each pig will require three square metres for humane husbandry. Even in covered areas, pigs like to have their own small house in which to lie down and sleep. In addition the earth, or what passes for it, should be damped down occasionally.   When it comes to disposing of the pigs - and here we assume that in one way or another you intend to eat them - you should find some-one skilled in killing the animals and butchering them into the appropriate cuts, which can include bacon pork and ham.*

Some religions ban the eating of pork, although the banning of meat-eating of any sort has tended to have fallen into disuse, due to the general unavailability of the product.

Lastly, be aware that pigs can harbour a variety of unpleasant parasites, which can be transferred to humans unless the animals are treated with suitable vetinary products. This will be only necessary if you keep them for more than six months.

I sat in the pilot's seat of the Evangelina for another uncounted hour in another uncounted work period.

Nadia Abdull sat beside me in the co-pilot's seat. She was talking on the intercom to Rollo who was down in the engine room. Collectively, they were trying to make things go. It was the same routine every day. Rollo and Easan worked their way through the systems, checking each one and then testing the interlocks with the pilot house. And every time, it was necessary for one of us to grab the stick and move it, or press a button or flick a switch, or sometimes in desperation talk into a microphone. The last was only if absolutely nothing else would work.

If there is anything pilots hate it's voice recognition systems. They seem like a good idea: no hands, no buttons. But sometimes the systems have trouble understanding the simplest commands. I have known pilots shout the word "stop" at a ship so loud that they have cracked glass, but the system, failing to understand the urgency of the request, has found it necessary to clarify the instruction. Once the ship is buried past the nose ring in planetary dust, clarification becomes unnecessary.

And of course, nothing stops a voice recognition system eavesdropping on perfectly innocent conversations. If you have one switched, on you are asking for trouble.

Often there was nothing wrong with the Evangelina's systems, but there was frequently something wrong with the controls. After a few days of the same thing Rollo and Easan had done a check on the routing of the controls from the engine room up to the pilot house and found that they passed through the hydroponic garden. The very place that had gained our interest on the computer screen.

With a certain lack of enthusiasm, despite the pretty picture we had seen on the virtual map, we mounted an expedition. Down in the lift, then along the passageway until we reached the door. Boxer took the lead. I had to hand it to him once more. He was a pretty courageous guy for a short-arse with one arm.

It was obvious from our approach that we expected to find people in there. No-one said anything. There was no reason for us to find anybody anywhere, but we all picked up metal bars as we passed through the main store room. I recognised them as pry bars for moving large items of engine spares. They were slim tubes drilled with small holes for lightening them, but I knew from experience that no human hand could break them. The bars were well balanced. We swung them laconically but they gave us little comfort.

At the door Boxer pressed a button. It opened. We walked over the threshold. It still looked like a hydroponic garden, but a bit overgrown. Vines and tendrils almost visibly crept across the entrance. There was a familiar whirring and a

217

gardening robot hove into view and started watering a few plants.

We moved into the space and stood there watching it. After a moment it seemed to sense that we were there and turned towards us.

"Are there people here?" asked Boxer.

The robot remained facing in our direction, if facing is what gardening robots do, but it remained silent.

"Hell," said Boxer, "it's a mute. Some of them were just not worth fitting with voice synthesisers, particularly the ones in here. No-one ever comes in here."

However, at his words the robot began to move away through a small space between the vines, and we followed it into what could only be described as a jungle.

"Our control cabling is going to be along the aft bulkhead," said Easan. "So we have to go right through to the back."

"Come on then," said Boxer.

The five of us stumbled through the undergrowth, brushing against the thickening mass of green tendrils, sweating in the increasing heat. Somewhere overhead banks of white lights bathed us in a pitiless glare. Around us moisture atomisers sprayed droplets of water into the air. We wiped our brows and pitched onwards.

"How do we know we're going in the right direction?" asked Nadia.

"Don't worry, just follow me," I replied. I was following the lines in the floor, and I had no reason to think they ran in any direction other than front to back.

Then suddenly we were in a clearing. Less of a clearing, but more of a space made in the vines and tendrils, and there in the space, amazingly, was a small metal house, apparently constructed from sections of ventilation duct.

"What's all this then?" rumbled Boxer, putting on his tough man voice and fooling none of us.

I approached gingerly and lifted the sacking curtain from the door aperture with my length of bar.

There was a muffled sob from inside.

"Hey, what's all this then?" said Boxer again, bending and looking under the sacking. "Come on out and let's have a look at you."

We stood around looking threatening, while two small children crawled out. They were clad in rags and sat looking up at us, wide eyed and frightened.

Suddenly, the vines behind my left shoulder burst apart and I caught sight of a figure diving towards me. Before I could turn I was cannoned to the ground, an elbow stuck in my windpipe and a bony knee in my right kidney. I gasped, but before I could make any move to retaliate there was a dull thud and the grip relaxed.

"Come on," said Nadia, "get up before she comes round."

I got to my feet, and shook myself. Nadia was standing over the prone body of a young woman, dressed in even less than the children. She lay with her eyes closed, a trickle of blood turning into a little puddle behind her right ear.

Nadia swung her iron bar lightly. She was not a lady to tangle with.

"Thanks," I said.

"Just protecting my relief," she replied. We both recognised that it would be weeks before the ship's systems could be relied on to do their thing without supervision.

Like the soft old guy we were getting to know, Boxer got down on his knees and started mopping the young woman's brow, and making clucking noises to the infants. They looked up at him amazed. They appeared to be twins. No-one ever had twins. Only a limited number of people were allowed to have even one child. The available space in the solar system was less than the space required by the existing population. What this woman was doing with children I could not imagine.

"I wondered what had happened to this little team," said Boxer

"What's this, another scam?" I said.

"Well no," responded Boxer, "I'd hardly describe it like that. Sometimes there are couples who really want children. Sometimes they are even allowed to. You know. They have waited their turn, and the female has been back and been desterilised, or apparently desterilised and then they try to have children. Well, there are a few problems with the whole business. One is that by the time you get permission it is often too late, or almost too late.

So what do you do? It's been hundreds of years since anyone last really put any thought into assisting partners to have children. Let's face it; it's the last thing the authorities want. As far as they're concerned, the fewer couples who have children the better. So sometimes there are people with money, with position, who have permission to have a child, and sometimes they can't manage on their own, so we help. What's wrong with that?"

He was right. There was little wrong with assisting people to have children when they have permission to do so. But this was not quite as simple. This girl was a surrogate mother. She had been paid to carry a child on behalf of a couple. We did not know the means of impregnation, but that hardly mattered. The whole business had been illegal for years. It was more or less the first thing that the nations on earth had done to limit population increase.

Before we could offer any reasons as to what could be wrong with the situation, there was a groan and the young woman opened her eyes. Boxer made soothing noises and gently held her down to stop her attacking anybody.

"Now now, Lydia," he soothed. "Take it easy."

She started upwards and snarled at me. Nadia stepped forward with her bar and swung it threateningly.

"OK OK," said Boxer. "*Take it easy.*"

Everybody, including Lydia, took it easy, and we all

gradually achieved the same level. Lydia sitting, Boxer kneeling and us squatting down on our haunches.

"So, how the hell did you get here?" said Boxer.

Lydia took a deep breath.

"You know how I got here," she said. "You know what happened to me. You know that you hired me and sent me down to one of those rooms, and sent some old guy down who was to be the father of my child. And you saw to it that I got myself desterilised. By that pretty doubtful doc you kept on this ship.

Well, when all the power failed I escaped. I didn't do it all by myself. Gary helped me."

"Gary?" questioned Boxer.

"Yes, Gary. He was one of the ones who'd turned into a green."

"What's all this about greens? Is there something here we should know about?" said Nadia.

It was evident from Boxer's expression that things were beginning to fall into place. "I suppose that the greens came here when we all got hungry. It would be an obvious place to look for food. Probably that's why they call them greens - people who live in the hydroponic garden."

"Yes," said Nadia "I'd worked that bit out. So how many are there?" The last question was addressed to Lydia who was beginning to look a bit more alert.

"Well, I suppose about twenty. The settlement's a bit further in. We weren't allowed to be in the settlement."

"Why did they make you build your little house here?" I asked, but my voice trailed away as I realised what the answer was, and got to my feet. The others got up with me and we stood looking out at the impenetrable vegetation. Lydia and her little brood were decoys. Anyone who came in here would come to her first and would go through exactly what we just had. Doubtless she received food in return for being the alarm system.

"OK," I said. "You might as well come out. We're not

going to hurt anybody." The last statement belied the fact that we were still carrying the pry bars,, but nevertheless, it might have helped. There was a rustling in the bushes and half a dozen hobos edged their way out into the clearing.

There were two men and three women. They all looked as if they had been living in the jungle for a long time. The men were bearded, and their hair was long and unkempt. The women were equally unkempt. Their clothing was made from the remains of body suits, bits of pressure suits and parts of protective clothing. One of the men wore the shoulder pads from a cryogenic welding kit. He looked like a gladiator.

I noticed that they were all looking at Boxer.

One of them spoke. "We're going to have him," he said.

He nodded at Boxer.

In response Boxer drew himself up to his full height, just above my shoulder.

"What have I done?" he asked, a genuine picture of innocence. " I don't recognise any of you except for Lydia. What did you do here anyway?"

"I worked as a chef," said the spokesman. "But we never got enough to eat. There we were, making fantastic food for bloody plutocrats and we got starvation rations."

"Ah yes," said Boxer. "Now I can see you clearly, I think it was me who hired you. So what's your problem?"

"In the end we had little choice really. We either starved or we left, and your manager made sure we had no chance of stealing anything. It was cruel."

"I'm sorry, I didn't know," said Boxer simply. "I never said that anybody should be kept on short rations. It was one of the things I never saw any point in trying to regulate. I didn't see how I could possibly regulate how much people ate."

"Of course you knew," said the chef. "Someone programmed those cleaning robots to keep an eye on us. I tell you, if one of us tried to put anything into our mouths a cleaning robot would slice a finger off sometime. We never knew when it was going to happen. You could be working away - and you know there were a few cleaning robots down in the galley - you could be working away and quite suddenly *whack*, and you'd look up to see a cleaning robot retracting a ceramic blade and you had a couple of fingers not attached."

The chef held up his right hand and I was shocked to see that the majority of his index finger was missing.

"It looks like someone knew how to fix those robots. I thought I'd sorted it but someone must have passed on the technology."

"What do you mean?" asked the chef.

"How do you think I got this?" said Boxer. And he recounted in some detail the loss of his arm. If I hadn't heard it already I would have become a bit queasy. As it was I was already queasy at the sight of the missing finger. I decided to make a point of keeping a lookout for cleaning robots. There must still be some about, programmed to cut bits off people.

The chef was a little mollified by the story. I suppose if you've lost a finger it must seem pretty bad until you meet someone who has lost an arm. He looked sideways at the other four. There was no doubt that he was the leader and I could see it in the eyes of his friends that whatever he said, they would go with him.

"Come on," said Boxer. "If there's anything we need here it's a good catering department. We're going to start off anew. Now there's only me in charge, and these guys." He waved his arm in our direction. "They're going to drive the ship."

The chef stepped forward and took Boxer's hand, crushing it in a vice like grip. "OK," he said, "we'll go for it, but two things. If you double-cross us there's nothing else for us to worry about. You'll be dead, and probably you lot as well." The chef nodded in our direction.

We tried to look as if none of it had anything to do with

us. I wondered what sort of weapons they had to hand.

"And the second thing," he continued meaningfully, "is get rid of those robots."

This seemed like a logical step. After all, any of us might happen to pass a cleaning robot while nibbling at a snack from the Evangelina's newly discovered storage system. Who had the faintest idea what triggered the bloodthirsty mechanoids? Easan nodded, and I knew it would be dealt with at some time, though I might have to remind him a couple of times, particularly since he had the rest of the ship to fix.

"Perhaps you could take us to the forward bulkhead?" suggested Easan.

The chef, Gary, turned on his heel and led the way forward. We followed, brushing aside tendrils and vines until we came to an ordered open space. Before us were groups of hydroponic tanks, each containing lines of plants. On one side of the tanks was a cluster of shelters. Gary clapped his hands and more people emerged from the shelters. A pungent odour was evident.

"This smells like shit," said Nadia.

"Yes, we use animal excrement to fertilise the plants. They grow better."

"I'm glad you kept the pigs alive," said Boxer.

"No thanks to you," was the reply. "What would have happened to them if we weren't here to look after them?"

Of course, they might not have died. This ship was so large that there were tiny pockets of civilisation developing all on their own. Perhaps the pigs would have broken out of their pens, and reproduced with such alarming frequency that they would have populated the ship.

"Where are they?" asked Boxer.

Gary beckoned us to follow and we did so obediently. We took a right turn away from the shelters and broke through the vines and tendrils into a large open area. It contained multiple pig pens, absolutely full of clean pink snorting porkers. When they saw us they bustled up to the fence closest to us. Of course, we had never seen live pigs. We had never seen any living animals. Back on earth there were said to be places where many species were kept alive, otherwise they would become extinct. But for us, brought up in the wasteland that is the solar system, being close to live animals was a new experience.

Gary reached over the fence and stroked one or two of them on the tops of their heads. They seemed to love it, and all but one or two were vying for his attention. The ones that were hanging back were marked with a blue paint splodge.

"So, what's the problem with them?" I asked.

"They're next for the chop," replied Gary. "It's a strange thing, but they seem to know. Pigs have always been considered to be intelligent, but over the years they appear to have been making progress. If we follow the Darwinian theory it's possible that the smartest pigs have found ways of living longer and having more offspring that the dullards. Even if they are eventually terminated, the longer they live, the more intelligent pigs they will produce. But it doesn't make any difference, we get them all in the end."

"What? You're going to kill them?" said Nadia.

Gary nodded. There was obviously no point in keeping domestic animals just for fun. Even on the Evangelina where there was lots of space, it was still necessary to make the best use of it.

"One pig produces several different cuts of meat. Some religions used to ban the eating of pig meat, for some reason, but now it hardly matters. No-one eats meat anyway unless they are in places like this. Here you can enjoy pork, ham and bacon. There is nothing in the world like a bacon sandwich made with home-baked bread. I like to cook the bacon in its own fat and then mop up the fat with the slices of bread before putting the bacon in the middle."

We had only just found out what sandwiches were, and

so we were only too keen to try anything new. I felt sorry for the pigs, but sacrifices sometimes have to be made, and we could comfort ourselves with the thought that they would have had a pretty good life.

As we turned away from the pens we were confronted by a group of about fifteen men and women clad similarly to Gary and his group, in cast off space-ware of one sort or another.

They were led by a tall overweight man with a shaven head and a threatening attitude. He spoke.

"What's this we hear about the ship going back to work?" His question was addressed to Gary.

"That's right, Stadler," replied Gary. "And we're going to go back to doing the cooking."

"You speak for yourself," said Stadler. "What makes you think that we all want to go back to work? We like the ship as it is. We've got food and space and warmth. What else could we want?"

"You know as well as I do that this situation can't go on as it is for ever," replied Gary. "We're providing light and heat using an emergency generator hooked up to the system. Eventually it'll run out of fuel. Then we die."

"Who are this lot?" asked Stadler.

"I'm Boxer," said Boxer. "It's my ship."

Stadler looked towards Boxer; his eyes narrowed and we all took a firmer grip on our pry bars. But then he seemed to lose interest in our leader, and his eyes wandered over the group, finally settling on Gary again.

"We think you should put it to the vote. If we don't want to go to work then we won't. That's all there is to it. And there's not a damn thing you can do about it."

Behind Stadler the rest of the group looked aggressively in our direction. I looked round. We were a pretty uninspiring team. Three guys, one with only one arm, two women and Lydia and two children, none of us exactly in the prime of physical

226

fitness or trained in any form of combat. It was beginning to look as if our plan was failing.

Nadia spoke. "I don't know whether you expect us just to throw in our lot with you and get this thing fixed, and then to keep it going, and end up as the only people working while you lot just take it easy and take advantage of our graft. Well, think again. If we're not going to get this ship working again, doing the job it's supposed to do and incidentally keeping us all safe and comfortable, we'll just get back into our tugs and hit it for the horizon. We are in a situation where we all have to stick together and get on with it. Boxer is going to make sure that there is an end to the maniac mechanoids, and we think he'll do a good job and look after us. He knows how to manage a ship of this size. We know how to drive it and maintain it, and you lot know how to provide the services. So it's all or nothing. You've been lucky so far. These systems have kept going without anyone looking after them. But what's going to happen if they go wrong?"

"We're still going to have a vote," said Stadler.

"What's the point of that?" asked Boxer. "Today we could vote to carry on and make the ship work, and then we'll come across another group and have to have another vote. The only way we can carry on is if we all start work again and just get on with it. I think you should rely on me to look after you. Believe me, I want it to work and I want the workforce to be happy in what they do, and comfortable in their living environment. What point is there otherwise?"

"What point is there in letting you be in charge? There's nothing better than being here. We all know that. So why don't we leave things as they are? We're alive, and we have the means of survival. Working is not going to make any difference."

It seemed that Stadler was not going to let it go.

"Haven't you heard?" asked Nadia. "There are going to be passenger flights back to earth soon. And the only way to get on them is to have some form of credit. You can get that credit here. We can all get it. In the end we can be on our way back to the home planet. There is no other chance of doing that, and the alternative is to die out here without ever having seen it."

This suggestion caused a hum of interest amongst the group behind Stadler, as well as a hum of interest amongst us. It was a worthwhile suggestion, and was something we had heard of as a possibility. As a result of the somewhat unexpected fall in population, the earth needed people back, but no-one was going to take us there for nothing.

"Everyone who wants to go back to work, step over to this side," said Boxer.

Everyone except for Stadler shuffled over, until he was standing by himself glowering us.

"You wanted a vote. Now you've had one," said Boxer, "so you might as well get over here and get on with it. What did you do anyway?"

"He was a pastry chef," said Gary.

"Aha, a baker, that's great. You could get us some fresh bread baked for tomorrow morning. Then we can have bacon sandwiches," declared Boxer.

Stadler glared at him, shrugged and turned away.

"Don't worry," said Gary "The rest of us'll make sure he gets on with it."

The group gradually dispersed leaving us, and Gary and Lydia and her children.

"On we go then," said Boxer.

And without further discussion we shuffled our way towards the forward bulkhead, still, I noticed, following the lines on the deck of the hydroponic space.

Eventually we came up against a bulkhead, and with some difficulty, due to the density of the vegetation, found the damaged control cables. They ran vertically down the space in cable trays. There were hundreds of wires descending from above us and disappearing through the deck into the space below.

"Here they are," said Gary unnecessarily.

Easan stood in front of the cables and gave them a hard look. When that had no result he began to examine them more closely.

"Look at this," he said, pointing at the base of the cables, at the point where they disappeared into the deck. We all looked closely, and sure enough I could see that they seemed to have been nibbled by something.

"There are rats in here," said Gary.

We had only heard of rats. They were unpleasant rodents, which lived on all the detritus created by humans, but I had no idea that they existed anywhere but on earth.

"Don't forget, this ship is really a small world," said Boxer. "We should have prevented them boarding from the yard, but we were never that efficient, and obviously they were there because at some time ships from earth had docked there. Rats are resourceful and resilient and they're not picky about what they eat."

"Obviously not," said Easan, pointing to the nibbled cables. "But at least we don't have to look far to solve the problem."

Once the control cabling was fixed we were able to get on with the job, and finally there we were, Nadia and I in the pilot's and the co-pilot's seats. There were also seats for the Chief Engineer and the Assistant Engineer, but Easan and Rollo were away in the engine room, patrolling the chequer plate between the prime movers to make sure that nothing was going wrong during the build up to full speed.

We had drawn lots, and had agreed that one of us was to be captain and one navigator. All I can say is that it seemed like a good idea at the time, but it had ended with me as the navigator. That was probably bad enough, but Easan was chief engineer. Hell, I'm whingeing but what could I say. In one stroke I'd made my lover the woman in charge and my best friend chief engineer of a ship the like of which none of us had ever seen before, and were unlikely ever to see again.

One of the navigator's jobs was obviously to navigate. I reached above my chair and flicked the switch for the navigation system.

Ahead of me the holographic representation of the sector solidified. It was an unnecessary embellishment. The data showed up on the monitor at my left hand and I was able to read out the co-ordinates and punch in a required course for Io.

"OK" said Nadia. "Let's have ten per cent."

I pushed the sticks forward and waited for the great black ship to move. It was not instant. There was a low rumbling deep in the bowels as the main engines responded to the slight action of the fingers on my right hand. It grumbled and built up into a distant roar, and we felt the ship start to move forward.

Before we had built up much speed Nadia gave the course command and I activated the forward thrusters to bring the nose round onto the correct heading. This was some ship. The thrusters were bigger than the main engines of the average shuttle. The movement was ponderous. The controls were stressed so that the force required to move the ship had some relationship to my own physical input. I sweated as I pushed the thruster control to the side and felt it moving slowly under my hand. Eventually I judged that I had the swing right and released the lever. It centred once more, but the movement had been initiated. The stars swam across our field of vision. We had the impression of being in control of something vast; something so big that there was no comprehending it.

Solar Flame and Solar Flare remained hooked up to the airlock. Who knew when we might need them?

"What do you think of this then, my boy?" said Nadia.

The vast ship rumbled in a way that made us feel that we were part of it. We were small parasites within a great body. And like some parasites whose existence relies on them having active control over the bodies in which they are living, we controlled this great beast, and in return it was doing our bidding.

I called Easan. "How's it going down there man?"

I heard his voice echoing round us. "Hey, this is a dream. These engines would drive a planet. You can take it on up, but slowly."

There was enough thrust in the great engines to pull the ship apart if we gave it everything at once, and although logic dictated that there must be some sort of control somewhere to stop some gung-ho pilot doing such a thing, we had failed to find it yet.

And so, almost seamlessly, we were embarking on yet another phase of what was turning out to be a great adventure. And we even had an objective. Nadia had voiced what we might have been thinking about unconsciously. There was a possibility that we might make it back to earth. It was a remote possibility, but we had heard the rumours. Up to the time we had arrived on the Evangelina the cost of the passage had been so far beyond anything we could see as a possibility, that subconsciously we had already dismissed it. Now, on the huge emoluments that Boxer had offered us, we might even be able to save up to pay for the trip.

But first of all we had to get the ship working again, and that was going to necessitate a visit to Io.

CHAPTER 17

The Suncruiser 55 – General Guidance

Thank you for choosing a Suncruiser 55. It is the latest and smoothest Suncruiser ever. It features more power than any previous model and houses its pilot and co-pilot in greater luxury. There is also space for two further passengers. The pilot house features the very latest in holographic navigation instrumentation and computer assisted control systems. The Suncruiser 55 helps you to go where you want in a style for which Suncruiser have become famous.

As well as a control station which features hand stitched leatherlux seating and deep pile genuine wool type carpeting in colours and patterns of your choice, the passenger areas feature relaxation couches which can be programmed to mould into your body shape, or to provide a full body massage.

Although intended as a day cruiser the Suncruiser 55 features two sleeping berths and of course the necessary accoutrements to allow you to maintain personal cleanliness.

We expect that your Suncruiser will be totally reliable throughout its life, but just in case, all Solis regulations are complied with, and a full compliment of deep space survival suits are lockered under the relaxation couches in the recreation area. We make the best use of the available space.

The power plant is configured for maximum speed and acceleration, and the engine compartment can be accessed from the passenger spaces. Even owners who have limited knowledge of mechanics will be impressed by the wonderful engine features. The power units appear to float in the engine space, due to the concealment of the auxiliary machinery behind easily removable panels. They shine, they twinkle, and when you put the hammer down they silently propel you up to a maximum velocity, which would allow you to outrun any other short range cruiser available today. Yes, in either its standard cruising form or its full race configuration, the Suncruiser is the one for you.

In the event of any problem with your craft please get in touch with Suncruiser Central right away. As part of the guarantee process we will supply you with a rental craft while we carry out the repairs. The time taken for our mechanics and their recovery transport to reach you depends on your location in the Mars/Jupiter region. But rest assured, we'll be there as quickly as possible.

We were in geo-stationary orbit round Jupiter, on the opposite side of the planet to Io, so they could not see us.

Boxer was on some sort of a high. He was in his element. The ship was more or less back in action. At least, it was in orbit and he had fifty of the best staterooms refurbished and occupied by fifty very good-looking whores. The catering staff, formerly of the hydroponic garden, had worked particularly hard to restore the fixtures and fittings to a condition where the financial aristocracy of the solar system could enter any one of them and feel at home.

The one thing the ship was missing was a Madam. Boxer had told us that it was just not possible for him to administer the brothel. Yes, we had to face it, that's what it was.

"Traditionally," he said, "there are two means of managing a group of working girls, the first is with fists and threats and is usually carried out by a male, and the second is by means of care and consideration. The second means is the one I favour, and I need a lady with the appropriate experience to carry out the job. My last Madam took off in one of the lifeboats, probably with the captain, and none of the girls down here have quite the qualities we need."

"I think we can help you there," I said.

I saw Nadia raise her eyebrows, but I carried on, and

related our experience during our wait for the Trojan shuttle.

"And I thought you were pining away for me," was her only comment.

"The one problem we've got is that we have to get down there to the Io facility and go and talk to her, and there's no way we can take either Solar Flame, if it was working, or Solar Flare. As soon as we get over the Io horizon their systems will register the ship and they'll be calling us up. They might even welcome us home, but then they'll hardly let us get away again."

"Don't you worry," replied Boxer. "When we built this ship we thought of everything. One of the accessories we installed was a Suncruiser. It was just about the most expensive single item, and so far we've not even used it. So your visit to Io will be its maiden voyage. It's so fast that there is no reason why we should even move from this position. It'll get to you Io in no time."

Uncharacteristically, Easan remained silent. He must have heard of the wonders of the Suncruiser. And so in a couple of hours Easan and I found ourselves togged out in body suits, which would have blinded the unwary with their brilliance.

"No-one will have the faintest idea who you are," said Boxer. "Your story is that you've been transported in your ship out to Europa and now you're doing a tour of the Jupiter moons. The Suncruiser is so fast and so expensive no-one will doubt you for a moment."

There was no doubt that it really looked the part. It was a long slim shape, covered in black glass and fitted with great big engines. Of course the shape was entirely cosmetic, but it did look expensive. It was hanging in a bay close to the stern of the Evangelina and was the sort of accessory intended to be used by playboys, who had come to the cruise ship in something not quite so exciting.

"OK," said Easan. "Let's go."

I could see that he was absolutely determined not to enjoy it.

We got ourselves in through the hatch and slid down into the contoured pilot's and engineer's seats. I sank into the leatherlux of the pilot's couch and fingered the controls. Easan reached up and began to flick switches. Dials glowed and the engines began to hum. Boxer appeared on the screen.

"You guys OK?" he asked.

"Yeah," I replied. "Let's go to it."

Boxer could be seen on our VDU operating controls. We felt the little ship slide out through the hatch in the hull of the Evangelina, and I knew that it was now hanging on an arm in space, connected to the cruise ship by a single claw.

Easan blipped the engines to ensure that they were operating correctly. He frowned at me, and I interpreted this as an indication that everything was well.

I told Boxer to let us go, and almost without any noticeable change we found ourselves moving away from the Evangelina.

"OK," said Easan. "Take it away!"

I pushed the sticks forward and Eva - for that was what the little craft was called - leapt forward, pressing us into the control seats. The mother ship was immediately out of sight, and so I pulled the control stick back, changing the orientation of the craft. A thruster in the nose fired up, and we felt the Eva changing direction until we were flying over the Evangelina, upside down. That is, upside down in relation to the Evangelina. I rolled the ship through one hundred and eighty degrees port to starboard and set course for Io. In response to this tiny manifestation of enthusiasm Easan rolled his eyes skyward.

Eva's substantial view ports gave us a grandstand view of Jupiter as we took up a suitable orbit and blasted towards Io. The coloured stripes of the great planet are caused by jet streams racing in opposite directions, and we could see the eddies and imperfections at the joins of the banding. The great red spot passed beneath us; its diameter is the same as that of the earth, but in minutes we had passed over it and were heading into the area controlled by the Io space admin.

As we approached the spacelock on Io, Easan called the control and asked for clearance to lock on. We decided that he would do the talking because it had always been the convention that the pilot made the contacts, and hence there was a good chance that some-one might recognise my voice. As it was, we were free and clear.

"Io control, this is the yacht Eva," said Easan.

"Yes Eva," responded the control. "We have you on our screens. You can come in to port seven point three. You will see the guide light flashing when you get a little closer, then just come in on the beam."

"OK," said Easan. "Here we come."

I powered Eva towards the tower, which stuck out from the top of the Io base like a blasted tree on a burnt out landscape. Below it the bulbous form of the rest of the base floated in the sea of magma, which seethed and bubbled on the surface of the least inhospitable of Jupiter's moons. As we approached I saw the high density flash of the approach light and then the landing line illuminated in a crisp segment. I lined up the nose onto the apogee and flicked in the landing lock. The silicone chips in our mainframe took over the craft and we made our way slowly downwards. I sat back and looked at Easan. He was gripping the arms of the engineer's seat just like he always did when the computers were in control. I took this as compliment.

The Eva eased down. We listened to the throttles closing and the thrusters jetting back and forth until finally we hovered next to the lock on the space-port. There was a solid thump as the lock hit the side, and then the sound of it cranking up. Then the engines shut down.

I never ceased to be impressed by the ability of the computers to get it right, even though I knew that the problems they were solving were pretty simple. Joining one mechanical object to another in free fall was so easy I could do it myself.

Our computer spoke. "Gentlemen, you may now make your way to the Io base. You have twelve hours before you should return to reprogramme this system."

"What does that mean?" I asked.

"That's just to remind us that we can't stay here for ever. Eva doesn't really exist in the real world, just as the Evangelina doesn't, and so they have to make sure that we don't stay for too long. If we fail to return, this thing will go back to the Evangelina under remote control."

"What!" I was aghast. "And just leave us here."

"Yeah, what has anybody to lose? If we were sufficiently important then it would hardly matter that we were left on an inhospitable space station, or even an inhospitable planet come to that. Money will solve all problems."

"But we don't have any," I said plaintively.

"We just have to make damn sure we're back here in time to lift off. Better set your watch," said Easan. We set our watches against the ship's chronometer.

We were soon in the main lounge of the Sunspot Hotel, decked out in the astounding suiting provided by the spare clothing lockers of the Evangelina. Evidently the rich and famous out for a good time did not believe in being conservative.

We were waiting for Egghead. From our previous visit we expected that, if he was still doing his thing on this forsaken pillar of metal, he would be through the lounge within the hour.

The one thing we were good at was waiting. Easan and I had probably done as much waiting as anyone alive. We had spent days waiting when travelling across the solar system to get to the more distant spots. When we were at work, most of our time was spent waiting. Waiting certainly beat working your balls off in the foundries of Io, or half a dozen places like it across the central belt of the solar system.

So today, to have to wait the one hour and seven minutes before Egghead showed up was of no account to us whatsoever. As he slid across the room I waved to him. He rushed up to us, as if to ensure that little attention was paid to him. It struck me that I was forgetting how to conduct myself in civilised society.

"Hey!" he said, smiling and extending a vertical palm.

"Hey!" I replied, clasping the upstretched fingers, How you goin?"

"Fine, man," he replied, taking in our finery at a glance. "My, you boys come into some credits? Last time we met, you were on your way to end of your lives at the killer station."

"What do you mean, killer station?" I asked.

"You were on your way to the Trojans to do your thing with the asteroid recovery system - yeah?"

"Yeah - so what."

"No-one's come back yet. That is, except you guys. I expect they'll sort it out soon. They always do, and then we start to see a few people coming through on their way back to their home bases."

"I have to tell you, we're into a whole new world, but it's too complicated to explain right now. Take us to your leader," I said.

"What? To see Moma?" he asked.

I nodded, and he shrugged and started out into the metal corridors, only glancing back occasionally to see if we were following.

We were. The debris seemed to be visibly deeper. I had a job to believe that it had been only a few months since we had been here.

I noticed that no robots met us at any point. The lifts were silent, although they still worked, failing to acknowledge instructions apart from carrying out the deed.

In one of the lifts I could contain myself no longer. "So, what's with the mechanical aids? They don't seem to be quite what they were."

"You're right," said Egghead. "We've had a strike back in the maintenance section. To tell the truth we think it's more like sabotage. It's pretty eerie. One day everything's talking to us just like they always do, boring the shit out of us. And the next day, nothing. Total silence. Of course you can tell there aren't many cleaning robots doing their thing any more. When they break down they just get taken back to base and left there, or that's what we think. There are hardly any doing the rounds now. To tell the truth, I miss them."

I remembered Egghead's problem with the cleaning robots. You'd think he would be pleased to see them go. There's nowt so strange as folk, as the old saying goes.

We descended the many decks in the lift and, following the diminutive balding figure, found our way back into the accommodation area of the station. We felt ridiculously noticeable in our colourful suiting and when we met occasional inhabitants hurrying on their way to work, or back to their tiny living space, we found that their eyes followed us until we were finally out of sight around the curve of the corridor. Egghead scurried along, kicking debris into the side as he went.

We followed closely and soon we were at the familiar door. Egghead looked up into the camera and the airlock door clicked.

Soon we were inside, and there behind the bar was Moma. She leaned towards us as we entered and cracked a smile, which almost blinded us in the UV light. Her even teeth gleamed whitely, just as they had on the first occasion of our meeting.

"Hi, boys," she gushed, coming round the table to hug us. First Easan, and then me.

"Wow, Sulliman. It's great to see you. You've come back to me now? You thought over what I said to you then?"

"Which, what you said?" I answered.

"You know," she replied, putting a well manicured hand

on my upper arm and squeezing lightly. I was flattered.

"No, not that, Moma," I replied. "But I have something even better. In answer to your second question, I've got a job for you."

Moma's face fell at first, at which I was even more flattered, but then she cheered up and began to show some curiosity about what we had to offer.

As we described our adventure, where we were and the part she could play, she looked even more cheerful. We described the Evangelina and what we had on board in the way of facilities, and then waited for her response.

I realised that she was trying to take it all in, and then trying to decide what to do.

"How long have I got?" she asked.

Easan looked at the watch on his left wrist. "It looks like about seven and a half hours," he replied.

Moma cursed and looked down at her own watch.

"OK, I'm going to have to do a little thinking - you got something for Neville?" She gestured in the direction of Egghead.

"Neville! Hey, I don't know," I replied.

"Well, if you want me then you gotta take him," said Moma. "He's my son." Egghead smiled uncertainly, not being quite sure whether being Moma's son was a good thing in these circumstances, or whether being part of the crew of a cruise ship was really his idea of a beneficial career move.

"We've got lots of room," I said, "and so we're only too happy to take him. He can train up as anything he chooses in the hospitality business. He could even continue to be a guide. We keep getting lost, so I'm quite sure that our visitors will."

"You'd better go next door and wait," she said.

"OK," replied Easan, "but if we don't get back to our ship in seven hours it's going to leave without us and we will become a problem for you, rather than a solution."

"Just get a beer and go next door," she said. And so we

got a beer and went.

After only a couple of the available seven hours Moma put her head round the door and beckoned us out. With her in the small space was the diminutive eastern girl with whom Easan had spent what had appeared to have been an enjoyable half hour on our previous visit.

"I'm with you guys," said Moma, "and this is Poppy. She's going to take over this establishment. After all it's here, and so I'm leaving it in her hands. It's not that I don't trust you, but if it all goes tits up at least I might have something to come back to. That is, if its possible to get back?" She looked at me questioningly.

I shrugged. There was absolutely no knowing how things would go from this point on. It was certainly one step at a time, and however it went we were living in more luxurious conditions than would be possible for anyone remaining on Io.

"I suppose I don't want to die here." She indicated her surroundings, which I took to mean the whole of the Io station. "So let's go".

And so we went. We were a curious little group. Egghead took the lead, as one might expect, carrying a duffle bag over his left shoulder. We followed in our brightly coloured clothing and bringing up the rear was Moma, carrying nothing, clad in her red jump suit, protecting her shoulders with a short leatherette coat, and partially covering her face with a blue iridescent scarf. I had told her that unless she had anything to which she was particularly attached, there was already almost everything one could possibly need on board the Evangelina. This was particularly true of things that might interest ladies. Although make-up, perfume, shampoos and scented bubble baths were frowned upon throughout the known solar system, on board the cruise ships every one of these items was a necessity. And of course the same went for the more alluring traditional forms of female dress.

Nadia, despite being naturally very beautiful, had

collected a variety of these products and spent much of her off-duty time trying them out, with considerable effect on me.

Of course, there came a time when we had to leave the safety of the workers' accommodation and enter the public area of the station. We had decided that the easiest way of dealing with it would be for us all to separate. Easan and I could proceed together towards the ship, disguised as we were as the solar system's richest playboys, and Egghead and Moma would make their way individually to the port, attempting not to attract too much attention from any stray mopo who might be out there. In the public areas of the Io hotel, Moma was particularly vulnerable, even with the scarf.

We crossed the wide area of the hotel lounge, skirting the low tables and the uncomfortable chairs. As usual they were full of travellers waiting to go somewhere, or possibly having just come from somewhere, but not knowing what to do next. There were a couple of guys I recognised from the Eugenia base. After all, it is a small solar system. And I noted that they looked up, thinking they recognised me. But they were in that situation where you think you recognise someone, and so you look straight at them in the hope that they will look straight back at you, and even better, remember who you are and re-introduce themselves.

They looked straight at me, but did not say "Wahey, hello Sully, how's it going?" Instead they waited for me to look back at them, which I did. But I showed no sign of recognition, and that and our playboy attire must have convinced them that I was someone other than Sulliman Smith, the moderately well-known tug driver from the asteroid belt. If Easan recognised them he gave no sign. He just looked straight ahead, avoiding eye contact with anyone.

Easan and I made it to the entry of the spider arm, on the end of which snuggled the Eva. We were quickly joined by Egghead, and from this position some metres above the floor level of the hotel lounge we felt safe enough to look back across the space. We were alarmed to see Moma engaged in conversation with a black uniformed member of the Morality Police. We shrank back into the shadows so that we could just see the two figures out in the bright artificial light of the public area.

The mopo looked up in our direction in response to a gesture from Moma and then they parted, he stamping off in the direction of the lifts, and she heading towards us.

"What was that?" I asked.

"Don't you worry," she replied, "that was just one of our private police force. We've got many of them on the payroll. They get paid either in money or in kind. I just told him that I was off to take a rich client round the world."

"Not too far from the truth," responded Easan, not quite getting the joke.

We made our way back to the Eva, and sank back into the contour seats. Moma and Egghead were silenced by the sheer luxury of the environment and I realised that I had got used to it, during the weeks that we had been immersed in this new world. I pressed the button to cancel the count-down to the automatic launch system. Eva welcomed us back, and we heard the outer door closing, sealing us off from Jupiter's least inhospitable moon.

Easan called the control, indicating an intention to depart. The control room operator responded with an instruction. "Eva, please file a flight plan immediately." Easan looked at me, but we were unprepared and it showed in the resulting silence. "Please remain where you are," said the control room operator.

"I don't think so," I said. "Strap yourselves in guys, we're off." Easan reached up and initiated the prime movers, and almost before they were up to speed I pressed the button to detach the lock. Eva dropped off the spider arm, and through the glass beneath our feet we could see the molten surface of Io approaching at alarming speed. It was only the low gravity that saved us. Before we became part of the landscape I pushed the throttles forward and gave the nose some upward thrust. Eva responded like the racing craft she was, pressing us into our seats to a point that prevented any movement and we powered away into space.

"Eva, did you get my last message?" asked the CRO plaintively. The acceleration reduced to the point where I could lean forward and adjust the heading of our little space craft, so that we would fall into a trajectory which would bring us back to the Evangelina on the other side of Jupiter. I did not bother to answer the control room.

CHAPTER 18

Solar System Administration Authority – Retirement Information

Due to the increasing health of every worker in the solar system, retirement has been abolished. This has had two effects; the first is that the workforce has become more stable. Once a worker is recruited there is no need to subsequently replace him or her until death. And the second is that there is no necessity for entertainment facilities to be provided for people who are not working.

Of course death will still occur, but later in life, and more suddenly. No-one now can expect to suffer from any debilitating illnesses. There are drugs to deal with them all, and injuries can in all cases be dealt with in one way or another. However, the medical and surgical advances that have taken place cannot eliminate death altogether.

Therefore, though it is acceptable for you to change jobs as time passes, it is not possible to give up work altogether.

It is accepted that in some cases married people cannot both be working simultaneously. It is always necessary for a woman lucky enough to have been given permission to become pregnant to stop work in the seventh month. The woman who has a new-born baby to look after can also be supported for six months after the birth, after which time the child can enter the standard nursery facilities and the woman can be employed once more.

The changes in work cycles will generally be administered by the management of the facility where you are employed. Particularly hard physical labour cannot always be avoided, in such places as the foundries on Io, but foundry workers will be re-assigned to lesser tasks when the annual medical tests indicate a lack of physical strength. The range of

245

tasks available will be promulgated at that time, and the administrators of SSAA will provide suitable advice and assistance.

We were gathered in the Evangelina's conference room for a management meeting. Boxer sat at the head of the table in a new body suit, the empty sleeve tucked neatly in at the shoulder. We, the operational staff, sat along one side and the hospitality crew, Moma, Neville and Gary the chef, sat along the other.

Boxer called us to order and we stopped chattering. It was our first meeting. "Now," he said, "we've got things to do before we have our open day. For those of you who don't know, when a cruise ship arrives at a new venue it is customary for it to issue invitations to anyone who might have the money or the influence to be useful, while it is in the sector. Of course it has to be done pretty carefully. If we got the wrong person there is just a chance that they might do something to close us down. But more importantly for those of us round this table, we have some clearing up to do first. So let's go round and see how we're getting on. Nadia, what have you got?"

Nadia cleared her throat and consulted her notes. Meetings were a new thing for us. As tug drivers we were more used to the mushroom approach: being kept in the dark and having shit thrown over us.

"All the pilot's control systems are working and I have found the ship does exactly what I want when I want. At present we are in geo-stationary orbit around Jupiter, and you will note that the ship is maintaining station perfectly with no unwanted thruster operation."

We had noted it.

"Anything else? Any problems?" asked Boxer.

Nadia shook her head. "There is one thing," he went on. "I hope you've noticed that I have done nothing to try to influence your choice of roles. This means that we have a female captain."

"So what's wrong with that?" asked Nadia defensively.

"In itself, nothing," said Boxer. "And when we started off on this road to recovery it wasn't too important. I was just relying on you guys to rescue us. But now, thanks to you, we are in an entirely different situation. The ship is about to go back into action, in a world where the men are still in charge, and in any case where men and women are kept completely separate. And we have a crew where men and women work together. You may wonder how we can possibly make such distinctions in a flying whorehouse. My answer is that our guests are all rich men, probably in positions of considerable influence and I honestly don't want to be constantly explaining that this lady is not available to them. They all seem to have a thing for girls in uniform. There are a couple of choices. You can change your minds and make Sully the captain or else you," he nodded to Nadia, "can just keep out of the way."

"I think we all want to keep out of the way," I replied. "Am I right guys?"

I looked round the room and the others nodded in agreement. Most of them, anyway. Easan remained resolutely silent, and unmoved.

Boxer picked up the differences of view. "Actually, I have no problem with the guys getting out there and sampling some of what we have to offer. In some situations it's necessary for engineers to go and fix things." This was true. All of us had seen engineers wandering about trying to fix things whenever we had travelling on the shuttles.

"So that's settled then," he said. "The only person who's going to go out into the public spaces, once we have clients aboard, will be Easan."

Time was passing and so far we had only had input from one person.

Then everybody looked at me, and so I spoke briefly about the navigation system and how it worked, and how there had been nothing wrong with the navigation system ever. Even when there had been no power the system had remained up, hibernating, using its independent power source. I was quite proud of it.

Boxer moved on to Easan. "What about the robots?" he asked. "Anyway," he went on, "I thought that robots were incapable of harming humans. What was it, the first law of robotics?"

"That's just something made up by an author years ago," replied Easan. "There is a problem with the robots. I've had a look at their central control system and there's nothing in it telling them to do anything but get out there, clean up the place, and come back at specific times for maintenance. So the change to their programming must have been carried out on each individual unit. Obviously, since it's been applied to catering staff, someone must have connected them to a terminal and loaded up the identity information on each of the kitchen staff, together with the change to the programming. And they must have fitted the weapon instead of a brush. What we have to do is to identify the rogue units, cancel the changes to their programming, and then change the blade back to a small brush for cleaning out cracks and crevices."

"So, when can you start?" asked Boxer.

Easan went on. "We've sorted out all the rest of the systems, so now everything's working properly we can start right away. I'm going to need one of the catering staff to help me; otherwise we'll have a job identifying the modified robots. We need to wheel each one out in front of a catering person who is eating something, then when it makes its move I'll press the stop button."

"Is it dangerous?" asked Gary.

"Yes, a bit," was the reply.

"That's fine then. You can have Stadler, When would you like him?"

"I'll meet him in the galley in..." Easan looked at his watch. "At the beginning of the next work period."

"Moving on then," said Boxer, assuming that Easan was speaking for the whole of the engineering department, "how are things with our girls?"

"Oh my!" Moma smiled. "You have treated them too well, and recently they've had too little to do. There's nothing worse than a bunch of comfortable whores with time on their hands. They've thought up all sorts of things which they believe will make their lives better; that is – even better."

"Well, what do they want?" asked Boxer, evidently surprised that they could possibly want anything.

"Firstly, they want regular hours. They think that after twelve hours work they should have twelve hours sleep to recoup. Secondly, they think they should have the same food as the guests, and thirdly, they want a bigger percentage of the fees you get. But I've told them they get nothing more than they get now, which is, as far as I can see, the best deal in the business. If anyone makes trouble I'll transport them down to Io, and replace them with one of my girls from down there."

"And so?" said Boxer.

"They've changed their minds. They know which side their bread is buttered on. And here it's real bread and something like butter. They can't get that anywhere else in the solar system. But I think they should be given something they haven't asked for. They can't keep doing this for the rest of their lives. Most of them will last for another ten years at most, even with a bit of surgical assistance. You need to find a way of giving them a pension, and a means of finding somewhere to live outside this thing." She indicated the ship with a wave of her hand.

"They could join the catering staff," said Boxer.

"Come on," replied Moma, "they'll have spent 20 years on their backs by the time they get too old for it, and then you expect them to go to work in the kitchen? You know that's not on."

For myself I couldn't see what was wrong with that. The Evangelina was probably one of the most luxurious venues in the whole solar system. Even if they retired to the catering staff's quarters they would still have more room to themselves than they would have as a single woman living on any of the satellite stations. Besides which no-one gets to retire. If you are the sole occupant of any living space you have to work to support yourself, and in the worst situations your living space could be nothing more than a bed with a curtain round it.

Of course many of the younger whores thought that their way out of their situation was to be chosen by a rich or influential man, but it seldom happened. They only had to look around to see that. In twenty years of work, few women managed to hook a man who would look after them in retirement. Others were like Moma. They had been married, and being in this protected environment was better than being stuck with a violent husband.

"That's a good idea," said Boxer. "What do you think guys?" He turned to us, and suddenly we were transformed from being the operations team to being his financial and policy advisors.

Nadia was the one to speak. "I don't think it should be restricted to the whores. What about the rest of us? Yes, I think we should find a way of giving these girls some security. Not many people in our world can say they have any, and with modern health arrangements we can keep fit into old age, and therefore keep working until we drop. What the hell *is* old age? Sometime I'd like to be able to give up being a tug pilot, and for the first time in my life I can see that there might be a possibility of something different when I get on a bit. But don't forget we're in Boxer's hands - sorry hand - here."

Boxer nodded. "OK, we'll give it some thought. Anything else."

Moma shook her head. "We've got everything more or

less in place. There'll be problems. There always are. But we won't see them until we start work."

Boxer nodded to Gary, who shuffled his papers and cleared his throat.

"And the catering department, how's that?"

Gary spoke. "It's good. To tell the truth it's better than it ever was. Now we that don't have to worry about the robots we can get on with our work. I've done a stock take of the supplies and we seem to have enough stuff in the store rooms for quite a few years. The livestock is healthy. Of course, the pigs have benefited particularly from the situation while we were out of action, and therefore with your permission, some of us are going to continue to live in the hydroponic garden and look after them.

And talking about the garden we do have one problem; I'm not a social worker, but what about Lydia, or more particularly her children? How are we going to educate them? Have we got anyone here with teaching qualifications or even teaching ability?"

"All tug pilots have to do a course in tutoring," answered Nadia. "They found it's the easiest way of passing on our knowledge and skills. One of us could do it."

"And finally," said Gary, "we have to do something about the rats. We see them occasionally in the galley so there must be loads of them living in the ducting and in all the places where the cleaning robots can't get a brush or a vacuum nozzle. If we don't sort them out they're going to start getting into the staterooms. And what will the girls think of that?"

"OK," said Boxer, "we've still got a few problems, but we're on course for our opening day in seven Jupiter days. I'm getting the list of guests together and I'll let you all have a look at it in a day or two. Even better, perhaps those of you who know a bit about Io and about the management of the Eugenia mining operation could let me know what you think. Thanks very much, that's all for now."

Boxer left us to it, and I beckoned to the rest of our team. I had an idea. When I explained what I had in mind Nadia said she would go and tell Boxer about the people we thought could be invited to the opening. And I agreed to go and help Easan.

The following morning found us in the cleaning robot maintenance area. It was a dark cave in the lower regions of the ship. The robots had no need of illumination; they were able to use sensors to determine the limits of their environment and the objects, which were in their way, and so the hanger was lit by a blue glow. Some of the tubes had failed in a way that resulted in stuttering illumination, which gave us the appearance of being characters from antique black and white films. The robots were lined up, attached to their re-charging points. The one thing Easan had been able to do was to instruct them to return to base and not to move until told otherwise. Having done that he had switched them off. Now he went to the central console and collectively released them from their digital bonds.

Stadler stood with us behind a small table, looking extremely concerned. On the table was an assortment of tit-bits from the Evangelina's larder. I particularly liked the look of small sandwiches with the crusts cut off, and small items skewered on little sticks. I was there to stand next to him and press the stop button as soon as the blade appeared from its little slot on the side of the unit.

"Don't worry, boy," said Easan to the bait, "Sully's got the quickest reactions in the solar system. These things will never get anywhere near you."

Easan wheeled the first of the robots out in front of the table. It looked like most of a metal egg on a flat base, shiny and slightly scarred from contact with the bulkheads and protrusions of the cruise ship. The oval top, which came up to a level just above my waist, was studded with its optics. There were eight irises evenly spaced, so it could look in any direction. They were opaque. Beneath the irises were a number of grills, which indicated the presence behind them of the distance sensors, which would keep it heading in the right direction. Down the sides were the pods, which contained the tools of its trade, but we knew that there was the possibility that one of them was a blade. We had chosen this technique because Easan thought that if the units were not shut down while actually in action, they might have been programmed to defend themselves from anyone who connected up a computer to their programming port.

"Here we go then," said Easan, switching on the robot.

The protective covers of its optics slid back and it was suddenly alive. It rolled forward until it was within range of Stadler, who stepped back. I hardly blamed him. Somehow the robot had become extremely sinister. I stood beside the mechanoid with my fist poised to smash the red button. On this model it was placed on top of the curved surface which I could not prevent myself from thinking of as its head.

Stadler inched forward reluctantly and snatched a sandwich. But even as his hand extended towards it, the pod on the left hand side of the robot clanged open and almost faster than the eye could follow the robot extended a small brush and collected the crumbs from the sandwich and then vacuumed them up with a small nozzle. We all breathed a collective sigh of relief.

"Don't get confident," advised Easan. "We know the things are here, but we don't know is how many there are." He pushed another robot into position and switched it on. It came alive as the shielding slid back from its irises. It moved forward towards the table. Stadler cautiously extended his hand towards the next sandwich. The pod opened and in a blur the blade extended. I smashed my fist down on the red button, and the act was frozen. The blade gleamed darkly on the end of its arm, only a few centimetres above the table, and Stadler's hand. Stadler dropped the sandwich and stood immobile in shock.

"Wow," said Easan "I don't think we can do that again, but now it's got the safety on I can check to see if there's a defensive programme installed."

Stadler looked behind him, and when he had located a stool, staggered backwards and sat on it, breathing heavily. I rubbed the outer edge of my fist, which had been bruised by the impact with the stop button. Easan plugged a cable into the robot's communications slot.

I watched him at work, pursing his lips and narrowing his eyes in concentration. "Yep," there it is," he remarked. "I've got the rogue programme. I can completely expunge it so that when we put the brush back that'll be it."

"Yes, but don't forget my plan," I replied. "We should keep one or two available for action if we need them. But you can remove the identities of the catering staff, so that even if the programme is still there, they won't have any targets." Easan grinned and gave me a thumbs up. I nodded to Stadler and indicated that he could go. He did not need telling twice.

"There is one thing we could do," I said. "We could maybe set one of these things up to exterminate the rats. If we put some bait down and programme a robot, that should sort out the whole thing. But of course we need a rat identity card."

Easan looked through the available illustrations of rodents on the terminal screen, and added one to an ID card.

"There he is then, Rattus Rattus, king of the rubbish dump. I'll just add his details to this robot and there we are." The addition took a few minutes, and then it was just a matter of fixing the rest. One at a time we wheeled a robot forward into the light, or at least what little light there was. Easan would connect up the terminal and I would switch the thing on and then stand with my fist a few centimetres above the off button while he disabled the more aggressive aspects of its programming. Once this was achieved he would access the instruction module and open up the instrument pods on the sides. I would press the stop button, and we would remove the blade and replace it with the little brush that the robot would use for cleaning out cracks and crevices.

Later we had our own meeting: Easan, Nadia, Rollo and I. Nadia had met with Boxer and given him the names of the people we thought could be invited to the opening party. The names included Sediki, Hassan and Macgregor, all of whom were sufficiently important as to meet the general criteria Boxer had set for the guests. She had also got him to include Tranter, who was not all that important, but we had plans for all of them and we did not want to leave the odious little slug out.

Of course, once we had the robots sorted out, there was little for us to do other than walk about and look interested. I enjoyed wandering through the public rooms where there was more room than I had ever seen anywhere. There were a variety of spaces for different levels of client. The smaller compartments had an air of intimacy, with low couches and dark drapes round the walls. The larger ones were no less luxurious, but lacked something. Not that the clients would notice. All of them had wonderful concealed lighting, which was intended to show off the girls in the best possible way.

My exploration ended in Moma's domain. As well as her dark mahogany coloured desk there were couches, on which there were usually a number of young women reclining and passing the time of day. Moma kept a real coffee percolator going, which in itself was sufficient reason for my visit.

Moma had by this time made friends with Nadia, so my excurions were guilt-free. Nadia herself seldom left the pilot house during the work periods. It is difficult for a captain to give up the habit of standing at the viewports and studying the heavens, and then checking all the dials and read-outs on every console. This took some time on the Evangelina, which had dials to indicate everything. She felt the need to be there just in case something went wrong. Indeed it was necessary for someone to be in the pilot house all the time, just in case the orbit degraded and the navigation system failed to recognise it. The thought of the ship plummeting into Jupiter without us noticing was sufficient motivation for us all to take our turn at watchkeeping during the non-work periods. Even Boxer took a turn sometimes to give us all a rest.

Boxer spent most of his time in what we had come to know as the control room. Actually nothing was controlled from it, except for which video cameras you use to, look into the myriad spaces of the cruise ship. He was also able to monitor the teelink, which he used as a means of communication with his contacts on Io and the Eugenia base.

Easan prowled the corridors. It was difficult to say whether he was doing this to ensure the continued successful operation of all the systems, or in order to get closer to one or two of the young women who could be seen occasionally, clad in figure-hugging sports gear in the ship's gym, or rubbing themselves down with nutritious oil to improve their skin tone. Whichever it was, everything continued to work successfully. The thrusters operated, the orbit was maintained and the cleaning robots did their stuff, even the one programmed to dispose of the rats. We discovered that rats are quite partial to other rats, so once it had killed the first, further rats came on the scene in order to eat it. Of course this resulted in their demise and so on. Every day one of the catering staff collected most of the bodies and added them to the ship's recycling system.

Rollo remained in intriguing obscurity. Easan assured us that she was doing everything asked of her, and she took her turn in the pilot house without complaint, but other than that we saw nothing of her. We all had our own spaces, and she seemed to be making use of hers.

Essentially, we were all adapting to the new life we were leading in a way which could be expected of ship's crews. We took the good things on board and made the best of them, and were capable of putting up with considerable hardship. The one thing we had in common was a desire to get our own back on the management of the organisations which had sentenced us to death

at the Trojans. And we knew that they had it coming to them in a
few days.

CHAPTER 19

Etiquette for Cruise Ships – Underground Docx

It may be that you are faced with the need to entertain. It is an unlikely requirement - after all, out there amongst the asteroids there's not much excitement, and not much reason to deal in etiquette of any sort. All we do out there is work, whatever line of business we are in, from the lowest immigrant – the guys who labour in the foundry – to the executives who administer the Acme Mining Corporation on behalf of the Rais. We would also include the Morality Police at all levels. Well, they won't be reading this will they? But don't kid yourselves, they could well be on the receiving end of some pretty high level entertainment at some time.

So, let's start at the beginning. There is a natural requirement for food and drink to be served. None of those nutrient tubes and recycled drinking fluids are on the cards. If your guests got a glimpse of any, they would think they'd been short changed. So you need real food. Your synthesizers can do that, but how to serve it, that's the question.

Let's start with the table. Always use white linen on tables seating four to eight people. The tablecloth, the covering for the table, should be devoid of creases – ironed in the old style. Each place-setting, the items on the table at each seat, should have at its centre a plate. We know no-one uses plates, but you have to find them. They can be white or tastefully coloured or patterned. On the right of the plate should be a knife, and on the left a fork. More sophisticated settings can have a smaller knife and a spoon outside the first knife and a smaller fork outside the main fork.

You will want to serve alcohol, and your synthesizer,

258

properly programmed, can produce any sort you want, if you have the programmes available. (Order the programme from us now – click on this link).

But given the booze, you should get the glasses right. The most elaborate table settings will require three glasses. A longish glass, for water (not thirst relief fluid,but the real thing), a smaller balloon glass for white wine and a large balloon-type glass for red wine. Page 1 of 4 ...

And so the day came. The last thing we did was move the Solar Flame and the Solar Flare into the cargo hold. Nadia just locked them together and moved them as one. There was little room on either side of the hatch, and when the job was complete they filled all the available space.

Once this had been done, we repaired to the pilot house, from which we could monitor all the activity. We were all gathered there except for Boxer and Moma, both of whom were dressed in their best gear and were posted in the access area to greet the visitors.

The first arrival was familiar to us; it was Cygnus Two. "Well, look at that," said Nadia, who was more familiar with the exterior of the ship than I was. After all, Easan and I had spent most of our time inside it. We clustered round the monitor, which was connected to the camera in the access area. Sure enough, our old friend Trantor appeared. It was evident that he had tried to smarten himself up, but his body suit was still ill fitting and his sparse hair was failing to stay in place, despite the obvious application of quantities of some sort of hair gel. With him was Hassan, the Acme Mining base manager at Eugenia. Hassan was tall and dark-skinned with close-cropped curly hair. He wore Acme coveralls. Small badges dotted the short sleeves of the garment and his name was embroidered over the left breast. It was an unsuitable garment to be wearing for a clandestine visit to an orbiting whorehouse.

Boxer greeted them and passed them on to Moma. We changed monitors as she conducted them into the main reception area and sat them on two low divans. We could see them looking round in amazement at their environment. Boxer would have been pleased. There was no sound, but we could tell that they were being asked what they would like to drink. Here it is necessary to bear in mind that usually they only drank a liquid which passed for water, and which had almost certainly *been* passed in the past.

They said something, and Moma went away. Within a count of ten a young woman appeared with two long glasses containing what we had come to recognise as mojitos. They eyed the drinks suspiciously, but looked up at the retreating rear of the girl with greater enthusiasm. This was not surprising. All the whores had spent considerable time in the gym making sure that their rear view would be particularly attractive. This girl also wore a body suit which was shaped to expose her lightly muscled back down to the cleft of her buttocks. She swayed her way out of sight, absolutely aware of the effect that she was having on the two men. "That's Celestine," said Rollo, to our surprise.

We turned our attention to the viewports again to see a Suncruiser holding station about 100 metres away from us. It was an earlier model than the one in which Easan and I had visited Io, but nevertheless it still looked purposeful; all curved aluminium and black glass. Who could own this craft? It hovered. The lock was extended and locked on. We mentally heard it crank, and the Suncruiser was part of the Evangelina.

We dashed into the control room and picked out the monitor showing the access area. Sure enough, Macgregor strolled into view. Macgregor was a short man, whose expanding waistline was disguised by his very well tailored body suit, cut high in the collar in very muted colours. He was followed by Sediki. Although we expected all this to happen, because after all we had put them on our list, we were still struck dumb by the sheer effrontery of these guys.

There they were, the moral upholders of the asteroid belt, visiting a place which was completely immoral. Macgregor based the success of the Cygnus fleet on his rigorous support of an environment in which men were separated from women. And there was Sediki, the head of the Morality Police, whose instructions, if followed, would have resulted in the deaths of Nadia and Rollo.

We saw Boxer introduce them to Moma, who led them off to the 'VIP' spaces. Soon Sediki, who was still clad in his black uniform, was seated on a divan next to Macgregor. We continued to watch and our indignation increased as we saw the pair being served champagne by a whore clad in nothing more than a bejewelled G-string.

Time passed, and gradually the locks filled up with a variety of craft, and the reception areas hummed with noise. It was the sound of easy conversation, which we had learnt resulted from a moderate intake of alcohol. We watched as the whole group, who now numbered about forty, were shepherded by Gary, clad in his best chef's gear, towards the dining area. They moved along and were guided to their seats at a number of four and six seat tables. Each table was covered with white linen, and equipped with silver knives and forks, napkins and glasses. We had found that drinking from glasses instead of sucking liquid through plastic tubes from similarly constructed containers, resulted in an amazing difference in taste, and that even applied to water. Members of the catering staff appeared with white napkins draped over their left arms, and bottles of red and white wine in their right hands. They leaned forward and questioned the guests. They received answers to their questions, and poured either red or white wine, the former into larger balloon-shaped glasses, the latter into taller slimmer ones. Boxer, who was by now viewing the scene with us, rubbed his hands.

"Look at that!" he exclaimed. "You don't think this was achieved automatically do you? I spent weeks training these guys to do what they do, while you lot were sitting in those seats back there flicking switches! I taught them how to lay the table, how to polish the glasses, how to fold the napkins and how to pour the wine. And that is the result." He pointed at the scene.

We were impressed, but our enthusiasm was tempered by our anticipation of an impending event, about which he had no knowledge.

And when Boxer next spoke he heralded what we had all been waiting for. "What's that cleaning robot doing there?" he exclaimed.

Sure enough, a single gleaming cleaning robot had appeared from the serving area and was beginning slowly to move between the tables in the direction of the centre of the room. It was making no effort whatever to do any cleaning. Had it been an old fashioned mechanoid, its head would have been swivelling from side to side, but this was unnecessary for a model with irises all round the periphery of its 'head'."

"What's that thing doing there?" asked Boxer again, turning to Easan who had taken on the responsibility for all things mechanical.

Easan shrugged, but I felt that we owed it to the one armed man to tell him what was going on, and so I outlined the plan. "What?" said Boxer. "You mean to tell me that when that thing sees Sediki, or Macgregor, or Hassan or Trantor it's going to hack one of their extremities off with its hidden blade? You can't do that to me! The rest of this bunch will be back in their ships like rats deserting a space ship on a slingshot, and they'll be off to their stations and bases, and no-one will ever come back again! As well as places of pleasure, cruise ships are sanctuaries! They are safe for everybody! Stop it now!"

It was apparent to me that, for once, we had not really thought out what had seemed like an excellent plan. We looked at each other. Easan's expression seemed to say "so what?" Nadia looked upset. Rollo remained her inscrutable self.

"Come on," said Boxer. "Get down there and stop it! Surely you can disable it from the central control?" Easan shook his head. "Well get down there and press the stop button, now!" said Boxer.

I gestured to Easan, and we got going.

Down in the restaurant we made our way between the tables, feeling pretty conspicuous in our dark flight crew coveralls, amongst all that white linen. People began to look round at us, but we were undeterred and sped up when we sighted the cleaning robot, only a few tables away from where Sediki and Macgregor were sitting, sipping their glasses of red wine. We could not see Trantor and Hassan, but they must have been somewhere more distant.

The conversation gradually reduced to silence, until finally we could hear the hum of the mechanoid's gearing. Sediki was facing in our direction. He looked at the robot, which was now only about two metres away, and then at me. Macgregor, who was sitting with his back towards us, looked round. We had no doubt whatsoever that the robot's programming had already checked their facial characteristics against the IDs Easan had loaded up, and that it was preparing, if that's the right word for what a robot does, to unleash our retribution.

I made a dive forward and succeeded in smashing down the stop button at the moment that the side pod had opened, but before the blade had made an appearance. They had no idea what had happened. I fell sideways and rolled under a table, at which four well-dressed men were sitting. They lurched backwards, and as I knocked two of the legs away the crockery and glasses cascaded over me. I looked up and was shocked to see that as one of the guests was attempting to regain his balance, he had grabbed the table cloth from the next table and pulled it towards him, clearing a second table of plates, glasses and cutlery.

I got to my feet, brushing bits of broken glass and porcelain out of my clothing, until I was standing by the robot, breathing hard. Illogically I found myself picking up a napkin and polishing up the dull bits on its carapace. Easan gave me one of his raised- eyebrow looks, unslung a portable terminal and plugged it into the port on the robot. He punched a few keys. looked up and me and nodded. I put my hands on the metallic surface and began to push it away.

"Just a minute," said Macgregor. "Just a bloody minute. I recognise you!"

I stood up and looked back. There seemed to be no point in running away, and since Boxer had said that the cruise ship was a sanctuary, surely it applied to us as well as to all of them.

"You are Sulliman Smith," said Macgregor. "I sent you, and you," he nodded at Easan," to the Trojans. The last we heard was that you were on some sort of a slingshot and you'd be back in about a year, if you were lucky. I thought I'd seen the back of you, and now you've turned up here! What the hell's going on?"

I was thankful that he was unaware of what we had intended for him and Sediki, because he was a man used to getting his own way.

The noise in the room was gradually increasing again as the guests lost interest in the odd figures in uniform, and an immobile robot, and gained interest in the first course of the meal, which was being distributed by the waiters, pressed into action by Gary.

I leaned close to Macgregor's ear and suggested a meeting after the meal. He had got over his surprise and dipped his head in agreement. For once Sediki was struck silent, possibly from embarrassment, at having been caught in the only place in the solar system where the Morality Police had no jurisdiction.

We retreated to the control room to watch the rest of the meal taking place. There was a fascination in seeing people eat something other than paste squeezed from a tube. The first course was a small portion of caviar, the eggs of the sturgeon. A legendary dish, made all the more rare by the fact that the sturgeon had been extinct for hundreds of years. This was followed by a choice of braised venison or a good wedge of Kobe beef. It was all re-constituted in the ship's galley. Boxer had tried us out on the Kobe beef, which was a new menu item after he had found a description of the way in which the meat was tenderised on a history programme.

"Imagine that," he said. "The meat was tenderised by having virgins sit astride the young bulls and massage their flanks with their inner thighs." I had a problem imaging it.

They moved on to an assortment of desserts and I noted that despite the apparent sophistication of the clientele they all seemed to like ice cream, with cream and cherries. I'd had some and it was wonderful.

A couple of hours later we were gathered in the Evangelina's conference room. Macgregor and Sediki sat on one side of the table, and we sat on the other. Boxer was acting as chairman. Trantor and Hassan were not sufficiently important to be included.

I started the discussion off. "You gentlemen can see us here because we were lucky enough to be rescued by this ship at the edge of the Trojans. The survey out there identified a rock which was on its way somewhere, instead of being in orbit with the rest of the asteroids. We thought we could change its direction using the tugs, but Solar Flame broke down. Hence the slingshot.

Anyway, now that we're in this no-blame environment, I might as well tell you why we were in trouble in the first place. You – well, your company - hadn't bothered to equip the Cygnus tugs to the Acme standard. I agreed that we'd accept the blame and keep Cygnus out of it, otherwise you might lose the contract."

Macgregor began to look just a little less confident, but he realised that as long as we kept quiet, all would still be well. Sediki was certainly not going to spill the beans. He'd have to tell someone where he'd heard it if he did.

I went on. "And as for the business at the Trojans. Acme

hadn't bothered to make sure the survey was done properly, and the rock we had been assigned to move was actually a comet. Everything would have been OK if firstly the mods to the Solar Flame had been done properly, and secondly if you'd given us the right spares. The whole thing was the joint responsibility of Acme and Cygnus, and you would have been responsible for our deaths if we hadn't been lucky enough to come across the Evangelina. So don't look at us as if we're criminals. You nearly killed us."

Macgregor's eyes widened and he sliced his hand, palm-down, from left to right as preparation for a negative response. It was a gesture he must have used a hundred times to strike fear into the people he happened to be negotiating with at the time.

"And before you start telling us we're going to face some sort of disciplinary action for failing to assess the risks properly, and losing the Solar Flame and Solar Flare, *and* associating with members of the opposite sex," I indicated Nadia and Rollo who were sitting further down the table.," you need to consider your own position. According to Boxer, the Evangelina does not exist, therefore you don't exist, and we don't exist. So there's really nothing to be done here except come to some sort of agreement about what to do next... sir."

Macgregor signalled some sort of agreement. Sediki glowered, but was struck dumb. There was absolutely nothing he could say to defend himself, and he must have realised that he should count himself lucky if he managed to get back to Eugenia with his reputation intact.

"What have you got in mind?" asked Macgregor.

"We're prepared to give you back the Solar Flame and the Solar Flare. We'll bring them down to Io at a pre-arranged time and you can put them back into service. They're fine except for the Solar Flame's thrusters. We'll fix it, if you can find a way of sending us the spares. We want to have the opportunity of recruiting our replacements, and we want a passage to Earth on the first available shuttle."

Rollo, on my right, leant towards Easan and whispered in his ear. Easan in turn poked me in the ribs and inclined his head towards the door. "Will you excuse us for a moment?" I asked, and we pushed our chairs back and left the room.

"So what's going on?" I asked. Easan was a mite apologetic. "Rollo and I don't want to go. We like it here. There's lots of machinery for us to look after, and probably the most luxurious environment in the known universe. Certainly a damn sight more luxurious than you're going to find on earth. We hear it's pretty primitive down there, so you're going to have your work cut out just to survive. Besides, we've found other reasons for staying, both of us."

"OK, so you're out. Nadia and I'll manage I'm sure, but we might need your help to get back to Io." Although I said the words I could hardly contain my distress at the loss of my engineer, and more realistically, my only friend. But there it was; there was no turning back.

We filed back into the room and sat again.

"So, gents. What's it to be? If you don't want to help us we have to abide by Boxer's code and let you go, back in your Suncruiser and off to Eugenia. It's a pity for us, we'd like to punish you in some way for being complete bastards, more than that, complete hypocrites. That seems to be your worst crime: pretending to be one thing when actually you're entirely another. You turn out to be human, which is not a crime, but pretending to be other than human is. And so is punishing others for being human. So, in a way, I find myself appealing to your humanity, now that we know you *are* human. And if we make a deal, don't forget you can have the tugs back. They must be worth quite a bit more than the price of a passage back to the home planet, plus a bit of pocket money. It's going to be the easy way out for you, and leaving us here without a deal leaves the possibility that at some time we'll rat on you. I appreciate that there's a bit of mutual trust involved, but I don't think that any of us have any choice."

Macgregor was beginning to look relieved, and I was beginning to feel quite pleased with myself, having discovered an unexpected talent for negotiation.

Macgregor slowly lowered his chin into the folds of his neck. It was a signal of agreement. "When can you get the tugs back to Io?"

"Whenever you get the spares for the thrusters to us. Easan'll give you a list before you go."

"I think we've got a stock of spares on Eugenia," said Macgregor. "If not they're all at the Trojan station. It'll take some time to get them here if that's the case."

"You'd better hope it isn't," I replied. "We might get impatient."

"OK, OK," interjected Boxer. "Let's wrap this up. You guys get back out there and enjoy yourselves."

"You must be joking!" spat Sediki. They were his first and only words, and were uncharacteristically informal.

Then they were gone, leaving us sitting there, facing a whole new future, for the second time in only a few months. Nadia and I held hands under the table, as if to assure ourselves that at least the two of us were together. We were going to miss our engineers.

"So there we have it," said Boxer. "You guys have not exactly been up front with me, have you? I thought I had a regular crew, and now I find out that my whole pilot house team is deserting me, and you would have taken the engineers with you if they'd wanted to go. Where would I have been then? Actually, I don't care to much about losing you two, but I would have been really pissed if the engineers had decided to go with you."

We hung our heads. Here was a man who had been as honest as anyone had ever been with us, and we were kicking him in the guts. It was also a bit disappointing to know that he didn't really care that we were going.

"Look Boxer," said Nadia. "We'll go down in one of the

ships and collect the spares for Solar Flame, and while we're there we'll find a new captain and navigator for you. We just wanted to go to somewhere where we could be together in a proper way, sort of married."

"You can be sort of married here. You're the captain. You could sort of do the ceremony yourself. You don't have to go to Earth to be sort of married."

He had a point, but we were resolute. For some reason, which we could not quite identify, we needed to take the step.

"Boxer. We're really sorry. But we have to do it." It was strange that when we did not know that we could do it, it never entered our heads, but now, with the whole plan more or less in place, there was nothing else to be done.

"I don't blame you," he replied, grasping my arm with his only hand. "If I were you, and I was hooked up with a lovely girl like Nadia, I'd probably want to do the same thing. Take your time preparing for it, make lists, find out what you can take with you, and try to get all of it into your baggage. And ask me if there's anything you want, which you think I might have."

We were very grateful. I knew what we needed that Boxer had, but at that particular moment I did not think I'd mention it. Earth could be, I had heard, a pretty scary place.

CHAPTER 20

EarthLink Information Sheet for Returning Colonists

The EarthLink Organisation takes no responsibility for the health or safety of passengers returning to earth after a prolonged stay in the populated areas of the solar system, and it is suggested that you read this document carefully, as it contains information that may be of use to you once you land.

You will be aware that whatever your role in the colonies, you were safe. The Morality Police ensured that miscreants were quickly apprehended, and illegal activities were limited to the means of increasing one's personal experiences outside those that were technically allowed by the law. Essentially you had no real concerns about your personal safety.

It is important to understand that earth is different. You probably realise that the reason you are being encouraged to return is that there are now fewer people on the planet than there used to be. The population of the earth used to be so great that much of the available land had been built on, and it was not longer possible to feed everybody due to the lack of agricultural space, no matter how intensively farmed. Despite the developments in the aquaculture, fish almost ceased to be part of the diet. As a result the population has naturally fallen. If there is no food then people die, and those who remain alive are more interested in where their next meal is coming from than procreating.

Therefore the world government has also had difficulty in financing even the simplest regulatory activities. The first things to go were such things as street cleaning and street lighting, and then other services including, in the end, the police.

Because of all of this the smaller nations became almost completely overbuilt. Britain, which had been one of the original civilized countries according to some, became a lawless wasteland, with gangs of violent men and women fighting each other for domination of the urban areas. Other counties with lower population densities have been less afflicted, but never-the-less all areas are potentially dangerous, and all passengers are recommended to be cautious and watchful.

EarthLink does not offer protection or assistance once you have landed, although the Arrivals terminals, in the airports we use, are manned by our personnel and our security. Our destinations are limited to temperate areas. The tropics have, at least in part, reverted to jungle and disease is rife. Of course the lack of street cleaning and rubbish disposal has also resulted in the spread of infection.

We would recommend that you trust no-one and keep together as a group, until you gain the confidence to strike out on your own.

GOOD LUCK.

During our visit to Eugenia in the Solar Flare we did the things that we had promised Macgregor we would do, and the things we had promised Boxer we would do. Macgregor had concocted a story that allowed the tug to land at the base, which was actually more or less the truth. He said we had been sent back to Eugenia for some spares, which were being held there. All he failed to mention was where we had come from, and where we were going back to. He had also told the authorities on the base that we had permission to take two passengers back with us, although it was left up to us to find them. Fortunately, the tug retained some segregated accommodation in case, when it was a cargo ship, there was ever a need to have both men and women carried on it.

So, once connected with the lock on the base, we were directed to temporary accommodation while a hired hand got the spares together and someone loaded them into the tug. From there

I made the hazardous journey to the women's quarters in the search for either a navigator or a captain. For a second time I met Gelda, again because her space was closest to the entrance to the tunnel. I told her what was required, particularly that whoever chose to come had to be prepared either to be captain or navigator. I sensed that Gelda herself was not too keen. Of course it was not everybody's gig, but she promised that she would broadcast the requirement. All the volunteer had to do was to turn up at the Solar Flare when the tannoy announcement required all the flight crew to board.

Easan did the same thing in the male quarters, and it did not surprise me when Damon proved to be the volunteer. Like us, he was finding working for Cygnus a really unpleasant job. It was difficult enough just getting on with it, but with the handicap of the Cygnus approach to operations it was close to impossible. Damon was a diminutive and youthful captain of Slavic origins. I thought he would do well.

When the spares were loaded we trundled off to the Solar Flare, with Damon in tow. Everything went well, although I registered the puzzled expressions on the faces of the morality policemen who were manning the access areas. They must have been aware of Sediki's way of dealing with tug drivers, and wondering why on earth he had given them the instruction to leave us alone. I would have loved to have seen their expressions as the lady of the party showed them her "permission to board," and walked into the lock with her luggage.

She was a tall, willowy young woman with very pale skin and flint blue eyes. Even though she was not smiling, her expression seemed to carry a hint of amusement. Her hair was an untidy blonde halo, which she obviously made little effort to keep in order. But if anything this added to her aura of glamour. She dropped her kitbag into the corner and turned to face us.

"Hi guys," she said, "I'm Sonia Rodriguez. Pleased to be with you."

Her voice seemed somehow familiar.

"Don't you remember me?" she asked. I looked at her, and I was sure that if we had met I would have remembered. I shook my head cautiously, because her crisp enunciation was vaguely familiar.

"Yes you do. It wasn't that long ago. The Salvager!"

Of course, the Salvager. We were honoured.

"How are Nadia and Rollo?" she asked.

Before I could answer Damon rushed forward. "Hello Sonia, I've heard of you!" he said, shaking her by the hand enthusiastically. She was probably a head taller than he was, and I thought it would be better to leave it to them to decide who would be captain and who would be navigator.

"Hi Sonia," I said, "I'm Sully and this is Easan. You and Damon are replacing Nadia and I. Easan and Rollo are going to stay on the Evangelina to help you out. There is just one small thing. If you end up being captain, Boxer isn't going to want you getting out there with the guests in your uniform. They won't be able to keep their hands off you."

"Don't let it worry you," replied Sonia, "I'll be happy to keep out of the way. It'll save me from having to deal with that particular problem, if you see what I mean."

So now the Solar Flare had three captains, but we did not draw lots for the honour of driving. It was necessary for me to either sit in the seat, or else to operate the Commnet to speak to the control room. So I sat in the seat, and Easan sat next to me, and the others sat in our passenger seats and relaxed. On the trip back we got to know each other. We found out that Sonia was not gay, and so I was relieved. After all, she was a very attractive woman. It remains difficult for me to understand why we should think that heterosexual females might be attracted to gay females, particularly glamorous ones, but there it is. I thought that Nadia might still be a bit suspicious when we tumbled out of the tug back at the Evangelina, and she saw that one of our number was

273

the delightful Sonia. But they were friends, they had spent time together, and they knew each other, so I hoped that it would not be a problem.

When it came to it Nadia and Sonia were so pleased to see each other that I was entirely forgotten at the meeting, and when the time came to hand over, it was no surprise that Nadia handed over to Sonia Rodriguez and I handed over to Damon. It was a tearful moment. Nadia and I hugged Boxer and Moma, and then Rollo and Easan. We had become far more than fellow travellers in the Cygnus fleet. We had supported each other through, what, for us, were life-changing experiences, and if any of us had broken we would not have survived. What could I do except thank Easan for his help and support, although the words just did not seem to be sufficient? Even though hugging was not quite in our line, we hugged. "Thanks for not being a complete arsehole, Sully," he said. Appreciation at last, I thought.

Eventually it was time to board and so we slid, respectively, into the driving seats of Solar Flame and Solar Flare, and initiated the flight sequences which would detach us from the Evangelina and get us back to Eugenia base.

Possibly for the last time in my life, I took a ship away from its mooring and set course for my destination. It was odd driving with the engineer's seat empty, so to overcome my feeling of loneliness I called up Nadia on the Commnet. She responded and I looked round, hoping to see the Solar Flare. But it was nowhere in view. If you can see a ship when you are on passage you are probably too close. So I looked out at the carpet of stars visible though the viewports and the stippled globe that was Jupiter, still dominating the starscape. I tried to get a view of Io, the starting point of our adventure, but it was somewhere on the other side of the great planet.

In the days that followed we moved through the process of ceasing to be tug drivers contracted to the Cygnus Corporation, and became passengers on our way to the mother planet. Nadia was housed in the Eugenia female section, while I lived in the male transit accommodation. Macgregor released us from our contracts and provided both tickets and credits for our onward voyage. I had a meeting with Trantor, who was almost tearful as he wished me well. I uncharitably felt that his emotion was somehow linked to his feeling that someone who had this level of influence with Cygnus was worth cultivating. I remained distant, although I wished him a happy life out there in the asteroids.

And on we went, moving slowly but steadily towards our chosen destination. We left Eugenia in a transit craft, which connected up with the Mars to Earth shuttle, the Winged Serpent. The shuttle was a large craft, and in keeping with the length of the trip we, the passengers, were given a modicum of space. It was operated by the EarthLink company, which maintained Earth rules, and so once on board Nadia and I were able to see and talk to each other. We also made ourselves known to the crew and so were able to obtain a modicum of preferential treatment, as fellow flight crew. Many pilots and engineers regarded tug crews as some sort of lower order, and it was only if they were aware of what we actually did that they showed us any respect. Luckily the EarthLink crew knew.

So when the craft set course for earth we were housed in the first class accommodation, and had the opportunity of watching the departure from the viewports of the pilot house. Mars is spectacular from an orbiting spacecraft, principally because, due to the much lower gravity, orbits can be set much closer to the surface. We seemed to pass only a few metres above Olympus Mons, the largest volcano on the planet. It is vast, extending hundreds of kilometres at a gentle slope away from the caldera, and as we passed over it we could see a light mist around the base, the results of the initial stages of terra-forming. We flew on and at points around the equator we could see human habitation, tiny groups of structures all collected under transparent domes, their locations governed by the points from which space craft could take of and land with the greatest ease.

The Winged Serpent did an accelerating orbit and then vectored off into space. We watched as the red planet became smaller and smaller, and was eventually reduced to a red disc, and then a red dot. Then we turned our eyes forward, straining them to see old earth.

But it was no go. Earth was too far away, and so we retired to our recliners, and allowed ourselves to be tranquilised. Indeed the only people who were not tranquilised were the crew, who remained awake and alert for the whole voyage, and as a result experienced a couple of months of extreme boredom.

When we awoke we were in orbit again, this time round the blue planet. I had always wondered why that was its name, but sure enough as we looked down, all we could see was ocean. "Don't worry," said Max the captain. "There is land down there. Most of it is covered with living units. We're scheduled to land you in what used to be Spain. If you go further south than that it's too hot. Further north and there are so many people. But you've read our hand-out. So, what we're going to do is take the transit down to Barakas – that's still an open space in Madrid. It used to be an airport. If you'd rather go somewhere else there are some spots we can land, like on the bigger roads. There aren't many powered vehicles now, so they can avoid us."

I described my dream, the small house next to a lake where we could bring up a family and hunt for fish, and build real fires. Max understood. He had the good fortune to be in a job where he spent some time working on the Earth - Mars route, and the rest at home on the surface of the planet.

We got into the transit with a dozen others, all of us almost speechless with excitement and were soon on our way down. The transit skimmed the atmosphere, losing speed and generating heat, as spacecraft approaching earth have always done since the first one carried out a re-entry manoeuvre, and then swooped over the sea. We could see wind generated waves, and large vessels moving slowly on the water. As the transit approached land we saw large islands seemingly made up completely of towering structures. The pilot made an announcement. "Those of you on the starboard, sorry, right hand side of the transit can see the floating cities which make up Atlantis. Atlantis is the place where the very rich earthsiders live. I doubt many of you will have an opportunity to visit it, so have a look at it while you can. The boundaries of Atlantis are fortified and armed, to guard against attack by pirates."

The transit zoomed over land and we could see mountains and plains. It looked to us as if the mountains rose directly out of the sprawl of concrete which formed the cities and, by the look of it, the spaces between the cities. We slowed as we flew inland over the peninsula and eventually saw the open area, which was identified for us by the pilot as Barakas. The transit slowed and hovered over the central concrete apron, then lowered itself slowly to the surface, blasting dust and debris in all directions with its thrusters. Around us the old airport buildings were still standing, although the concrete was pitted, and the steelwork red with rust.

Having chosen to disembark in a quieter area, we remained in our seats in the pilot house while the rest of the passengers filed down the gangway on to the surface, carrying their minimal baggage. The heat reflected from the apron began to leech into the ship, and in response the pilot boosted the air-conditioning.

"We'll wait until they make it to the arrivals hall," he said. "After that they're on their own. If they don't have anyone here already it's going to be hard for them. And for you, if it comes to that. But we'll take you up to the north and land on a road, so that you can make it to the mountains more easily. Most people who come in from Mars or the asteroids have problems with open spaces, so you may have some adjusting to do. And keep your eyes and ears open for scavengers."

The transit lifted off from Barakas and eased its way north, following a ribbon of tarmac for only a few minutes. "How will that suit?" said the pilot, pointing downwards. I looked down and saw that the concrete buildings had petered out and the green on the mountainsides had become visible. Over to starboard I could see a lake. "Those stretches of water are actually reservoirs built ages ago," he said, " but they've survived and filled up again since the population began to fall. We generally like to leave people in this area because even though it's hot, there is some space and not too many predators."

"Predators?" I questioned.

"Yes, predators. They're mainly human, but in the green stuff there are a few bears and wolves. So keep your eyes peeled in the country as well as the city."

We thanked him, and as soon as the ship landed on the tarmac we climbed down the gangway onto the surface, and then walked off to the side to watch it take off. With an ear-splitting roar the thrusters lifted the transit vertically until it was about 40 metres above us. Debris of all sorts was blasted into the air around us, and dust swirled upwards, until we were clutching our bags to stop them being blown away and coughing in the dirt-laden air.

Then it became quiet and the transit arrowed upwards; a silver bullet disappearing into the cobalt blue that was the earth sky. We watched it as it became smaller and smaller. Finally it was a speck, a chip of light shimmering at the extremity of our vision. And then it was gone, and we lowered our gaze to take in our surroundings.

It was the first time we had really considered our new situation seriously. In the sorrow of parting and the excitement of travel, the result of it all had not really entered our heads. We had just known that it was the right thing to do. Once all was quiet we began to register the sounds of earth. Distantly we heard a high-pitched whine, which seemed to be gradually becoming louder. There was no sound in our immediate vicinity and the tarmac stretched away from us in both directions, completely empty, shimmering in the afternoon heat. It sloped slightly. Down the slope the buildings seemed to crowd on either side of it, until eventually it was lost in shadow. Up the slope we saw that it twisted between the trees until it finally disappeared into a dark chasm.

The noise from down the slope got louder and louder until its source became visible. It was a two-wheeled vehicle being controlled by a human, who was sitting astride it and leaning forward over the transverse bar at the front, which as far as we could see was the means by which it changed direction. The rider saw us and slowed until the vehicle was stationary alongside us. He killed the engine, and removed his goggles.

"What do you want?" said Nadia.

"Yeoww! Feisty female!" exclaimed the rider. "I want to help you. You need things, don't you? You've just got off that transit so you don't know much. You've hardly got any stuff. So how are you going to manage?"

"I think we'll be OK," I replied.

"Oh no you won't," he said. "There's no way you'll be OK. You need some shelter, and time to draw breath, and that's where I come in. I'd like to offer you some accommodation for a start, so you have somewhere to stay while you're trying to work out what to do next. Why did you come anyway?" He sat back in the seat twirling the goggles in his right hand, waiting for us to answer. He was absolutely right. We knew nothing. Earth might have been where every human in the solar system had originated, but to us it was still an alien environment.

"What's in it for you?" I asked. "Come on, how do we know we can trust you? We came because we're fed up with having our whole lives controlled by the Morality Police out there." I gestured upwards.

"I came for the same reason," he said. "But you have to do something. Otherwise you don't survive. And you have to trust someone, sometimes even the first person you meet. Don't worry about me. If I ride off now what are you going to do? Go on up the road? Go down the road.

? Strike off straight out into the suburbs. I can tell you there are dangers everywhere. You're lucky I found you. Those guys in the transit know something. If they'd let you out at Barakas there would have been a dozen people like me offering to help you. Most of them ready to hit you on the head at the first dark corner or, if they're more sophisticated, ready to take you to a building, lock you in and then make use of you in a variety of ways. You," he nodded towards Nadia, "are particularly at risk. They go in for sex for money in this world. It could be one of the downsides of a free society. And men like you," he nodded at me, "are in the way."

"OK," I said. "But watch it." I lifted the edge of my flight jacket to expose the butt of the 1911 Colt that Boxer had given me.

"Yeowww! A gun. Wonderful stuff," he said. "No worries. I'm Nathaniel." He held out his hand. I took it. "I'm Sully and this Nadia."

Nadia looked surprised. "What are you doing with that?" she asked, pointing towards my waistband, rather belligerently I thought. I felt hurt.

"You remember that Boxer suggested that if he had anything that I though we needed I should ask." She nodded. I pointed at the butt of the Colt. "And I've got a good stock of ammunition too."

"Well, watch you don't shoot your toes off," she said.

"Now, just come along with me," said Nathaniel. "We'll go on foot, although I have to push this thing back down the hill until we get to my building. Nathaniel's hostel for returning spacemen. Tell you what. You can have a room for a week, until you find out how much everything is worth and then let me know what you think you should pay me for the space. It's difficult now isn't it? You've got credits, but you have no idea what they can buy or how long they're going to last, or even how you're going to get more. What's in it for me? Well, we all need people, and I've constructed a network by doing just what I've done today. We all help each other."

There seemed to be no doubt that Nathaniel knew the ropes, and what our problems would be, so what more did we have to lose? Our lives, of course. But I knew one thing, that we had gone through a great deal of difficulty to get here, and I certainly did not include an early demise for either of us in my plans.

As a result of our meeting, sunset found us in the spaceman's hostel, as Nathaniel called it. Sunset was something special. As the great orb lowered itself towards the horizon the sky was suffused with a red glow, which darkened as into scarlet and then purple. Nathaniel spoke. "That's a fire somewhere in the mountains to the west. It may not be happening today, but surely something's been burning out there. Mostly sunsets are like this. There's a lot of fire on earth."

And so we made our base at Nathaniel's hostel, and every day we went out into the country. First we went up the road until it disappeared into a tunnel. We had been warned not to go into any tunnels at all. There was no lighting, and they harboured many of the least friendly of the area's inhabitants. Effectively, the tunnel was the end of this particular road. Nothing went into it and nothing came out. Occasionally a four wheeled road vehicle would pass us going up the hill. It would reach the end of the tunnel, turn round and start down again. Most of these vehicles were oddly shaped, often with small wheels on the front and big wheels on the back, or the other way round. They were all extremely noisy and sometimes gave off black smoke. When we heard one we would dive into the side and remain out of sight until it had disappeared.

Sometimes we went down the hill until we were

overcome by the sheer density of the buildings. They towered on either side of the road, blocking out the sun at all times of day except noon. There were some people here. The most reliable sign was washing. It hung from windows, it festooned balconies and it was even strung between buildings. We saw people leaning over balconies, sometimes talking to each other, but we saw few people on the ground.

Then we did the very thing that Nathaniel said we should not do. We branched out into the suburbs. We were navigators, which was fortunate, and so we found our way to and from the hostel mainly by checking the direction of the sun, and looking at our watches. There were a few maps, and over the time we were exploring we were improving them. Occasionally we would enter a building. This was the most daring and dangerous part of the exploration. It was impossible to know what one would find in there, but Nathaniel had told us that not all the buildings were occupied, so it became our objective to find sort of habitation and stake a claim. Usually we would find out how well occupied a building was as soon as we went in the front door. There tended to be a well armed male sitting in the stairwell.

We entered a tall block down the hill, and before our eyes had become accustomed to the gloom I felt some-one grab me and heard Nadia scream. It was our good fortune that she happened to be carrying an iron bar, which she had picked up at the side of the tarmac, and because she was a woman they had not bothered to grab her. She swung the bar and hit my assailant behind the knees. He fell to the ground moaning, giving me time to extract the Colt from my waistband. I worked the slide on the gun to put a projectile into the chamber and its threatening metallic sound caught the attention of the three men who were edging forward to attack us again. The two of us backed up against a retaining wall and I pointed the weapon at them. They were a raggedly-dressed trio. "OK, OK," said my attacker, rubbing his calf muscles. "You win. We don't want any trouble.

You can go." I knew at that moment that I could pull the trigger three times and they would be lying dead on the floor. They were only a couple of metres away, and they knew it as well. I gestured with the muzzle and they stepped back against the most distant wall in the lobby. We edged to the door and were on our way.

"There you are," I said. "I knew it would be useful." On the other hand I had to admit it was not quite as useful as an iron bar in the hands of a well co-ordinated young woman with lightning reactions.   Once on our own again we kissed. We discovered that violence can be stimulating.

Further up the hill we found extensive areas of individual habitations surrounded by their own plots of land. Most of the plots were cultivated. Most of the houses had roofs, but occasionally there was one that had burnt down, or had been damaged in some other way. We could see that there were more houses than people here, and, curiously, that most people wanted to live in close proximity to others. This might have explained the popularity of the large blocks, which gave the appearance of being heavily populated, even the ones with trees growing out of the roofs.

In all of this we began to make a track from Nathaniel's place to a roofless house with a view over a stretch of water.   In the water we saw there were enormous fish, which we fed with scraps of food from our limited supplies. The scars on their backs made them distinctive. Nadia liked to feed one which she called George.

We realised that Macgregor had supplied us with a large quantity of credits. This was the currency used all over the planet, although it was difficult to see on what its value was based, since having a plot of land on which to grow vegetables seemed to be beyond price.

So there we were on earth, hardly giving our previous lives a thought, except when we looked up on dark nights at the Milky Way above us, or at red twinkling dot that was Mars or the bright morning star that was Jupiter. It was already difficult to believe that we had spent our whole lives out there. Now we looked around us at what was earth, and looked forward to being on it, to spending our lives on it. Now we looked at the sunsets, which every day were beautiful and long lasting. And even though they were like that because somewhere some part of the planet was burning, we enjoyed them. Actually, we were enjoying everything. We were enjoying our new life, and more than anything we were enjoying being together. It was what we had come here for.